PIONEER MICROBIOLOGISTS OF AMERICA

Paul Franklin Clark is Emeritus Professor of Medical Microbiology at the University of Wisconsin. He is the author of numerous scientific articles in the field of viruses, especially poliomyelitis. His major published works include "Alice in Virusland," an address as president to the Society of American Bacteriologists, and *Memorable Days in Medicine: A Calendar of Biology and Medicine*, Alice Schiedt Clark, co-author, published by The University of Wisconsin Press.

PAUL F. CLARK

PIONEER

MICROBIOLOGISTS

OF AMERICA

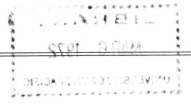

*I want to know the steps by which men
passed from barbarism to civilization.*

VOLTAIRE

Paul F. Clark

*Emeritus Professor of Medical Microbiology
The University of Wisconsin*

THE UNIVERSITY OF WISCONSIN PRESS · MADISON, 1961

Published by

THE UNIVERSITY OF WISCONSIN PRESS

430 Sterling Court, Madison 6, Wisconsin

Printed in the United States of America by the

George Banta Company, Inc., Menasha, Wisconsin

Library of Congress Catalog Card Number 60–11441

Preface

These tales of early American microbiology are dedicated to the memory of Barnett Cohen, first archivist of the Society of American Bacteriologists, first editor of *Bacteriological Reviews*, and long-time associate professor of physiological chemistry, Johns Hopkins Medical School.[1] His untimely death in 1952 deprived us of the history of American bacteriology which he had intended to write during the years of emeritus activity. His genial spirit and broad grin encompassed us all; his active mind and wise counsel have left us with warm recollections. In connection with our chronicles, I have appreciated his initiative in fostering symposia on the history of bacteriology in the regions where the annual meetings of the Society of American Bacteriologists have been held; they have served as excellent bases from which to take off. Much of their material belongs, however, to the more involved adult productive life of microbiology in this country rather than the bursting infancy and teen-age period that I am attempting to survey. It has taken more restraint than I have been able to muster to keep entirely within my determined time boundaries; I have weakened repeatedly. This has been especially true in considering the lives of men who have died before the completion of their three-score years and ten, and in telling the stories of some of our major achievements.

Practically all individual professional titles have been omitted. The terms doctor and professor have had widely different significance in our own land during the three centuries of this history, as well as in other countries; they have no accurate meaning without involved explanations or knowledge of individual cases. In some of our states, as for example, California, the practitioner of chiropractic is a doctor, and

---

1   W. M. Clark, An appreciation of Barnett Cohen, *Bact. Reviews, 16* (1952), 205–9.

here in Madison the chiropodists use that title in the telephone directory. On the other hand, most British surgeons continue to employ the "Mister" of the barber surgeons of the fourteenth and fifteenth centuries; in William Welch's early Hopkins period, when his niece referred to him as Professor Welch, he remonstrated, "You must never call me professor. Only dancing masters are called that."[2]

A rambling chronicle such as this stems from everyone and everywhere. I am a part of all that I have met. I am writing this not only for students in microbiology, but also for others who may wish to know more about this exciting period, its conflicts, its hopes, its men, and some of its achievements. These were made possible through our energy and because in the early period, there were no artificial barriers to travel and to the exchange of ideas. Because of personal interest, I have doubtless overemphasized the University of Wisconsin and the medical aspects of our science; if my work had been chiefly in dairy or soil bacteriology, my choices for stress would doubtless have been different. Actually, the pathogens were the chief agents in awakening our interest in the microbic world. Only later did the other microorganisms assume their rightful position.

My apologies to all and sundry for my temerity in undertaking this broad-brush picture and for the inevitable errors. I have used the term America in the usual inaccurate sense meaning chiefly the United States. I regret the exclusion of our neighbors north and south who have so commonly worked with us. In our period scientific names have tended to change more frequently than those in daily use; the robin has had at least three different scientific names in my lifetime. In these chronicles I have commonly used the names employed when the papers were under discussion, for example: *Bacillus typhosus* rather than *Eberthella typhosa* or *Salmonella typhosa*, and *Bacillus prodigiosus* rather than *Serratia marcescens; Endamoeba blattae* Leidy persists, but our important pathogen for man has become *Entamoeba histolytica*.

Bearing in mind that journeys are where stories live when they are at home, may we journey together from the Atlantic to the Pacific and visit with some of the men who have given us a strong hand in the upbuilding of Pasteur's dream. Although these tales are chiefly about Americans, it will be apparent that they had their origins in Europe; there is no national science; in such fields, we *are One World.* Mani-

2 Simon Flexner and James Thomas Flexner, *William Welch and the Heroic Age of American Medicine* (New York, 1941), p. 126.

festly, this book is largely a personal story of men and achievements rather than the mature judgment of the professional historian in the interweaving of the innumerable threads. I shall be happy if it gives some perspective to beginners in microbiology and to other interested seekers.

> *Why did I write? What sin to me unknown*
> *Dipped me in ink, my parents or my own?*   POPE[3]

Madison, Wisconsin   Paul F. Clark
May, 1959

3   Alexander Pope, *Epistle to Dr. Arbuthnot.*

Acknowledgments

The sources that have contributed to such a book as this are innumerable and range the world over. I am grateful to colleagues from other departments in our University for interest and for help where I have been weak—to R. C. Stauffer, W. B. Sarles, A. J. Riker, W. C. Frazier, Merle Curti, Noble Clark, who have given valuable counsel, and especially to O. N. Allen, who has given aid repeatedly. In our own department, Michael Lysenko and C. V. Seastone have given worth-while suggestions; I am greatly indebted to Frances Holford, who has read the whole manuscript, has polished rough statements, and has pulled me out of several pitfalls. Letters from colleagues elsewhere have been acknowledged in the bibliography. L. S. McClung, archivist of the Society of American Bacteriologists, has responded promptly to my calls for the loan of local histories. To librarians near and far, especially our own medical librarian, Helen Crawford, I voice my appreciation; they are a wonderfully helpful lot. Above all, I owe, as always, deepest gratitude to my wife of half a century; without her encouragement, this task would never have been undertaken and without her continuing aid and criticisms, it would never have been completed. Manifestly no one save the author is responsible for his statements of opinion, for his sins of commission, and especially the many of omission. That notorious Virus de Vejéz,[1] always latent, becomes, as the years go by, increasingly virulent, or our resistance becomes less.

The Wisconsin Alumni Research Foundation has provided some funds for trips to other libraries and for student aid in typing the manuscript in its several incarnations.

1   T. M. Rivers, Virus de Vejéz, *Bact. Reviews*, *17* (1935), 213–47. Personal copy from the author, quoted liberally by P. F. Clark, Half-century of presidential addresses of the Society of American Bacteriologists.

Contents

Contents

List of Illustrations

1

FOUNDATIONS OF EARLY BACTERIOLOGY

CHAPTER I

Beginnings in Other Lands

We think our fathers fools, so wise we grow,
Our wiser sons, I hope, will think us so.   POPE

Why should one attempt to chronicle and, if possible, to interpret early American microbiology, the optimistic crusading enthusiasm that prevailed, and any recompense we may have made for the inspiration and the knowledge derived from the older countries? Were there, as Winslow delighted in saying, an unusual number of "giants in those days?"[1] How significant were their contributions to the development of world microbiology?

The term bacteriology has until recently been used commonly in this country rather than the more accurate, broader one, microbiology, chiefly because most of the disease-producing organisms discovered during the thrilling, expanding Pasteur-Koch period were bacteria. These took the center of the stage and have held it until recently when filterable viruses have shoved them into the wings. All are microorganisms whether they belong to the animal or to the vegetable kingdom, or whether one is studying them as significant biologic units or as disease-inciting parasites. Although my major interest has always been in the medical field, I shall scan more briefly other areas and beg any who may wish to amplify.

I am defining "early" in this book roughly as the Victorian era, although it will be necessary to begin much further back, and I shall consider the period as closing not with the death of the good Queen in 1901, but with World War I, when the philosophies and optimistic dreams of that era, many of them, manifestly unfounded, were shattered by Mars and Moloch. When necessary for the story I may extend my account beyond the end of the war, but commonly 1916 will be my final date for reasons that will be made clear. I cordially agree with Agnes Repplier: "Nothing is so unmanageable as a date. People will be born a few years too early; they will live a few years too long. Events will happen out of time. The closely linked decades refuse to be separated."[2] I hope we can catch something of the spirit and the achievements of the period, the exuberance, the atmosphere of inquiry, the conflict, the suspense, the difficulties, the frontier movement into the "brave new world" with its immense importance in medicine, in public health, in agriculture, in the dairy and other industries, in the broad field of biology itself, and in the intimate life of each family. How rapidly did the discoveries of Jenner, Pasteur, Koch, Lister, and the many other investigators in Europe percolate down through our press, schools, colleges, legislatures, and to the man in the field, in the factory, and on the street? Who and what were the men in this country responsible for bringing this biological revolution to our shores? What institutions gave them their opportunities?

In recent years, we have become so rich, so proud of our know-how and efficiency, that I have set myself this task partly to show how much in early microbiology, as is true, also, in the other sciences, we owed primarily to European investigators, and how little initially to ourselves. Local pride is so strong and hero worship such an integral part of human nature, that one finds on every campus an astounding number of men with "international reputations." If we have no saints, we create them. And how shall we define international fame? Almost every mature productive scientist has acquaintances in other countries through publications, letter, or in person; does that constitute an international reputation? Most biographical sketches published at the time of a man's death have only slight critical value. We are all brought up to appreciate *De mortuis nil nisi bonum*, but certainly that does not mean that we should canonize each reasonably competent man. Is not a candid picture of our predecessors more stimulating, more possible to emulate? They were but men of varying abilities; they stood on the shoulders of others just as later comers have used their shoulders. Writers in other countries have not infrequently neglected the work of our scholars, and we have done the same in reverse, but contributions of importance are ultimately recognized. Quoting Sidney Smith, Osler stresses that "it is not the man who first says a thing, but it is he who says it so long, so loudly and so clearly that he compels men to listen to him—it is to him that the credit belongs."

All the broad fields of microbiology had been plowed and planted and had yielded a considerable harvest before we in America, save in rare instances, had become aware of the importance of the microbial world in us and around us. The importance of the *first* course in bacteriology given in this country seems slight. The first course did not produce the seed from which the second and subsequent courses were derived, as in the primary case of typhoid fever upriver for those acquiring the disease from drinking the bacteria-laden water downstream. The courses and much of our knowledge and inspiration sprouted from seed grown in Europe, and although the seed was not wind borne, it was widely disseminated and came to fruition in many areas at about the same time.

With our characteristic American genius, we have in microbiology as in other fields, emphasized practical applications. In stressing this fact, one is certainly not minimizing their importance. Pasteur has well said, "There is science and the applications of science, bound together as the fruit to the tree that bears it."[3] Until recently scientists have agreed with Pasteur that no sharp dividing line exists between pure and applied investigations. Important fundamental concepts and advances have come in working out applications as well as in research carried on from pure curiosity.

Thomas Henry Huxley, in one of his essays on education, states that "the great end of life is not knowledge but action." He says further,

I often wish that this phrase, "applied science," had never been invented. For it suggests that there is a sort of scientific knowledge of direct practical use, which can be studied apart from another sort of scientific knowledge, which is of no practical utility, and which is termed "pure science." But there is no more complete fallacy than this. What people call applied science is nothing but the application of pure science to particular classes of problems. It consists of deductions from those general principles, established by reasoning and observation, which constitute pure science. No one can safely make these deductions until he has a firm grasp of the principles.[4]

Is not freedom of initiative, even if not always wise, the chief point rather than this overemphasis on pure versus applied science? Have not the appalling expenditures for defense, the direction of effort by uninformed political bodies, the wastefulness of our clashing governmental agencies, and the draining of our colleges and universities of suitable manpower by the larger stipends these other institutions can offer caused us to forget this main issue?

Our adaptations of the methods that Pasteur used in the preservation of wine made pasteurized milk broadly obtainable in our cities when it was rarely available even in the capitals of Europe. Although the method of preserving food in glass jars by sealing them hermetically and heating was used by the confectioner Appert as early as 1804 in Paris,[5] long before the days of bacteriology, large-scale commercial canning of foods became a common practice in this country before it did in Europe. Another of the many examples of practical applications that might be cited is the tuberculin testing of cattle. Although this originated in Europe (Guttmann, Bang, Nocard), it was carried out more extensively in this country with the slaughter of the infected cows; so that by the end of 1940, our Secretary of Agriculture could state that the entire country had reached the "modified accredited status,"[6] that is, in each county, less than five per one thousand of all animals tested reacted positively to the diagnostic dose of tuberculin. With this elimination of bovine tuberculosis, nonpulmonary tuberculosis in humans, as for example scrofula, the King's Evil, became for us largely a disease of the past.

We would not minimize the achievements of our early bacteriologists. They were thrilled crusaders; each poured plate of water or milk was a discovery; they made progress in spite of lack of funds, inadequate methods, and the antagonism of personal interest. The progress in medicine from the overwhelming yellow fever epidemic in Philadelphia in 1793, with its rumbling wagons and the dismal cry "Bring out your dead," to the crucial control of yellow jack at the beginning of the twentieth century which was achieved not by ineffective general quarantine but by ridding an area of certain mosquitoes, is a dramatic tale worthy of a Shakespeare. Even though none other has quite the qualities of major disaster and suddenly achieved success as this, yet the simpler tales also show achievement and are fraught with tragedy and comedy. These were neither myths nor miracles but encouraging, exciting facts. And yet, in 1918–19, let us admit it, we were as completely helpless as in the yellow fever epidemics, as one after another of the strong young men in our army cantonments fell over and died from influenza.

A few decades earlier evidence of evolution and presentation of theories that could explain some of the mechanisms of the *Origin of*

Species by Darwin,[7] Wallace, *et al.* had inflamed the emotions, jolted some religious conceptions, and had incited further studies. The human mind was hardly ready for another almost equally explosive awakening. Biologists were no longer harmless scientists; much as the physicist and chemist of today have revolutionized our thinking and our world by terrifying control over atomic forces, so the biologists began to transform the thinking and modes of life of the western world during the latter half of the Victorian era. The ferment was widespread, but Europe, with its older institutions, more mature in scientific development, made more fundamental advances in these early decades than were made in this hemisphere. Indeed, most of our first bacteriologists learned their lessons from European leaders.

The discoveries that made everyone wake up, that brought bacteriology directly home to each family were those of men such as Koch, Pasteur, Behring, Löffler, and Lister in Europe, and Theobald Smith, William Welch, T. J. Burrill, and Erwin F. Smith in this country. They proved that common diseases that were sickening and killing children and adults, cattle on the farms, and crops in the field were caused by microbes. Here, too, we find that men of vision had glimpsed the truth long before the 1870's and 1880's. Microorganisms, not too different in form from those observed in the studies which overthrew the doctrine of spontaneous generation and made plain the microbic origin of fermentation, were proved to be specific inciting agents in tuberculosis, diphtheria, typhoid, and other common diseases. I wish I might convey something of the excitement and the spirit that prevailed. It was a major crusade with men joining in the march from widely different fields. There were no bacteriologists, so physicians, zoologists, botanists, physicists, engineers, and old-fashioned naturalists enthusiastically took over the new tools and the new thinking. The promise of hope was not remission of sins, but better crops, better living, and freedom from the great plagues. We need a Chaucer to relate each tale; we shall see what the "clerk" can do. "And gladly would he lerne and gladly teche."

Although our major theme is microbiology as it has developed in this country, our history was closely bound with that of the mother countries for more decades than we have been a more or less independent federation. We derived our peoples, our laws, our literature, and most of our ideas, customs, and infections from these sources. If we need evidence, the recent world wars have shown that we are still indissolubly tied. It has become increasingly apparent that we are one world, closely involved with our earlier origins in the East as well as with our more immediate Western World. As we shall see, disease-producing microorganisms such as those causing bubonic plague, yellow fever, and cholera, to name only a few, have been harsh teachers of this fact. Man, even with his strong, frequently stupid self-interest, has become convinced that plague-bearing rat fleas and mosquitoes carrying the yellow fever virus do not recognize political or geographic boundaries, or fences around homes and factories.

In the field of our chronicles therefore, we must trace briefly the early speculative ideas as to the origins of life and disease. These were found commonly in religious beliefs and poetry, somewhat later in more exact observations and only recently in convincing experiment. These are integral parts of our own history and must be told.

Early Concepts of the Origins of Life and Disease—the Slow Decline of Magic and Superstition and the Rise of the Idea of Contagium animatum

Our medical historian Garrison[8] states: "The common point of convergence of all medical folk-lore is animism, *i.e.*, the notion that the world swarms with invisible spirits which are the efficient causes of disease and death. Primitive medicine is inseparable from primitive modes of religious belief." Benevolent gods must be worshipped, and appeased by penance and prayer if we have sinned; demons and witches must be exorcised; fetishes and charms must be employed; devils must be cast out.

Tied in with these convictions were the commonly accepted ideas of abiogenesis, that living things grew spontaneously from nonliving matter, water, air, and putrefaction. Fleas, bugs, and lice were supposedly produced from filth; fish from mud, and eels according to Aristotle, from Earth's guts.

Our ancestors believed that the stars, the conjunction of planets, and comets circling in their orbits were causes of dire epidemics and other earthly events. Astronomy and mathematics were developed early and the magic astrology grew up along with these sciences, flourishing into the seventeenth century. If the tides follow the sun and the moon, why not epidemics and the characteristics of individuals born, shall we say, under Taurus. Horoscopy, palmistry, and other superstitious means of fortunetelling still persist.

Mixed in with these ideas and practices, strange to the informed modern mind, we find evidence of customs that arouse our admiration. Cleanliness as a religious virtue, to be pure before the gods, was widely practiced. Modern archeologists have unearthed conduits for drinking-water, drains for sewage disposal, and even water closets in the more advanced lost civilizations as in India, Mesopotamia, Crete, and, in this hemisphere, among the ruins of the Incas.[9] The idea of contagion in certain diseases such as so-called leprosy dates from early history, though the causative agents were thought to be gaseous products from the sick. It is commonly agreed that these concepts came to our western world largely through the Hebrews and their ancient writings. But chiefly to the Greeks, we owe an unbounded debt, the beginning of release from the bondage of superstition. A few quotations from the early literature, both Hebrew and Greek, will give us a clearer idea of their thoughts and practices.

We find the authors of Leviticus (about 500 B. C.) giving directions for isolation and quarantine of those ill with leprosy which shows that they believed that this disease was communicable and therefore preventable (Chaps. 13–15 and 22), "And the leper in whom the plague is, his clothes shall be rent, and his head bare, and he shall put a covering upon his upper lip, and cry, unclean, unclean."

"All the days wherein the plague shall be in him he shall be defiled; he is unclean; he shall dwell alone; without the camp shall his habitation be " (Lev. 13: 45 and 46.)

"He shall therefore burn that garment, whether warp or woof, in woolen or in linen, or anything of skin, wherein the plague is: for it is a fretting leprosy; it shall be burnt in the fire." (Lev. 13: 52.)

But the gods or the one God was not ignored; in the Old Testament, God, wrathful because of the sins of his people, is portrayed repeatedly bringing plagues upon them. "The wrath of the Lord was kindled against the people and the Lord smote the people with a very great plague." (Num. 11: 33.) "And if ye walk contrary unto me and will not hearken unto me; I will bring seven times more plagues upon you according to your sins." (Lev. 26: 21.)

In the New Testament, the work of devils and evil spirits is given the greater prominence. "And they brought unto him all sick people that were taken with divers diseases and torments, and those that were possessed with devils, and those which were lunatick and those that had the palsy; and he healed them." (Matt. 4: 24.) And in giving instructions to his twelve apostles, Jesus said, "Heal the sick, cleanse the leper, raise the dead, cast out devils." (Matt. 10: 8.)

One approaches the Greek philosophers, too, with deep respect. In dealing with disease, it is chiefly to Hippocrates (460–377 B.C.) that we must direct our attention because he and his school gradually discarded much of the contemporary magic, the fear of angry gods, and emphasized dependence on clinical observation; for example, the description of mumps is a gem of accuracy. The Hippocratic School of Cos insisted that universal natural law prevails. "No one disease is either more divine or more human than another, but that all are alike divine, for that each has its own nature, and that no one arises without a natural cause." These writings on, "Airs, Waters, and Places,"[10] are epidemiological studies with emphasis on the influence of the external environment on the incidence of diseases. With marshy waters "in the summer there are epidemics of dysentery, diarrhoea and long Quartan fever."

Although epidemics are given a prominent place in Hippocratic writings and endemic diseases are also featured, yet Adams agrees that "certain it is that not the least reference to contagion in any shape, is to be found in any of the Hippocratic treatises." This is remarkable "more especially as the contagiousness of certain diseases would appear to have been the popular belief of his age." The Greek historian Thucydides[11] (471–400 B. C.) of the same period, recognises contagion in the great plague of Athens during the Peloponnesian War.

Appalling too was the rapidity with which men caught the infection; dying like sheep if they attended on one another; and this was the principle cause of mortality. When they were afraid to visit one another, the sufferers died in solitude, so that many houses were empty because there had been no one left to take care of the sick; or if they ventured, they perished, especially those who aspired to heroism. . . . No one was ever attacked a second time or not with a fatal result.

Manifestly, this recognises also specific immunity.

The gods played prominent parts in the *Iliad* and the *Odyssey*, aiding their favorites and influencing the outcome of voyage and war. In causing epidemics, we find many references, especially to Apollo, the Fardarter. His answer to the scorned father who came to rescue his daughter, a prize of war, from the bed of Agamemnon is typical.

So he [Chryses] spoke in prayer, and Phoebus Apollo heard him and came down from the peaks of Olympus angry at heart, his bow and covered quiver on his shoulders. The arrows rattled on the shoulders of the angry god as he sped, and he came like night. Then he sat down far from the ships and sent an arrow towards them; dreadful was the twang of his silver bow. First he shot the mules and the swift dogs; and then he shot a sharp arrow against the men and smote them. And the crowded pyres of the dead burned on unceasing.

Nine days throughout the camp fell the missiles of the God and on the tenth, Achilles called the host to an assembly.[12]

But as to the nature of Apollo's arrows, this remained a shrouded mystery with possible inklings among a few philosophers and poets until experiment, the microscope, and the sharp Renaissance mind came to enlighten us. Poets seem to have had especial insight, or was it merely poetic imagination? The Roman Epicurean author, Lucretius[13] (99–55 B.C.) in his *De Rerum Naturae* writes: "And first, I've taught above that seeds there be of many things life giving, and that, contrariwise, there must fly many round, bring disease and death." Varro,[14] a contemporary of Lucretius, is also frequently cited. "Attention should also be paid to any marshy places thereabouts; and because certain minute animals grow there, which cannot be detected by the eye, and which get inside the body from the air, through the mouth, and nostrils, and give rise to stubborn distempers."

With the fall of Rome in the fifth century, came the sinking of western Europe into the Dark Ages. The earlier break in the flow of medical and scientific knowledge from Greece, the collapse and withdrawal of Roman organization, and the overwhelming invasions from the north brought broken aqueducts, broken economy, and a break in the progress of learning. Many pagan habits and customs, including a large element of magic and the supernatural, added to the confusion. As Christianity gradually became the dominant religion, the precept that disease was a punishment for sin became increasingly prominent with prayer and penance as the accepted means of prevention. Notwithstanding these ideas and also the horrifying delusions of witchcraft and devils, believed even by the better educated persons, including prominent physicians, the church and the monasteries became the refuge of learning during this long latent period. Towards the end of the Dark Ages, "cathedral" schools such as that at Chartres about A. D. 1000 became important, especially in medicine. In the succeeding centuries, the great universities began to bud: the University of Paris, 1110; Bologna, 1113; Oxford, 1167; Montpellier, 1181; and Padua, 1222; the last two became famous in medicine.[15]

In eastern Europe, Constantinople, established by Constantine in

A. D. 330 as the capital of the Byzantine Empire, remained an important center of learning until its overthrow by the Turks in 1453. The changes that had been taking place slowly then became accelerated. In the spread of the refugee scholars all over Europe, in the development of printing, and in the introduction of gunpowder changing the methods of the ever recurring wars, one observes important elements of the Renaissance. Leonardo, Copernicus, Galileo, Martin Luther, and our first real bacteriologist, Antony van Leeuwenhoek, whose observations we shall soon describe, are all part and parcel of this great marvel.

The idea of contagion with its fears was repeatedly forced upon the people by violent epidemics such as the plague of Justinian (A. D. 543), the overmastering terror of leprosy with the harsh measures of banishment and isolation brought from the East by the crusaders, and still more widely by the fury of the Black Death of the fourteenth and later centuries. The grisly details of the panic and the pest houses, of the dying, and of the dead during the plague years are told by many. Hecker,[16] one of the more conservative historians, estimated that in the plague year of 1348 one-fourth of the population of Europe died of the disease; others gave figures as high as half or four-fifths for several cities. All authors of the time, both medical and nonmedical, agreed that the plague was contagious. The mode of transfer commonly accepted was by corruption of the air "with poisonous vapors" from the sick and the dead as well as from decomposing organic matter, a mixture of ideas that seemed not to trouble them. The plague was also attributed to stars and meteors. All the regular forces of control, the family, the church, the law, and the medical profession were shattered. Fields went untilled, the people, even physicians, fled from the cities when they could. Black Death ruled; contagion was his frightful weapon, a more powerful teacher than even "the terrible swift sword."

The following extract from "The First Day" of Boccaccio's *Decameron*[17] tells of the popular ideas of contagion and the plague of the fourteenth century. "And this pestilence was yet of farre greater power or violence; for not only healthful persons speaking to the sicke, coming to see them, or ayring cloathes in kindness to comfort them was an occasion of ensuing death; but touching their garments, or any foode wheron the sicke person feed, or anything else used in his service, seemed to transfer the disease from the sicke to the sound, in very rare and miraculous manner."

In the next century, however, Hieronymus Fracastorius of Verona gave to Boccaccio's "rare and miraculous manner" some basis of the reasonable. He is well known for his poem *Syphilis sive Morbus Gallicus* (1530) from which the name of this venereal disease is derived. But he merits greater recognition for his treatise *De Contagione et Contagiosis Morbis et eorum Curatione* published in 1546.[18] In a study of epidemics including some that would now be named plague, typhus fever, syphilis, and foot and mouth disease, he predicated probable modes of spread through "seminaria" by three means, by direct contact, by fomites, and by air. In his own phrases,

We shall define contagion as a certain precisely similar corruption which develops in the substance of a combination, passes from one thing to another and is originally caused by infection of the imperceptible particles. Its seminaria have great activity; they are made up of a strong and viscous combination; and they have not only a material but also a spiritual antipathy to the animal organism. . . . An especially good instance of the contagion that infects by contact only is that which occurs in fruits, as when grape infects grape, or apple infects apple; so we must try to discover the principle of this infection. It is evident that they are infected because they touch, and that some one fruit decays first. . . .

In discussing contact through fomes, he says "Now all substances are not suited to become fomes [that is, inanimate objects, such as bedding, clothing, etc.] but only those that are somewhat porous: . . . on account of their pores, the germs [seminaria] of contagion can be stored up, and they cannot be altered either by the fomes itself or by external factors, unless these are excessively active; for instance, they have no defense against fires. . . ." As an analogy of infection at a distance, he suggests,

Who would imagine that tears could be drawn from us, even from a long distance, by onions and garlic; that pepper, iris or ptarmicum could make one sneeze?

. . . .

The remedies which have power to extinguish and destroy the seminaria are very hot or very cold, but especially those which are called "burning," or akin to burning, whether you prefer to use fire or those remedies called caustic. For by these means, the germs [seminaria] are extinguished, and in such a way that once they have been destroyed, the whole imminent disease is utterly destroyed at the same time, since nothing is left over that can generate offspring.

A further reading of this rather involved essay makes clear that Fracastorius conceived his "seminaria" as chemical substances, susceptible to evaporation and diffusion rather than as living microbes. He did however point out that each disease had its own "seminaria" and was therefore specific; he analyzed the modes of spread as though he were dealing with living organisms. Along with this clear reasoning, he still retained some ideas of his period, calling upon atmospheric phenomena and conjunction of the planets to explain widespread epidemics.

Wright in her translation of *De Contagione*, gives the word "seminaria" as "seeds" or "germs." Winslow suggests that germs, as germs of an idea, would be preferable. But our sixteenth century seer came remarkably close to the concepts of the late nineteenth century. In the section on treatment directed towards the principles of contagion, he states that fire will destroy so that nothing remains that can reproduce (*nihil enim remanet, quod praeterea sobolem gignatur*). This gives point to Fracastorius' wide acclaim as one who pushed forward amazingly the concept of *contagium animatum*. Most rarely is there complete priority in scientific discovery.

One of Fracastorius' followers in the next century, the seventeenth, was Athanasius Kircher[19] (1602–80). In his *Scrutinium pestis* (1658), after giving suggestive quotations from Aristotle, Pliny, and other early authorities, he enunciated the doctrine of *contagium animatum* on the basis of his observations during the plague. With his lens (said to magnify about 32 diameters, but none of his instruments is known) he observed *vermes* (worms) in the decomposing bodies of persons dead of the plague, in the body of a dead "mermaid," in putrifying material such as meat, dead snakes, rotten wood, etc., and also in the blood of living sufferers. It has been suggested that he may have seen insect larvae and rouleaux of red blood cells, but unfortunately he left neither descriptions nor drawings. He surmised that insects, especially flies, might be carriers of the plague, but he continued to hold with the prevailing idea of the period, abiogenesis, that the organisms he saw arose spontaneously in putrefying organic matter.

Kircher's more critical biographers,[20] such as Dobell in England, and Torrey in this country give him little credit for anything new. Dobell describes him as the "veriest dabbler in Science" and states that his formulation of a doctrine of *contagium animatum* "had no more objective basis that similar earlier guesses." Torrey agrees and Hendrickson refers to Kircher's "incredible credulity and superstition"; "it is little wonder many modern students have been loath to grant him any significance at all." But whatever Kircher may have seen, quite understandably colored by the ideas of his period, his *Scrutinium pestis* attracted considerable attention; it went through several editions in just a few years, helping to keep alive the idea of *Contagium animatum*.

Overthrow of Doctrine of Spontaneous Generation

The beginning of wisdom is found in doubting;
by doubting, we come to the question, and by
seeking we may come to the truth.   PIERRE ABELARD

In 1667, only nine years after Kircher's publication, the simple direct investigations of Redi[21] in Arezzo, Italy, cast discredit on Kircher's statements and those of others as to the sources of the "worms" in decomposing matter. Even the experimental portion of the long conflict is so involved that we can cite only this beginning with Redi and the dramatic chapter closing with Tyndall and Pasteur. To test the view that "worms" arise from decomposing animals or plants, Redi placed several kinds of flesh in boxes, observed the decay, and watched the maggots appear and change into adult insects. At times he thought he saw flies dropping ova on the meat, a possible source of the maggots. To test this hypothesis, he placed fresh meat in three sets of small jars, the first left open, the second covered with fine gauze, and the third covered tightly with parchment. The meat in all the jars became decayed attracting flies by the odors. In a short time, maggots appeared in the open jars, and these later developed into flies. In the second series maggots developed on the surface of the gauze, but not in the meat below. The meat in the third series covered with parchment decayed, but no maggots appeared. He carried out many similar experiments with flies on different fruits and vegetables tracing the development of the ova through maggots to adult insects of several species and thus laid a careful foundation for his famous dictum *omne vivum ex vivo.*

More exacting experiments by Spallanzani (1729–99), a century later, and increasingly critical studies of Schulze, Schwann, and Schröder in the middle of the nineteenth century apparently settled the question.

ANTONY VAN LEEUWENHOEK AND HIS SUCCESSORS

There is nothing too little for so little a
creature as man. It is by studying little things
that we attain the great art of having as little
misery and as much happiness as possible.

JOHNSON TO BOSWELL FOR HIS PRIVATE JOURNAL

In the meantime, however, Antony van Leeuwenhoek (1632–1723) had come onto the scene and other microscopists such as his fellow

Dutchmen, de Graaf and Swammerdam, and Hooke and Grew in England. They opened the doors into the new world of microbiology.

Leeuwenhoek[22] examined with his simple lenses of high curvature "a little white matter" from between his teeth,

which is as thick as if 'twere batter. . . . I have mixed it, at divers times, with clean rain-water (in which there were no animalcules), and also with spittle, that I took out of my mouth, after ridding it of air-bubbles (lest the bubbles should make any motion in the spittle): and I then most always saw, with great wonder, that in the said matter there were many very little living animalcules, very prettily a-moving. The biggest sort had a very strong and swift motion, and shot through the water (or spittle) like a pike does through the water. These were most always few in number.

One exceedingly minute type "seemed to me e'en as if there were, in my judgement, several thousand of 'em in an amount of water or spittle (mixed with the matter aforesaid) no bigger than a sand-grain; albeit there were quite nine parts of water, or spittle, to one part of the matter that I took from betwixt my front teeth, or my grinders." From his sketches and descriptions it is commonly agreed that the smallest "little animals" were bacteria.

The existence of this newly discovered microscopic world and the finding that free oxygen was necessary to support the life of the microbes that were then known, reawakened the querying and the experimentation into the age-old question of spontaneous generation. Finally (is anything final?) the theory was overthrown by fifteen years of experimentation by Louis Pasteur,[23] especially through the persistence of sterility in flasks of meat infusions after prolonged boiling and free contact with the air by means of doubly curved goosenecks and by Tyndall with similarly boiled infusions in vessels open to the air in a dust-free chamber. Tyndall also aided by demonstrating the different heat resistance of vegetative cells and spores by means of discontinuous boiling. In granting acclaim chiefly to two men, Pasteur and Tyndall, the first primarily a chemist and the other a physicist, we must realize that they were but adding to the observations of other investigators who had gradually made more certain the seventeenth century dictum of Redi, *omne vivum ex vivo.*

Although all would now agree with Pasteur's statement that organized living beings (slime molds, bacteria, or mice) are not produced by spontaneous generation, yet practically all scientists have continued to hold that eons ago in the days when our planet was a watery primordial mass, conditions must have been ripe for the upbuilding from simple minerals of something akin to amino acids. In more millenniums, these must have acquired the property of replication into some simple ancestor of bacteria. This is of course speculation, but to scientists is much more acceptable than any notion of direct creation. In the last few years, however, exciting experiments have given more than suggestive foundations for these speculations.

Severable filterable plant viruses and at least two viruses producing disease in man, poliomyelitis and Coxsackie, remain infectious after a high degree of purification and subsequent crystallization. On theoretical grounds, it has been suggested, that the planets formed at much lower temperatures than formerly assumed and that they had reducing atmosphere. Following this hypothesis, certain animo acids, these building blocks of proteins, have been produced by subjecting a mixture of simple gases (CH_4, NH_3, H_2O, and H_2) to electrical spark and silent discharges for about a week. Recently Kornberg and associates have actually produced deoxyribonucleic acids (the chemical compounds regarded as the basis of all forms of life and closely tied in with hereditary nuclear genes) by enzymatic synthesis from deoxyribonucleoside triphosphates.[24]

A vast amount of evidence is now before us making it clear that just as the old distinction between organic and inorganic chemistry ceased to have any meaning after urea was synthesized, so now with our increasing knowledge of viruses and enzymatic syntheses, we must realize that no sharp line exists between that which we term animate and that which we have called inanimate. By tomorrow or day after tomorrow we fully expect that some simple self-replicating organic compound will be engendered in the laboratory. The biologist has complete faith in the infinite variety and complexity of nature. Would that we could find similar faith in man and his capacity to handle with wisdom the increasing forces at his hand whether animate or inanimate. A portion of Rudyard Kipling's introduction to a Hunterian medical lecture by Sir John Bland Sutton seems pertinent.[25]

"There is a legend," said Mr. Kipling,

which has been transmitted to us from the remotest ages. It has entered into many brains and colored not a few creeds. It is this: Once upon a time, or rather, at the very birth of time, when the Gods were so new that they had no names, and Man was still damp from the clay of the pit whence he had been digged, Man claimed that he too was in some sort a deity. The Gods were as just in those days as they are now. They weighed his evidence and decided that Man's claim was good—that he was, in effect, a divinity, and, as such, entitled to be freed from the trammels of mere brute instinct, to enjoy the consequence of his own acts. But the Gods sell everything at a price. Having conceded Man's claim, the legend goes that they came by stealth and stole away this godhead, with intent to hide it where Man should never find it again. But this was none so easy. If they hid it anywhere on Earth, the Gods foresaw that Man, the inveterate hunter—the father, you might say, of all hunters—would leave no stone unturned or wave unplumbed till he had recovered it. If they concealed it among themselves, they feared that Man might in the end batter his way up even to the skies. And, while they were all thus at a stand, the wisest of the Gods, who afterward became the God Brahm, said, "I know. Give it to me!" And he closed his hand upon the tiny unstable light of Man's stolen godhead, and when that great hand opened again, the light was gone. "All is well," said Brahm, "I have hidden it where Man will never dream of looking for it. I have hidden it inside of Man himself." "Yes, but whereabouts inside Man have you hidden it?" all the other Gods asked. "Ah," said Brahm, "that is my secret, and always will be unless and until Man discovers it for himself."

By studying the intimacies, the enzyme systems of physiology, we seem to be getting measurably nearer that discovery.

Fermentation

> Living things are found by a simple
> experiment to have powers undreamt of, and who knows
> what may be behind?   W. BATESON

The unraveling of another biological snarl, that of fermentation, proved still further the importance of microbes. The use of bread leavened by wild yeasts or certain accidental gas-producing bacteria dates from prehistoric times. Some of the methods are shown in the carvings in the tombs of the Old Kingdom at Sakkara (ancient Memphis), Egypt, dating from around 3000 B. C. The making of vinegar, beers, and wines has aided in food preservation and contributed to the gaiety and the tragedies of life in all lands and has stimulated universal wonder and fascinating legends. The dairy industry, both in primitive cultures and later among highly organized peoples, with its production of milk, butter, and pungent, delectable cheeses was another broad basis for interest in fermentation. Knowledge in these realms affected both food and drink so that eager interest arose in improving and controlling the rule-of-thumb processes of the ages.

Chemistry was making outstanding strides around the middle of the nineteenth century and leaders, such as Berzelius, Wöhler, and Liebig had great influence. Liebig[26] was an especially vigorous and intolerant person, and he flouted and scorned the biologists Cagniard de Latour, Theodore Schwann, and Friedrich Kützing, who independently presented increasingly strong evidence that yeasts, first described by Leeuwenhoek in 1680, were living agents, not just chemical substances, and that fermentation was due to the life processes of the yeasts. Liebig and his supporters continued to maintain that yeasts were nonliving chemical catalysts and that fermentation was due to chemical instability with the balance upset by these catalysts.

The clash of experiment and opinion went on for several decades. The brilliant leader of bacteriologists, Louis Pasteur, was drawn into the problem about 1854, and he continued to study various types of fermentation for twenty years, clarifying our knowledge of these obscure biologic processes, adding to our bacteriologic technics, and zealously trying to persuade the other chemists of the accuracy of his observations. His *Mémoire sur la fermentation alcoolique* (1860) and *Etudes sur la bière*[27] (1876) will remain as classical outstanding master-works, and his proof of anaerobiasis, life without atmospheric oxygen (1863), and that certain microbes removed only the dextro tartaric acid from mixtures containing both right- and left-handed crystals (1860), gave startlingly new conceptions and impetus to further experiment.

The chemists gradually (Liebig died in 1873) became convinced of the microbic basis of fermentation and aided in developing new methods of control in major industries. Büchner[28] in 1897 succeeded in pressing from the living yeasts a nonliving, noncellular active enzyme which caused alcoholic fermentation of sugar. The study of enzymes and elusive coenzymes is today one of the most subtle and rapidly advancing fields of investigation.

Microbes, the Specific Causative Agents in Particular Diseases

Although the microscopic world was described with increasing detail in the seventeenth and eighteenth centuries and although Fracastorius and his followers had shown that *contagium animatum* was highly probable, the bringing of these together, the experimental proof, was not forthcoming save in a few suggestive instances, until the latter part of the nineteenth century. Aside from the technical difficulties which were many, the celebrated "English Hippocrates," Thomas Sydenham[29] (1624–89) was a stumbling block who exerted influence both in Europe and this country throughout the eighteenth century. In spite of his acute clinical observations as shown by his firsthand descriptions of diseases such as scarlet fever, measles, and gout, Sydenham was perplexed over the rise and fall of great epidemics, a state of mind in which we still share. Unfortunately he reverted to a metaphysical explanation an "epidemic constitution of the atmosphere" varying with the year and dependent "upon a secret and inexplicable alteration in the bowels of the earth." The planets were also brought into the confused picture. Sydenham was thoroughly imbued with the miasmatic doctrine and includes "effluvia or seminia" in his discussions, but he paid little attention to the idea of infection or contagion. For example, he thought that in the absence of a suitable epidemic constitution of the air, plague could only be communicated by infection sporadically.

In the study and isolation of an infectious agent, large size and ease of demonstration have always been important aids to investigators. Redi in 1668 showed evidence that a specific dermatitis was caused by the body louse; *Sarcoptes scabei* was strongly implicated in the itch (scabies) by Bonomo in 1687; and the disease was actually reproduced experimentally in man a century later by Wichmann in 1786. Indeed the itch mite had been described by Avenzoar as early as 1281, although his writings are known only in translation. Linnaeus (1758) suggested the probable relation of a number of helminths such as *Ascaris lumbricoides* and *Taenia solium* and the human diseases now known to be caused by these worms.

Agostino Bassi in 1835, demonstrated that a fungus, later named for him, *Botrytis bassiana* was the causative agent in muscardine, a devastating disease of silkworms. Bulloch[30] states that "he is justly regarded as the real founder of the doctrine of pathogenic microorganisms of vegetable origin." And in 1839, J. L. Schoenlein identified a fungus, *Achorion schoenleinii*, as the cause of favus, a disease of the scalp of man.

A road-breaking cogent essay by Henle[31] (1840) using knowledge available at the time in human and veterinary medicine as well as in plant diseases, without adding any experimental evidence, showed that living reproducing microorganisms provided the most plausible explanation of the origin of many contagious diseases. Drawing especially on two diseases of known etiology, scabies and muscardine, and many contagious diseases of unknown etiology, Henle stressed the difficulties in determining whether an agent or body found in a given disease is actually the causative agent.

Even if living, mobile animals or distinct plants are found in contagious material, then they may have arisen accidentally just as in benign pus, or in all animal secretions when they have been exposed to the air for some time. And even if they would be found constantly in contagious matter and inside the body, then the objection would still be possible and at first hardly to be refuted, that they were only parasitic, even, if constant elements of the contagia, just as indeed one still hears maintained concerning the spermatozoa, that they are elements which may develop in the fluid and may even be significant for the diagnosis, without being therefore the active stuff of the fluid or of the semen. It could be empirically proven that they are the active part, if one could isolate the spermatozoa and the spermatic fluid and observe the powers of each separately— an experiment which one must probably abandon.

We must bear in mind that the simple technics for isolation and growing bacteria had not been developed by 1840 and that any theorizing, however persuasive, is colored by the notions of the period. We recognize in this essay, however, the germ, the "seminaria," that grew into the more complete criteria enunciated by Koch in 1884, and maintained ever since as bacteriologic ideals of the proof of etiologic relationships. Although the anticontagionists of this period freely admitted that certain diseases, such as smallpox, syphilis, measles, and the itch were contagious, "the big three," yellow fever, bubonic plague, and cholera together with typhus fever, had nowhere been controlled by quarantine measures. These facts were enormous stumbling blocks to the acceptance by well-informed physicians that these diseases were spread by contagion. The laity found it easier to accept the idea, because contagion in measles, mumps, and diphtheria was so apparent, and they were not aware of the contradictory evidence.

To a person of the twentieth century it does seem strange that just before the almost explosive development of microbiology, adherence to anticontagionism should have been so tenacious. It is clear, however, that only after the demonstration of latent and carrier cases and transmission through water and food and the demonstration of insect transfer as in malaria and yellow fever could contagion in the broader significance be established. Ackerknecht[32] emphasizes these points and the strong influence of the findings of the several cholera commissions in India in the conflict of evidence. "One of the most signal defeats of anticontagionism was the adoption of the importance and contagiousness of cholera by the Anglo-Indian medical men in 1866, after a resistance of more than 60 years."

Our colonial ancestors, strongly influenced by the necessity of hewing an existence from the new world, lived necessarily in the climate of opinion of their period. The importance of miasmas and emanations coming from rotting organic matter, the malign forces from earthquakes, comets, and erupting volcanoes, the "epidemic distempers" and "epidemic constitutions" of the great Sydenham were mingled with the suggestion that contagion might in some unknown manner be a factor in certain diseases. Through all these notions, especially in theocratic New England, was the strongly prevalent idea that the disease was the will of God and if it was occurring in epidemic proportions it was a direct purposeful visitation because of man's sinfulness or neglect. "To coerce the spiritual powers, or to square them and get them on our side was during enormous tracts of time the one great object in our dealings with the spiritual world."[33] Too strong efforts to combat or prevent epidemics were sacrilegious and should therefore be condemned. This idea still persists.

> *Medicine could not begin to be medicine until*
> *it was dissociated from magic and religion.*[34]
>
> *Diseases are not the work of God or demon.*   HIPPOCRATES

CHAPTER II

Early Centuries in America

O brave new world, that has such people in't. THE TEMPEST

We are likely to forget that in spite of wind and wave, resulting in more than a month of extreme crowding, hardship, and both contagious and nutritional diseases even in a good crossing, the early colonists were dependent on Europe for many of their material and cultural needs. Not infrequently, our leaders returned to the fatherlands for study and interchange of ideas. Only slowly did a degree of independence develop, and we are still bound by indissoluble ties even in this last half of the twentieth century. In wars, for example, any considerable clash in Europe has inevitably involved this country.

Our ancestors brought with them not only the literature, laws, and the cultural heritage of their homelands, but also the diseases, among these the communicable, such as tuberculosis, diphtheria, influenza, scarlet fever, dysenteries, measles, other infections of childhood, and periodic outbreaks of yellow fever and smallpox that swept through the colonies. Throughout the early seventeenth century the mortality among the colonists was frightful. Of the shiploads arriving both north and south during many years, one-half or more were doomed to death within a few months after their arrival. The meager statistics of the period, personal letters, and the lichen-covered stones in the graveyards give eloquent evidence of the high mortality especially among infants and children. Many of the colonists were ill prepared to dig their living from the soil; instead, hunger, inhospitable climate, especially in New England, and disease forced them to dig their own graves. Currie states that "in Philadelphia, New York, Baltimore and Charleston more children are annually destroyed by chronic cholera or bilious diarrhoea and by cholera in its acute form than by all other diseases to which they are subject in this variable and unsteady climate." And in Noah Webster's itemized descriptions of "Epidemic and Pestilential Diseases" from the earliest accounts of the Christian era through the eighteenth century, one finds evidence of crushing losses among both the Indians and our colonists.[1]

The lack of scientific knowledge and the usual lack of professional standards in a frontier country placed medical burdens on the few who had a little preceptorial training and on herb doctors, ministers, and laymen who were forced by circumstances to accept the responsibilities.[2] And medical practice was little, if any, better in Europe. A reading of Molières' biting satires, *Le Médecin Malgré Lui* or *Le Malade Imaginaire* sheds light on the contemporary practices in France.

Quarantine, Marine Hospital Service, and Boards of Health

The early biblical practices of isolation and the extreme measures against leprosy with some 19,000 leper houses, "lazarettos," in Europe by the thirteenth century have been mentioned. Although the practice is manifestly much older, the word quarantine derives from the Italian *quaranta* referring to the period of forty-day maritime restraint imposed by Venice (1403) on ships from epidemic areas.[3]

In 1647 the General Court of Massachusetts Bay Colony enacted a maritime quarantine statute because of the prevalence of disease, chiefly yellow fever, in the Barbadoes.[4] With the cessation of the epidemic two years later, the act was repealed. Such spasmodic attempts to prevent the spread of epidemics occurred throughout the seventeenth and eighteenth centuries in all of the seaport areas of our country. On June 22, 1797, again largely through fear of yellow fever, Massachusetts passed a law "Providing for the formation of health organizations in towns and gave these local boards of health the authority to abate nuisances which they considered dangerous to the public health." Two years later, as an aftermath of a severe outbreak of this disease in Boston, a local board of health was established with Paul Revere as its chairman; such a multiplicity of functions did he serve. Several colonies, for example New York as early as 1742, with a charter from George III, following a British practice, established a Marine Society for the purpose of improving maritime knowledge and for the relieving of indigent and distressed masters of vessels, and their wives and orphans.

The practice spread and, after we became the United States of America, our federal Marine Hospital Service was established by act of the Fifth Congress on July 16, 1789, under the presidency of John Adams.

Because of outbreaks of yellow fever in New York City and Philadelphia and the resulting terror and disruption of life, Congress passed an Act on April 3, 1794, permitting the legislature to convene at some other place than the seat of government "as the President may judge proper in case of prevalence of contagious disease."[5] In colonial days and up to 1878 maritime quarantine functions were legally in the hands of state and local authorities,[6] but because of the responsibility for care of seamen, the United States Marine Hospital Service became involved in the control and quarantine of vessels and their crews, especially those coming from ports where yellow fever and cholera prevailed. As early as 1833 Congress provided additional funds for boats and medical officers to aid in enforcement of quarantine regulations. Conflict between local and federal authorities was inevitable, especially as the knowledge of sources and modes of infection was so inadequate; hence local opinions ruled.

In 1879 a National Board of Health was established by Congress, a highly desirable step, but this created overlapping authority, resented by the Marine Hospital Service. Unfortunate political pressures caused the discontinuation of this early national board of health a few years later in 1883. Since that date, with changing times, differing titles and enlarging functions, including large-scale research with excellent buildings, equipment, and personnel, the Marine Hospital Service has grown into the more appropriately named United States Public Health Service. Recently this and other federal boards and divisions concerned with the public weal have been united under one executive head with cabinet status under the title of Department of Health, Education, and Welfare.

Massachusetts established the first permanent state health organization in 1869 and California the second in 1870; the other states followed rather slowly with a large number in the 1880's, when the bacteriologic surge was strong.

Inoculation of Smallpox—
The First Specific Preventive Medicine in America
COTTON MATHER AND ZABDIEL BOYLSTON

Smallpox was the dominating epidemic disease in colonial America during the seventeenth and much of the eighteenth centuries.[7] Boston for example, was afflicted with repeated epidemics. "In 1677 was seen a comet in April and May; an earthquake was experienced in England; and in Charlestown, Massachusetts, raged the smallpox with the mortality of a plague."[8] In 1698 Cotton Mather wrote,

The small-pox has four times been a great plague among us—often had one hundred bills, desiring prayer for the sick, been read in one day, in one of our assemblies. In one twelvemonth, about one thousand of our neighbors, have been carried to their long resting home. In 1702, 4.4% of the inhabitants died with it. The most violent epidemic was in 1721, when 6006, being 54.6% of the population had it; of whom 14.3% died.[9]

The following table from Shattuck's survey[10] gives a view of the prevalence and results of the disease through most of the eighteenth century.

	Ratio per 100 of the population				Natural			Inoculated		
Year	Cases	Deaths	Sick	Died	Cases	Deaths	Ratio %	Cases	Deaths	Ratio %
1721	6006	850	54.6	7.7	5759	844	14.8	247	6	2.4
1730	4000	500	26.6	3.3	3600	488	13.5	400	12	3.0
1752	7669	569	48.9	3.6	5545	539	9.7	2124	30	1.7
1764	5646	170	36.4	1.1	669	124	18.5	4977	46	.9
1776	5292	57	44.1	1.0	304	29	9.5	4988	18	.5
1778	2243	61	16.6	.4	122	42	34.4	2121	29	.9
1792	8346	198	46.0	1.0	232	33	14.2	8114	165	1.8

The first specific measure used in this country, as in Europe and before that for centuries in India and probably in China, was inoculation against the smallpox. The direct application of material from a pustule of an active case of this disease to a normal person was actually a hazardous large-scale experiment in microbiology. It was an active immunization by producing the disease at a chosen time and by a different route of introduction of the virus from that in the natural disease. The Reverend Cotton Mather of Boston, one of the first native Americans elected to membership in the Royal Society of London, became convinced of the value of inoculation through reading the *Transactions* of that society concerning the practice in Turkey and even before that through conversations with his negro slave. Mather wrote Dr. John Woodward of the Royal Society in 1716;

I am willing to confirm you, in a favorable opinion, of Dr. Timonius's Communication; and therefore, I do assure you that many months before I met with any Intimations of treating ye Small-Pox, with ye methods of Inoculation, anywhere in Europe, I had from a Servant of my own, an account of its being practiced in Africa. Enquiring of my Negro-man, Anesimus, who is a pretty intelligent Fellow, Whether he ever had ye

Small-Pox; he answered, both, Yes, and No; and then told me that he had undergone an operation, which had given him something of ye Small-Pox, and would forever preserve him from it; adding, That it was often used among ye Guramantese, and whoever had ye courage to use it, was forever free from ye fear of the Contagion. He described ye operation to me, and shew'd me in his Arm ye Scar, which it left upon him; and his Description of it, made it the same that afterwards I found related unto you by Timonius.[11]

When one of the periodic outbreaks of smallpox in Boston occurred in 1721, Mather tried to interest physicians. Most of them ridiculed or scorned the procedure, but Dr. Zabdiel Boylston was persuaded, and on June 27, 1721, initiated the practice in this country by successfully inoculating his only son, a boy of thirteen, and two negro servants. During the year 1721 and the first part of 1722, according to Hutchinson in his history of Massachusetts, "Dr. Boylston inoculated 247 persons and 39 were inoculated by other persons in Boston and vicinity. Of this number, six died or 2.1%; several of these were supposed to have taken the infection before inoculation. In the same period, 5759 took the disease in the natural way, of whom 844 died or 14.6+% and many of those who recovered were left with broken constitutions and disfigured countenances."[12] Both Cotton Mather and Zabdiel Boylston underwent persecution, bomb-throwing (both literally and from the pulpits of the Boston Divines), assault, and attempts of the courts and other physicians to suppress the practice.

In the Boston area inoculation house parties were common; here the persons could be isolated without a consuming boredom. At one of these John Adams went through the ordeal under the ministrations of Dr. Perkins. In April, 1764, he wrote to his fiancée, Miss Abigail Smith:

Just off to enjoy the Small Pox Saturday eve. Eight o'clock. My dear Diana—For many years past, I have not felt more serenely than I do this evening. My head is clear and my heart is at ease. . . . My room is prepared for a seven days retirement and my plan is digested for 4–5 weeks. My brother retreats with me to our preparatory hospital and is determined to keep me company through the Small Pox.

. . . .

We have new milk in abundance and as much pudding and rice and indeed anything of a farinaceous kind we please, and the medicine we take is not at all nauseous or painful. Five persons in the same room under the care of Dr. Lord are starved and medicamented with the greatest severity. No bread, no pudding, no milk (except half milk, half water) and powders that keep them sick and weak.

Inoculated patients felt pretty uncomfortable "just before the Pock

came out—some general languor, some fever and shivers." Then their
aches and pains departed, "Their spirits rise, tongues run and they eat,
drink and laugh like prisoners released." Abigail's brother and uncle,
who had been inoculated in another house, "have been here to see us
this morning."[13]

About a decade later another prominent layman, Benjamin Franklin,
was influential in introducing inoculation in the Philadelphia area. He
had lost a young son from smallpox in the 1736 epidemic in that city.
Inoculation steadily gained ground in the colonies despite the occasional fatalities and strong opposition. Any detailed history of inoculation in smallpox in this country is beyond the purpose of this narrative.
We should bear in mind, however, that in the eighteenth century smallpox was almost as common as is measles today, but with a high mortality rate, varying in the different epidemics, and ranging from 10 to
30 per cent. Therefore, a practice, even though it caused death at times
and did occasionally spread the infection and other communicable diseases, was thought permissible because it cut down total death losses
and prevented more widespread epidemics. In describing and listing
pestilence of many kinds in the colonies, Noah Webster observes in
1799 "It must however be marked that the smallpox in modern times,
will not exhibit similar effects as formerly, since the art of inoculation
has nearly banished the disease as an epidemic, from our cities, where
alone it used to prevail to any considerable extent."[14]

Vaccination against Smallpox

EDWARD JENNER AND BENJAMIN WATERHOUSE

With Jenner's announcement in 1798[15] of the use of cowpox, people
were ready for a relatively safe vaccination protection against smallpox.
The practice of inoculation, dangerous and stormy, passed into almost
forgotten history. Dr. Benjamin Waterhouse, first professor of theory
and practice of physic in Harvard Medical School, began vaccination
in this country. In July, 1800, he vaccinated his only son and three
slaves, and subsequently inoculated them with smallpox. Complete
protection in this group and later similar success with a group of nineteen other children caused the local Board of Health to announce that
cowpox was a complete protection against smallpox. The use of vaccination increased only slowly however because calf lymph was not
available and the method of arm to arm transfer of the virus was em-

ployed with its attendant dangers. Instances of the transfer of purulent infections, erysipelas, and even syphilis are recorded. With the gradual reduction of inoculation and slow adoption of the Jennerian vaccination, a highly susceptible population suffered repeated disastrous outbreaks of the smallpox during the century.

After 1870 calf lymph became available and control of production by the United States Public Health Service was gradually achieved. At least two strains of smallpox virus are present in the world populations, the one producing the more serious *variola major* with high mortality and the other, the more common one in the United States, producing *variola minor* with much lower death rates. An excellent record of protection against both types has been established by vaccination and this remains the only proved method of preventing epidemics of this once common and justifiably dreaded disease.

That our contributions in this and in other fields came slowly and that most of them were not road-breakers, is readily observed in any well-documented study, either before or since the end of World War I. Taking the *Newer Knowledge of Bacteriology and Immunology* edited by E. O. Jordan and I. S. Falk as a representative sample, this volume presented eighty-three essays in the important diverse fields, each paper written by one who had worked intensively in that field. (Only one author was from a foreign land.) The date of publication, 1928, ten years after the end of World War I gave an additional decade for development beyond our designated terminal date. The total number of references cited is approximately 5462, 4414 from foreign publications and 1048 from American, the latter about 19 per cent of the whole. If we were unaware of our relative position, these figures are convincing.

CHAPTER III

Critical Epidemiology
Before the Birth of Bacteriology

Oh let us never, never doubt,
What nobody is sure about!

H. BELLOC

Attention must be given to several noteworthy clinical investigations that proved modes of spread and contagion, with at least a probable *contagium animatum*, in certain diseases, before the specific causative microbes were known. In the nineteenth century the concept of "seminaria," planted by Fracastorius in the sixteenth century, was beginning to sprout on the basis of these epidemiological observations.

Diphtheria

PIERRE BRETONNEAU

Bretonneau[1] (1778–1862) of Tours, France, was one of these acute observers in the early part of the nineteenth century. In several extensive treacherous epidemics of the Egyptian disease, malignant angina (1818–55), he showed clear-cut evidence of transmission within the family and from family to family. In 1829 he described an epidemic in which each person in a girls' boarding school suffered from the disease with no other cases in the neighborhood. He emphasized the specific nature of the disease and in his final memoir (1855) wrote "it is vain to deny that contagion, if not the source of endemics, is the source of most epidemics." Because of the leathery characteristic nature of the false membrane in the throat, he gave the disease the name we continue to use, diphtheria.

Bretonneau also antedated (1818) the distinguished Parisian physician, Louis, teacher of a number of prominent American physicians (see Chapter XI), in observing the spread of typhoid fever by contagion and in describing the characteristic lesions in Peyer's patches. His name for typhoid fever, dothienenteritis, was too cumbersome to last. Louis, who gave the name that has persisted, subsequently remarked, "The contagious power of typhoid fever seems to me demonstrated by the facts and I accept it with no hesitation."

Measles

PETER LUDWIG PANUM

In 1846 a truly unique opportunity came to a twenty-six-year-old Danish medical graduate, Peter Ludwig Panum,[2] not yet through his hospital internship. An epidemic of measles raging on the Faroe Islands, located in the north Atlantic Ocean between the Shetland Islands and Iceland, caused the Danish government to send young Panum to see what he could do. The seventeen inhabited islands were rigidly isolated by the dangerous tides and currents and by governmental trade restrictions, so that no measles had been reported for sixty-five years, since 1781, thus creating a highly susceptible population of some 7,782 inhabitants. The first case (April 4 or 5) occurred in a carpenter who had returned from Copenhagen where he had visited in a household with several persons ill with measles. The next cases were two of his intimate friends. The disease spread rapidly on the immediate island and more slowly to the other islands providing excellent opportunity to trace the transmission. Panum followed the spread in fifty-two isolated villages, obtained complete records, and determined that the incubation period was of 13–14 days and that the infection commonly occurred when the primary case was in the eruptive stage. A lasting immunity was demonstrated in that all of the ninety-eight older persons who had had the disease in 1781 escaped the disease in 1846.

If among 6,000 cases of which I myself observed and treated about 1,000, not one was found in which it would be justifiable, on any grounds whatever, to suppose a miasmatic origin of measles, because it was absolutely clear that the disease was transmitted from man to man and from village to village by contagion, whether the latter was received by immediate contact with a patient, or was conveyed to the infected person by clothes, or the like, it is certainly reasonable at least to entertain a considerable degree of doubt as the miasmatic nature of the disease. . . . It is beyond doubt that the surest means of hindering the spread of the disease, is to maintain quarantine.

In many villages success in preventing general spread of the disease was obtained by house-isolation.

But apparently Panum had no interest in *contagium animatum*; gaseous emanations from the patient were, in his mind, the infectious material.

Asiatic Cholera

JOHN SNOW

John Snow[3] (1813–58) was another young physician who saw and seized his opportunity; he is better known in medicine as one of the earliest practitioners in anesthesia, using both chloroform and ether; he twice aided Queen Victoria in childbirth through the use of chloroform. He became an articled pupil of Mr. William Hardcastle, a surgeon, at the tender age of fourteen. His cholera experience began at the age of eighteen years during the first pandemic of that disease, when he saw the miners brought up from some of the coal-pits of Northumberland in the winter of 1831–32, after having profuse discharges from the stomach and bowels, and when fast approaching a state of collapse. In answer to Snow's inquiry, a relative connected with a colliery near Leeds wrote: "The pit is one huge privy and of course the men," who spend eight to nine hours in the pits, "always take their victuals with unwashed hands." Through care of patients, painstaking follow-up of case after case, searching for the unknown contacts with earlier cases, and from statistical studies, Snow came to the conclusion that fecal pollution and transfer of the unknown specific agents from the sick to the well through direct contact and through drinking water were responsible for the spread of cholera.

The culmination of his studies in this disease came as a result of the Broad Street pump epidemic in London in 1854. There were cases of cholera in London during the year but few in this area in the latter part of August. Within 250 yards of the pump in a two-week period from August 31, upwards of five hundred fatal cases of Asiatic cholera occurred. By laborious questioning Snow found that most of the cases were among people in the habit of drinking from the Broad Street pump and that few of those in the neighborhood who used other water acquired the disease. For example, "The keeper of a coffee shop in the neighborhood—where the pump water was supplied at dinner time, informed me (on 6th September) that she was already aware of nine of her customers who were dead." On the other hand "a brewery in

Broad Street near to the pump . . . with over seventy men employed had no cases of cholera 'at least in a severe form.'. . . The men are allowed a certain quantity of malt liquor and the proprieter, Mr. Huggins, believes they do not drink water at all." Also there was a deep well in the brewery. Snow told the board of guardians of St. James Parish that if they would remove the handle of the pump, the epidemic would cease. They took off the handle on September 8 and thereafter came a rapid decline with a return to approximately the usual cholera rate by September 20. Further studies gave convincing evidence: the brick work both of the well and the nearby (2 feet 8 inches) cesspool was in a badly decayed condition and the well was at a lower level showing drainage from cesspool to the well.

The different districts of London obtained their water from varied sources. In analyzing the statistical studies made by the Metropolitan Sanitary Commission in the several epidemics (1832–54), Snow found striking differences in the death rates from cholera in the different areas. Taking the figures from one epidemic, that of 1854, an experiment on a grand scale is provided with some 300,000 persons separated with no volition on their part into two groups; "one group being supplied with water containing the sewage of London, . . . the other group having water quite free from such impurity."

The following is the proportion of deaths to 10,000 houses during the first seven weeks of the epidemic in the population supplied by the Southwark and Vauxhall Company and by the Lambeth Company and in the rest of London.

	Number of houses	Deaths from cholera	Deaths in Each 10,000 houses
Southwark and Vauxhall Company	40,046	1,263	315
Lambeth Company	26,107	98	37
Rest of London	256,423	1,422	59

The mortality in the houses supplied by the Southwark and Vauxhall Company was therefore between eight and nine times as great as in the houses supplied by the Lambeth Company. These figures with a study of the sources of the water proved even to the sceptical the importance of water carriage of the specific agent. In spite of some confusion, Snow clung to the common thread, realizing that an obligate parasite propagated in the intestines and passed to others by ingestion of diluted excreta was the most probable explanation of the facts. In 1883 Koch isolated the cholera vibrio; numerous experimental cases both voluntary and accidental have proved its identity.

Typhoid Fever

WILLIAM BUDD

Harking back to the environmental teachings of Hippocrates that had prevailed for 2,000 years, the theory that filth and foul odors therefrom, the emanations which under certain atmospheric conditions could be seen rising from the dank decomposing muck of swamps, seemed to the eighteenth, nineteenth, and even the twentieth century mind a plausible source and cause of disease. Was not malaria more common in certain swampy areas as for example in the Campagna about Rome? The method of prevention then would obviously be to overcome the foul odors by counteracting gases such as camphor, fires, burning sulphur, or better still to prevent the accumulation of masses of decomposing vegetation or human excreta near human dwellings. Efforts directed against such public nuisances were among the first public health methods of our era.

Another early epidemiological study, one on typhoid fever by William Budd[4] of North Tawton, England, was of value in overthrowing the pythogenic or the rotting-organic-matter theory. He had practiced medicine in a rural area in Devonshire for over twenty years when, following a first case of typhoid fever on July 11, 1839, more than eighty of the inhabitants suffered from the disease and came under his care. He kept an accurate record of all the principal events, and published his first paper in 1856. Other papers followed, and in 1874 when he was retiring from active practice, he brought his observations and deductions together in a telling summary essay supporting the doctrine of contagion commonly known at that time in England as Snow's Theory.

In the first place there was no general system of sewers. . . . Each cottage or group of three or four cottages had its common privy to which a simple excavation in the ground served as cesspool. Besides this, it was a part of the economy of all who worked in the fields, as indeed of many more, to keep a pig, one of whose functions was to furnish manure for the little plot of potatoes that fed man and pig alike. Thus often, hard by the cottage door, there was not only an open privy, but a dungheap, also.

Nevertheless, these conditions existed for many years without leading to any of the results which it is the fashion to ascribe to them.

Much there was, as I can testify, offensive to the nose, but fever there was none. . . .

Meanwhile privies, pigstyes and dungheaps continued year after year to exhale ill odours, without any specific effect on the public health.

. . . .

For the development of this fever a more *specific element* was needed than either swine, the dungheaps, or the privies were, in the common course of things, able to furnish.

This specific element was furnished in the excreta of the first case. By excellent epidemiological studies, Budd traced the mode of spread of many of his eighty cases together with others in neighboring villages.

"The first thing to attract attention after the disorder had become rife in North Tawton, was the strong tendency it showed, when once introduced into a family, to spread through the household." By his studies, Budd showed a high probability that the "specific element" was in the intestinal discharges from fever patients and fresh cases occurred through contact with the feces. In one town "the little stream, laden with the fever poison cast off by the intestinal disease of the man who had been stricken with the same fever some weeks before, was the only bond between the cases."

In another series, "kept in strict separation from one another, as far as their persons were concerned, the common privy was almost the only connecting link left between them." "Neither dirt nor rotting manure cause the fever but some *specific element* breeding and multiplying in the body and passing to well individuals by various routes." It was not the esthetically objectionable and disagreeable rotting feces that were responsible for the spread of typhoid but some "specific element" in the stools from a previous case.

A clearer statement could hardly have been made until after the isolation of the specific organism by Gaffky in 1884. Typhoid fever was not reproducible in experimental animals, but numerous laboratory infections with pure cultures have since then given ample proof of the specific relationship of this microorganism to this disease.

Puerperal Fever

OLIVER WENDELL HOLMES AND IGNAZ SEMMELWEIS

If a pregnant woman be attacked
by erysipelas of the womb, it is fatal.   HIPPOCRATES

This bit of ancient wisdom, with stress on the modes of contagion, was emphasized early by one of our most loved poet-physicians. "The disease known as Puerperal Fever is so far contagious as to be frequently carried from patient to patient by physicians and nurses."[5] So wrote the young anatomist, Oliver Wendell Holmes, in 1843, later professor in the Parkman Chair of anatomy and physiology in Harvard Medical School (Holmes called it a settee). He was impelled to survey the facts of this disease because a neighboring physician had performed an autopsy on a patient who had died of puerperal fever and had himself died in less than a week, apparently in consequence of a wound received at the examination. In the interval, this physician had attended several women in confinement, all of whom, it was stated, were attacked with puerperal fever. Holmes is better known as a literary figure, the author of "Old Ironsides," the "Chambered Nautilus," "Autocrat of the Breakfast Table," and other writings, but to medical men, bacteriologists, and women in childbirth, he should be hailed as the first American who marshaled the grisly facts proving that a "poison," as he called it, of this frequently fatal disease was carried from previous cases or cases of erysipelas by physicians and midwives to the well women about to become mothers. Several British and Scottish physicians had preceded him by some decades in tracing transmission in puerperal fevers in the practices of certain midwives and obstetricians. Holmes cited about twenty ghastly series in England and Scotland, including especially those given by Charles White of Manchester (1773) and by Gordon of Aberdeen (1795). Gordon states: "it is a disagreeable declaration for me to mention that I myself was a means of carrying the infection to a great number of women."[6] We must, however, bear in mind the prevalent anticontagionist theories of epidemic disease so vividly depicted by Ackerknecht in his essay "Anticontagionism between 1821 and 1867." Not until more than a generation after Holmes's publication were the bacterial origins of this infection proved. Those who were forced in the earlier period to accept the idea of "contagion" felt that it was abhorrent and thought of the contagion as some unknown gaseous agent emanating from the ill and poisoning the surrounding air and environment. Most physicians preferred to assume an act of providence that could not be prevented.

Unfortunately, Holmes's essay was published in an obscure Boston journal that died the following year, so that for a decade, it attracted little attention, save locally, where the unorthodox doctrine almost caused his expulsion from the medical hierarchy. But Holmes was a Brahmin and was sustained personally if not intellectually especially by Walter Channing (1786–1876), professor of obstetrics in Harvard Medical School.

Omitting the detailed citations taken by Holmes from foreign medical literature, only portions of two of the several tragic histories from this country follow:

Certainly nothing can be more open and explicit than the account given by Dr. Peirson of Salem, of the cases seen by him. In the first nineteen days of January, 1829, he had five consecutive cases of puerperal fever, every patient he attended being attacked, and the three first cases proving fatal. In March of the same year he had two moderate cases, in June another case, and in July, another which proved fatal. Up to this period he remarks, "I am not informed that a single case had occurred in the practice of any other physician."

. . . .

Following is a series of cases which took place during the last spring in a town at some distance from this neighborhood [Boston]. A physician of that town, Dr. C., had the following consecutive cases.

No. 1, delivered March 20, died March 24.
No. 2, delivered April   9, died April   14.
No. 3, delivered April   10, died April   14,
No. 4, delivered April   11, died April   18.
No. 5, delivered April   27, died May   3.
No. 6, delivered April   28, had some symptoms, recovered.
No. 7, delivered May   8, had some symptoms, also recovered.

These were the only cases attended by this physician during the period referred to. . .

. . . .

The nurse who laid out the body of the patient No. 3 was taken on the evening of the same day with sore throat and erysipelas, and died in ten days from the first attack.

. . . .

The nurse who laid out the body of the patient No. 4 was taken on the day following with symptoms like those of this patient, and died in a week, without any external marks of erysipelas.

Holmes contrasts these histories with the favorable experience at the Rotunda Hospital in Dublin during seven years of the Mastership of Robert Collins when "there was one case of puerperal fever to 178 deliveries or less than six to the thousand, and one death from this disease in 278 cases or between three and four to the thousand." A reading of Collins *Treatise on Midwifery* shows some of the bases for this excellent record.

Because of puerperal fever in 1829,

it was deemed advisable at once to recommend that no patients, except such as were absolutely destitute, should be admitted; . . . until the entire wards of the hospital should have been thoroughly purified. We then had all the wards in rotation filled with chlorine gas in a very condensed form, for the space of 48 hours, during which time the windows, doors and fireplaces were closed so as to prevent its escape as much as possible. The floors and all the woodwork were then covered with the chlorine of lime, mixed with water to the consistence of cream, which was left for 48 hours more. The wood-work was then painted and the walls and ceilings washed with fresh lime. The blankets, etc. were in most instances scoured, and all stoved in a temperature between 120° and 130°. From the time this was completed until the termination of my mastership in November 1833, we did not lose one patient by this disease.[7]

Based on the evidence from the many series given, Holmes was forced to the following conclusions:

1. A physician holding himself in readiness to attend cases of midwifery should never take any active part in the post-mortem examination of cases of puerperal fever.

2. If a physician is present at such autopsies, he should use thorough ablution, change every article of dress, and allow twenty-four hours or more to elapse before attending to any case of midwifery. It may be well to extend the same caution to cases of simple peritonitis.

3. Similar precautions should be taken after the autopsy or surgical treatment of cases of erysipelas, if the physician is obliged to unite such offices with his obstetrical duties, which is in the highest degree inexpedient.

4. On the occurrence of a single case of puerperal fever in his practice, the physician is bound to consider the next female he attends in labor to be in danger of being infected by him unless some weeks at least have elapsed, and it is his duty to take every precaution to diminish her risk of disease and death.

5. If within a short period two cases of puerperal fever happen close to each other in the practice of the same physician, the disease not existing or prevailing in the neighborhood, he would do wisely to relinquish his obstetrical practice for at least one month, and endeavor to free himself by very available means from any noxious influence he may carry about with him.

6. The occurrence of three or more closely connected cases in the practice of one individual, no others existing in the neighborhood, and no other sufficient cause being alleged for the coincidence, is prima facie evidence that he is the vehicle of contagion.

7. It is the duty of the physician to take every precaution that the disease shall not be introduced by nurses or other assistants, by making

proper inquiries concerning them, and giving timely warning of every suspected source of danger.

8. Whatever indulgence may be granted to those who have heretofore been the ignorant causes of so much misery, the time has come when the existence of a *private pestilence* in the sphere of a single physician should be looked upon, not as a misfortune, but a crime; and in the knowledge of such occurrences the duties of the practitioner to his profession should give way to his paramount obligations to society.

The concept of contagion although confused and not usually associated with the idea of causative animalcula was slowly spreading. At the second annual meeting (1847) of the American Medical Association the committee on practical medicine gave attention to "the common occurrence of peritoneal inflammation in the individuals affected with the epidemic erysipelatous fever. . . . The close relationship between epidemic puerperal fever and erysipelas has been noticed by a number of pathologists within a few years past and it has certainly been established by incontestable facts that the two diseases almost invariably prevail simultaneously in the same localities." In that same year also appeared the most notable paper on this theme from faraway Vienna at the hand of a young Hungarian assistant in obstetrics, Ignaz Philip Semmelweis (1818–65).[8]

Far from being a library thesis, the studies of Semmelweis involved his daily life in the hospital, deaths of women in childbirth under his care, painstaking post-mortem examinations, including one on his most intimate friend, Kolletschka, a few days after a prick of his finger while performing an autopsy on a case of puerperal fever. The lesions in the two cases were so similar that Semmelweis' eyes were opened to the tragic truth. He showed that in the First Maternity Clinic that was having death losses of 9.9 per cent, the physicians and students were carrying cadaverous material on their hands directly from the post-mortem rooms to the lying-in wards where they were making vaginal examinations, frequently without even washing their hands. Enforced cleanliness and required scrubbing of the hands in a solution of chlorinated lime reduced the death losses promptly, eventually to the amazingly low figure of 0.39 per cent. Poor Semmelweis met with jealous opposition; he was bitterly attacked by his superiors and was denied the appropriate obstetrical appointment. He died disappointed and disoriented in 1865, one of our medical martyrs.

Philadelphia was the medical center of the period and there, about a decade after the publication of the Holmes essay, two professors of obstetrics, R. L. Hodge of the University of Pennsylvania and C. D. Meigs of Jefferson Medical College, pulled the paper from its quiet rest into the limelight by a series of lectures and published letters in which they ridiculed the idea of contagion in puerperal fever. They supported the theory of the miasmic, telluric, and cosmic origin of puerperal fever. Meigs was especially virulent in deriding the essay as the "jejune and fizzenless vaporings of a sophomore orator." He states further with regard to cases of puerperal infection, "I prefer to attribute them to accident, or Providence, of which I can form a conception, rather than to a contagion of which I cannot form any clear idea, at least as to this particular malady."[9]

But "the blood of the martyrs is the seed of the church." Holmes replied to these harsh attacks by a republication (1855)[10] of his original article with some additional references and material. He met each point of the opposition with logically arranged evidence, vigorously but without descending to name calling. "If I am wrong," he states, "let me be put down by such a rebuke as no rash disclaimer has received since there has been a public opinion in the medical profession of America; if I am right, let doctrines which lead to professional homicide be no longer taught from the chairs of those two great institutions." These two obstetricians are now recalled chiefly for their opposition to the proof of the contagiousness of puerperal fever. Actually they aided rather than hindered the advance of knowledge.

Contagion and Some Far-seeing American Physicians

Austin Flint (1812–86) of Buffalo, an excellent observer, later professor of medicine in several medical schools including Bellevue in New York and author of a series of our best textbooks of medicine, just missed an opportunity to point to drinking water as the transmitting vehicle of an epidemic of typhoid fever in North Boston, Erie County, New York, during the autumn of 1843. The *deus ex machina* could hardly have set up a more perfect natural experiment with a primary case coming from Massachusetts to the isolated community; the young man, severely ill, was unable to continue his journey, and died while lodged in the local Fuller's tavern. In the following weeks 23 secondary cases, 10 of them fatal, broke out among the population of

43 persons. All persons who became ill partook of the well water of the tavern whereas no cases occurred in three families that used their own wells. Flint attributed the difference to the better diet and living conditions of these wealthier families. In 1843 morbific emanations or mineral poisons introduced into the well could be suspect, but it was too early and the influence of anticontagionism was still too strong to permit the idea of living microbic agents transmitted through drinking water. In 1873[11] after reading the papers of Canstatt (1847), Riecke (1852), and Budd (1856), Flint realized his error and made out an excellent case for the contamination of the tavern well from a privy attached to the inn. On his behalf, we must state that he spent only one day at North Boston during which he performed one autopsy and questioned nine cases, while William Budd had spent years in the epidemic area.

Austin Flint came to our attention again the next year (1874), in an analytical paper in the *New York Medical Journal* on the "Logical Proof of the Contagiousness and of the Non-catagiousness of Diseases." He distinguished between "logical proof" and the "demonstrative proof" of the contagiousness in syphilis and gonorrhea, in smallpox, and in several cutaneous diseases. He again referred to the writings of Budd, and of Snow and of Simon "which seem to point to the presence of a contagium in drinking-water" during the cholera epidemics of Britain. From a review of the literature and from his own experience, he concluded that this disease is not spread by "fresh cholera-discharges." "Although not contagious, cholera is, however, portable." He declined to consider whether the special cause is a chemical product, a living organism, or dead organic matter.

In 1875 an excellent review article, "Bacteria and their Septic Influences," by L. A. Stimson appeared in the same journal. (This paper was abbreviated in the *Popular Science Monthly*.) Beginning with Leeuwenhoek, the author quoted liberally, giving the then recognized classification by Ehrenberg and some of his published pictures of morphological types of bacteria. Stimson especially emphasized the importance of the demonstration by Davaine of large bacilli in the blood of anthrax cases, probably the causative agent. Articles on Lister's methods appeared here and there, for example two were published in the *Boston Medical and Surgical Journal* in 1877, one of them by Robert White who had had personal instruction by Lister in Scotland.

Three decades after the Erie County epidemic, a paper by L. Woods of Pittsford, Vermont, presents good epidemiological evidence that an outbreak of typhoid fever in the autumn of 1875 was due to a contaminated well. Of 30 children in a school, 20 students became ill with typhoid fever. The surface well used by the sick students was manifestly subject to pollution from the next-door house, where there had been nine cases of typhoid fever. From this house ran a board sink-drain, liable to choke up and overflow, to within 5 feet of the school well. Slops from the house were thrown out of the back door only 15 feet from the well.[12]

Again, on September 4, 1876, one Otto Schmidt of Syracuse, New York, returned to his home, sick with typhoid fever acquired while visiting the Centennial Fair in Philadelphia. Dr. Ely Van de Warke gives us a clear-cut analysis of the circumscribed outbreak of this disease, 17 cases with 3 deaths, that occurred there a few weeks later. There was neither city sanitary sewer nor public water supply in the small community; privies near the houses, cisterns, and four wells served these necessary functions. After a long dry period, violent thunderstorms on September 20 swept the area filling up gutters and cellars and leaving scattered debris, showing that there had been ample chance for washing material from the Schmidt privy into the neighboring surface well. Fourteen days after the storm, the next case developed, the others in the following two weeks. Of the seven families involved in the disease, all used the Schmidt well; no one who used the other wells was attacked. By carefully mapping the distribution of the cases and their surroundings, Van de Warke eliminated sewer gas and decomposing vegetation, which were the favorite hypothetical causes of many infectious diseases at that time. The evidence, he insisted, pointed to a specific poison, probably a *contagium vivum*, spread from the feces of Schmidt to his neighbors via the polluted well water. As no apparent secondary cases developed, Van de Warke scoffed at the suggestion that typhoid fever was "contagious" from person to person calling that a "slipshod theory." But this idea of living microbes as agents in disease was spreading.[13]

Another Vermonter, C. S. Caverly,[14] contributed in 1894 an excellent detailed history of an epidemic of "acute nervous disease of unusual type" with some 130 cases and 18 deaths in the neighborhood of Rutland. His later report, 1896, with autopsy studies and co-operation from other physicians, showed that this disease, little known at that time, was part of a rather widespread epidemic of poliomyelitis. This first complete study in the United States pointed out many factors later generally accepted. Of these the most important was Caverly's recognition of nonparalytic or abortive cases subsequently shown by Wickman in Sweden to be so vitally important in the spread of this disease.

In the 1880's knowledge of bacteria began to spread more rapidly. Koch's papers on the demonstration and the cultivation of the tubercle bacilli, the simplicity of staining these organisms in sputum, and the whirlwind of discovery of other pathogens, chiefly in Germany, blew open the doors. Most medical journals began to publish articles especially on the bacterial diagnosis of tuberculosis and diphtheria. Scientific journals of broader interests such as the *American Naturalist* recognized the conflict over the doctrine of spontaneous generation, but the first article on bacteria in this journal was in 1887 by Theobald Smith, "Parasitic Bacteria and their Relation to Saprophytes." Even at that date Smith was probing into the rise of parasitism which he analyzed so tellingly in his last essay, "Parasitism and Disease."

A study of *Poole's Index to Periodical Literature* from 1802 shows a few papers that may be considered in our field in the popular journals as early as the 1850's. The *Popular Science Monthly* began to publish occasional articles on the conflict over spontaneous generation and on the clash over the germ theory of disease in such diseases as cholera, typhoid fever, and malaria. In 1856 *Harpers Magazine* published a series of four excellent unsigned articles on great epidemics from biblical times to the early nineteenth century. Selected quotations from contemporary authors made the descriptions graphic and terrifying, but suggestions of causes are restricted to angry gods and filth, save in the early *History of the Peloponnesian War* by Thucydides who strongly indicated contagion. *The Nation* from its first volumes (1865) showed interest in epidemic diseases and in that volume published a telling historical sketch of high quality on the much feared cholera; the article concludes, "We shall only express our firm conviction that cholera is not strictly speaking contagious but the germs of cholera are localized." But an article in the next year stated that although the physicians of Boston oppose the notion, "Dr. Snow, superintendent of health of Providence, Rhode Island, pronounces it the work of supererogation to attempt to prove it is not contagious." Two injunctions from Niemeyer of Tübingen, Germany, are given: "to avoid strange privies and to separate from those in ordinary use the discharges of cholera patients."

An article in the *Popular Science Monthly* in 1876 on malaria cites several epidemics giving "positive proof that malaria fevers are due to drinking water," but the observer stated further, "the sleeping quarters should not be below the second story and that exposure to the open air after sunset should be avoided." In an article (1877–78) by Bastian, the British proponent of the doctrine of spontaneous generation, one finds that the germ theory is "absolutely broken down and refuted."[15]

The controversy went on until the evidence became overwhelming; the anticontagionists had to be convinced. Ackerknecht suggests that had we been "forced to decide ourselves a hundred years ago, on the basis of the existing materials, we should have had a very hard time."

CHAPTER IV

The Period
of the Great Epidemics in America

Smallpox may be mistaken for the very little pox
or the very big pox (chicken pox or syphilis)

SIR WILLIAM OSLER

Disease should be combatted at its origin.   HIPPOCRATES

Although death rates were high especially among infants in colonial America and many epidemics raged as evidenced by contemporary records (Shattuck,[1] Stephen Smith[2]), tales, and tombstones, yet pestilences of even greater magnitude occurred during the first three-quarters of the nineteenth century. In seeking for an explanation, we must realize that eighteenth century Americans lived largely in isolated self-sufficient communities; horseback and coach transportation rarely provided the means for extensive contact necessary for large epidemics.

In the nineteenth century, along with the industrial revolution, we observe the rapid growth of our cities, improved transportation for man and the microbes he carries with him, and the development of factories along our power-laden rivers. The potato famine in Ireland during the 1840's (again a microbe, *Phytophthora infestans*, was a major culprit) and the economic and political disturbances in other European countries, notably Germany, brought droves of immigrants to our shores. "Between 1845 and 1855, the average number of newcomers admitted annually had risen to not less that 300,000."[3] The immigrants, especially those from impoverished Ireland, were crowded into the squalid slums of our larger cities. Many persons were without jobs, with little food, and used water from surface wells subject to contamination from a few overused privies. Given the specific microorganisms, these were ideal conditions for the spread of infectious disease. And some of the new arrivals brought such organisms with them.

All epidemic diseases were at that time classified under the general head of zymotic or fermentation diseases, and all fevers were thought to have a common cause, namely the miasmas emanating from putrefying organic matter. Benjamin Rush stated, "there is only one fever and only one cause, stimulus."

Yellow Fever

MATHEW CAREY, GEORGE M. STERNBERG,
CARLOS J. FINLAY, HENRY R. CARTER,
WALTER REED, JAMES CARROLL,
JESSE W. LAZEAR, AND ARISTIDES AGRAMONTE

Most terrifying have been the devastations of yellow fever in its erratic wanderings up and down our coast from 1647 until the early part of the present century. Although the disease apparently had its origin in Central Africa,[4] yet it has for centuries been endemic both there, in the northern half of South America, and in a number of the islands of the West Indies. An occasional severe epidemic has occurred in Europe, for example in Spain in 1800 with 60,000 fatalities, yet yellow fever has spread in more numerous epidemics over the western hemisphere, with estimated deaths in the United States alone of 500,000 from 1793 to 1900. Because of controversies, but more especially because of the brilliant contributions to knowledge of this disease made in this hemisphere, a history of early microbiology in this country must present the chronicle in considerable detail. It is our best story. Yellow jack, the black vomit, malignant yellow fever, the bilious remitting-fever, the Barbadoes distemper; by any name it smells to heaven, and each epidemic has given us terror and tragedy. For example, the Philadelphia outbreak of 1793 *et seq.* supplied the ocasion for striking contemporary accounts; among them were those by Benajmin Rush, Mathew Carey, and William Currie.[5] Selected passages will paint the picture of fear and death for us of more comfortable later generations. Carey's account (1794), dedicated to the American Philosophical Society, gives descriptions both of the disease and the reactions of the people.

The consternation of the people of Philadelphia at this period was carried beyond all bounds. Dismay and affright were visible in almost every person's countenance. Most of those who could by any means make it convenient, fled from the city. Of those who remained, many shut themselves up in their houses, and were afraid to walk the streets. The smoke of tobacco being regarded as a preventative, many persons, even women and small boys, had segars almost constantly in their mouths. Others placing full confidence in garlic, chewed it almost the whole day; some kept it in their pockets and shoes. Many were afraid to allow the barbers or hair-dressers to come near them, as instances had occurred of some of them having shaved the dead and many having engaged as bleeders. Some, who carried their caution pretty far, bought lancets for themselves, not daring to be bled with the lancet of the bleeders. Many houses were hardly a moment in the day free from the smell of gunpowder, burned tobacco, nitre, sprinkled vinegar, etc. Some of the churches were almost deserted, and others wholly closed. The coffee house was shut up, as was the city library, and most of the public offices —three out of the four daily papers were discontinued, as were some of the others. Many were almost incessantly employed in purifying, scouring, and whitewashing their rooms. Those who ventured abroad, had handkerchiefs or sponges impregnated with vinegar or camphor at their noses, or smelling-bottles full of thieves' vinegar. Others carried pieces of tarred rope in their hands or pockets, or camphor bags tied round their necks. The corpses of the most respectable citizens, even those who did not die of the epidemic, were carried to the grave, on the shafts of a chair, the horse driven by a negro, unattended by a friend or relation, and without any sort of ceremony.

ORIGIN OF THE DISORDER

In seeking for the cause of the epidemic, Carey comments further:

This fever does not seem to take its origin from any particular constitution of the weather, independent of infectious miasmata, as Dr. Warren has formerly well observed; for within these twenty-five years, it has been only four times epidemical in this town, namely in the autumns of the years 1732, '39, '45, '48, though none of those years, (excepting that of 1739, whose summer and autumn were remarkably rainy) were either warmer or more rainy, (and some of them less so) than the summers and autumns were in several other years, in which we had not one instance of any one seized with this fever; Which is contrary to what would have happened, if particular constitutions of the weather, were productive of it, without infectious miasmata.

William Currie also had eyes to see that the yellow fever did not arise, as Benjamin Rush insisted, *de novo*, within the city, but was imported from without and then spread by means unknown.

To ascribe the occurrence of the yellow fever in Philadelphia, after an exemption of thirty-one years, to a noxious and invisible change in the constitution of the atmosphere, without furnishing direct and unequivocal proofs that such change has taken place, is one of the tricks of ingenuity to impose upon and mislead unreflecting credulity, and is no more worthy of credit or respect than the Arabian Nights Entertainments, or than the conceits of the astrologers and conjurers in the ages previous to the revival of literature, when every disease as well as every natural phenomenon not obvious to the senses, was ascribed to the influence of the planets.

Benjamin Rush, along with William Shippen and John Morgan, was one of the leading American physicians of the Revolutionary period. His own account of the "Bilious remitting Yellow Fever as it appeared in the city of Philadelphia in the year 1793" clearly portrays the man, so well characterized by Garrison as "wrong headed as well as strong headed." His method of treating the disease, mainly by copious bleeding and vigorous purging, the exodus from the city of a third of the population, and the clash of opinion among the physicians both as to sources and modes of spread and the treatment are colorfully presented. (But lest pride in our own times should become too strong, we should also have either lived through or should read diligently about the 1918–19 pandemic of influenza.)[6] Rush stated: "I treat my patients successfully by blood letting and copious purging with calomel and jalap in doses of ten grains each for adults and six or eight for children and I advise you, my good friends, to use the same remedies."

"What" asked one, "bleed and purge everyone?"

"Yes" said Dr. Rush, "bleed and purge all Kensington."

Many physicians called these large amounts of purging drugs and the excessive bleeding—murderous doses. One is reminded of a famous contemporary British physician John Lettsom, one of the founders of the Medical Society of London, friend of America, and of its three well-known Benjamins of the period, Franklin, Waterhouse, and Rush; his motto was:

> I, *John Lettsom*
> *Blisters, bleeds and sweats 'em;*
> *If after that, they please to die,*
> *I, John, lets 'em.*

Although Rush was following the teachings of the illustrious Sydenham and the common medical thinking of the times, yet many wiser physicians followed Carey and Currie in realizing that the yellow fever had been introduced from without. It was inevitable that a serious clash must occur between the two groups. With the coming of colder weather in October, the number of new cases dwindled rapidly. As winter came on, Philadelphia was left with its economy ruined, some 4044 persons dead, a tenth of its population, many orphaned and many destitute, and painful memories of the death carts wandering through the city streets during the worst of the epidemic with the repeated cry, "Bring out your dead."

Soon after the fever left the city, the governor of the state addressed a letter to the College of Physicians, requesting to know their opinion of its origin; if imported; from what place, at what time, and in what matter.

The reply:

To the Governor of Pennsylvania

Sir,

No instance has ever occurred of the disease called the yellow fever, having been generated in this city, or in any other part of this state, as far as we know; but there have been frequent instances of its having been imported, not only into this, but into other parts of North America, and prevailing there a certain period of time; and from the rise, progress, and nature of the malignant fever, which began to prevail here about the beginning of last August, and extended itself gradually over a great part of the city, we are of opinion that this disease was imported into Philadelphia, by some of the vessels which arrived in the port after the middle of July. This opinion we are further confirmed in by various accounts we have received from the best authorities we could procure upon the subject.

Signed by order of the College of Physicians,
November 26th,   JOHN REDMAN, President[7]
1793

NINETEENTH-CENTURY YELLOW FEVER OUTBREAKS

We now jump almost one hundred years in our chronicle, from the eighteenth century outbreaks to the 1870's, when we shall find that in spite of intensive studies in field and hospital, the ravages of yellow fever had continued intermittently, and little advance had been made in the knowledge of the sources and modes of infections. One clearly established point, however, was that epidemics ceased in our cities with the onset of freezing weather, and further, that areas existed in the warmer islands of the Caribbean Sea where the disease was endemic and that from these areas, the disease was imported, at times, in the trading vessels. But what the cause and what the means of transfer— these were unknown.

Meantime, in the preceding decade, the germ theory of infectious disease had made only slight headway against the miasmatic and planetary ideas of the older centuries and against the more recent filth nuisance idea. Increasingly, some admitted that for yellow fever the germ theory of causation seemed plausible, but that it was not directly contagious, nor was it caused by the effluvia of swamps, nor by some unhappy conjunction of planets.

Repeated outbreaks of the disease in the delta of the Mississippi River reached a culminating epidemic in 1878, spreading from New Orleans along the coast and up the river as far as St. Louis. The American Public Health Association, founded in 1871, registers both the alarm and the ignorance concerning yellow fever in all of its early reports. The sixth annual meeting, in November, 1878, was devoted largely to reports on this epidemic. During the meetings, Surgeon General Woodworth, of the United States Marine Hospital Service, stated that "four score cities and villages of the Mississippi Valley were turned into mourning and a hundred thousand of the people were stricken in their homes and twenty thousand lives were sacrificed on the altar of a preventable disease."[8] Actually, however, neither Dr. Woodworth nor any of the other health officers of 1878 knew how to prevent the disease save to run far away.

As in so many instances throughout history, the alarm aroused the people, and they in turn were able to squeeze money out of the administration for investigation. A Yellow Fever Commission was appointed by the then existing but short-lived (1879–1883) United States National Board of Health. The commission consisted of Dr. Stanford Chaillé of New Orleans as chairman, Colonel Hardie, civil engineer also of New Orleans, Dr. Juan Guiteras of Havana, and, as secretary, Dr. George M. Sternberg of the United States Army. Sternberg had had previous professional contacts with yellow fever at Governor's Island, New York, in 1870 and in Florida in 1873, and two years later he himself had suffered a severe attack with slow recovery. In the division of labor of the commission, Sternberg, because of his interests, was assigned the studies on etiology. Much of his time, therefore, both during this period and later, was spent investigating the possible role of a dozen different easily cultivable bacteria, isolated from cases by himself and by others.

All of these claimants to the throne eventually proved to be pretenders, just common inhabitants of the normal skin or intestinal tract or at most secondary invaders. These painstaking investigations, many of them carried out on official order, were deeply discouraging to Sternberg, but all of the organisms, including Sanarelli's *Bacillus icteroides* and Sternberg's bacillus X, had to be ruled out.

George M. Sternberg, Pioneer in Bacteriology

In his early years, Sternberg (1838–1915) had led a life typical of the Army Medical Corps of that period with many shuttlings back and forth across the continent and, on the average, less than a year at each post. He had, however, begun to work in the infant science of bacteriology, and with improvised equipment, had seized a little time here and there to investigate the germicidal value of certain chemical and physical agents.

He was a man of restless, abundant energy and varied interests (field botany, paleontology, photography, sailing, etc.); he was always busy, not a good mixer, rather stiff and unbending, distinctly egotistical, not one you would choose as a companion on a fishing trip, but a persistent worker, and as shown in his later years, a successful administrator. He was our real pioneer bacteriologist; his early work was based on his own initiative and reading. His more important researches were those on thermal death points of bacteria, standardization of disinfectants, studies in yellow fever, and the isolation of the pneumococcus from his own saliva, as an early instance of a bacterial carrier (1880). Pasteur also isolated and described a similar organism the next year (1881), but neither of them at that time related the organism causally to pneumonia.

In 1885, however, Sternberg presented evidence that the *Micrococcus pasteuri*, as he named it, isolated from his own saliva during excellent health, the micrococcus discovered by Friedländer in the exudate of croupous pneumonia, and "micrococci of oval form in pairs and in chains," isolated from a portion of hepatized lung from a case of pneumonia at Bay View Hospital, Baltimore, were identical. He states further: "It seems extremely probable that this micrococcus is concerned in the etiology of croupous pneumonia, and that the infectious nature of this disease is due to its presence in the fibrinous exudate into the pulmonary alveoli." In 1886 he worked for some time in Robert Koch's laboratory in Berlin, where to his delight he successfully repeated the demonstration that he was a "carrier" of a pneumococcus virulent for mice.

While Sternberg was stationed in Baltimore, he enjoyed instruction and stimulus from both Welch and Councilman at Johns Hopkins Medical School. Sternberg aided our early bacteriologists by publishing the first general textbook of bacteriology printed in this country (1880), his own translation of a French text by Antoine Magnin. In

1884 he published an enlargement of this and in 1892, a comprehensive *Manual of Bacteriology*, which was used with profit by all American bacteriologists for more than a decade.

As an administrator, Sternberg successfully rejuvenated the medical corps of the United States Army by establishing the Army Medical School, arranging for additional training schools for the Hospital Corps, rearranging assignments, establishing sanitariums for tuberculous troops, and through his interest in yellow fever, by appointing the second United States commission, which solved much of the riddle of three centuries. Sternberg has been adversely criticized for the failure of the medical corps to prevent the high incidence of typhoid fever and other camp diseases among the American troops in the Spanish-American War. The medical corps was obviously quite inadequate to handle the sudden demands, and the Surgeon General must bear a share of the onus. All recognize the unfortunate effects of the ups and downs of government support.[9]

Returning again to the period of 1879, we find that the Spanish Governor General of Cuba had appointed a local physician, Dr. Carlos Juan Finlay, to co-operate with this first United States Yellow Fever Commission of which Sternberg was the secretary and the most active laboratory worker. Finlay had become interested in yellow fever because of its frequent occurrence in his home town, Havana, and was stimulated further by his associations with this commission.

Carlos J. Finlay, the Clairvoyant

Finlay,[10] an unassuming man with an international background, a Scottish father and a French mother, had much of his early training in France and other European countries, and received his medical degree at Jefferson Medical School in 1855. One of his sons describes him as a devoted husband and father, with much pleasure in the family circle, authoritative but affectionate, with broad concern in international affairs rather than local politics, charitable to the errors of others, and deeply interested in his profession and the welfare of his patients, even beyond their immediate physical ailments. He was tenacious in his convictions and inclined to be quick tempered and caustic in repartee. He enjoyed life, savored light wines with his meals, played chess and card games appreciatively, was a strong swimmer, fond of travel, and had a good bit of the wanderlust in his veins. In 1856 we find him fresh from medical school, seeking practice with his father, also a physician, in Lima, Peru, and in 1860–61 in Paris, gaining added experience in the hospital clinics and taking some special studies. In 1865 he married Miss Adeline Shine, a native of Trinidad of Irish ancestry, whose early education had been in the Ursuline Convent in Cork. She was deeply religious, provided richly for the happy family life and left three sons to carry on the genes and the traditions. One son, Dr. Carlos E. Finlay, was a physician. Finlay's family and his professional associates stress his extraordinary capacity for study and work.

With his sideburns, immaculate dress, and generous enthusiasm, he was a man of distinction in any company. His unusual charm of manner aroused the quick appreciation of casual acquaintances and the warm partisan devotion of his friends. Through twenty years of his active life, he carried on experiments in yellow fever with little aid and within the restrictions of a busy practice. Despite opposition and ridicule, he continued to preach his theory of the mosquito transmission of the disease. After his major contention was proved true, he was the happy recipient of honors from diverse sources and several nations.

The chief contributions of the first United States Yellow Fever Commission were two, the exclusion of many of the bacteria that had been claimed by their proponents as causative agents in the disease, and more importantly, the stimulation of continuing interest in yellow fever on the part of three men—Finlay, Guiteras, and Sternberg.

Finlay's first important paper on yellow fever, published in 1881, discarded his earlier notions of primary atmospheric influences and postulated some unknown germ as causative agent. In this paper he first suggested that mosquitoes might be "transmitters" of the unknown germ. Several observers, even as early as the Philadelphia 1793 outbreak, had noted the unusual prevalence of mosquitoes during epidemics, and Nott of Mobile, Alabama (1848), and Beauperthuy in Venezuela (1854) had advanced the idea that mosquitoes might be agents in the disease.[11]

Nott, in a rich, scholarly, slow moving essay, shows an extensive knowledge both of biological and medical literature, considers the infusoria of Ehrenberg (1838) and the complex story of the metamorphosis of insects. From a careful study of five epidemics in Mobile, he effectively disposes of the gaseous emanation theory, relates yellow fever to a locality, shows that it is not directly contagious, and requires a lapse of 10–20 days between the primary and secondary cases. He makes no suggestion of man-to-man transmission via the mosquito but thinks that "it is probable that yellow fever is caused by an insect, or animalcule bred in the ground." Beauperthuy's studies are less closely organized, but suggest on epidemiological grounds that mosquitoes may be involved in transmission, "obtaining the poison from putrifying organic matter in the water where they breed." But both of these papers were largely speculations and not followed as in Finlay's case with experiments to test the hypothesis.

In his 1881 paper Finlay presented five cases that had been bitten by one of the species of mosquitoes in the area that had previously fed on yellow fever cases in the third to the fifth day of the disease. One to two days had elapsed, in one case six days, between the possible "contaminating" and the "inoculating" bites. In two of these five cases Finlay reported "ephemeral signs without any definite characters." Of the other three, one was admitted to the hospital fourteen days later with a "mild attack of yellow fever perfectly characterized by the usual yellowness, and albumin in the urine which persisted from the third till the ninth day." The remaining two were reported as "abortive yellow fever" each with an incubation period of five days. No other cases occurred among the twenty nonimmunes under observation. Finlay was highly excited, but he considered these experiments only favorable to his theory but not incontrovertible. He hoped for further opportunities "outside of the epidemic zone . . . under decisive conditions."

Finlay knew of Manson's (1877–79) demonstration of the metamorphosis of filaria in mosquitoes[12] but, later in life, stated that, as he remembered it, the idea of an intermediary host for the yellow fever organism was suggested to him by an account of *Puccinia graminis*, a fungus highly destructive for wheat that requires another host, the common barberry, for the completion of its life cycle. In examining the epidemiology of yellow fever, he became more and more convinced that a mosquito as part of the cycle would satisfy the facts. A study of the local mosquitoes led him to continue to experiment with the one he had employed earlier, a small banded mosquito with ringed legs, a diurnal flyer, most active at twilight. He chose this especially because it lived close to human dwellings, laying its eggs in any neglected water receptacle such as a rain barrel, a sagging drain gutter, or a discarded can. At that time this mosquito bore the scientific name of *Culex fasciatus*, but taxonomists are never satisfied, and have shuffled it around among several genera and species. At the moment and actually for more than a decade, it has been carrying on as *Aedes egypti.* "A rose by any other name would smell as sweet." A yellow fever mosquito will be equally dangerous under any name.

We must remember that at this time the hypothesis of mosquito transmission was looked upon as a vagary of a disordered mind. Finlay defends his procedures in this manner: "In resolving to experiment on human subjects, I relied upon the inference that the quantity of virus carried by a single sting must be a minimum dose, capable of producing only the mildest forms of the disease ever observed in nature, and that a number of such bites would be necessary to occasion a dangerous attack." A careful reading of Finlay's subsequent papers, including that of 1886 and the paper of 1891 in which he summarized sixty-seven recorded cases, leaves one with the conviction that he was never able to carry on experiments as he had desired, "outside of the epidemic zone . . . under decisive conditions."

As the years continued, despite opposition, despite lack of adequate facilities, and despite pressure of his medical practice, Finlay continued his experiments and his publications, most of these in the Cuban journals, but periodically, complete articles in English appeared in the medical journals of the United States and Scotland. It is a tale of persistent courage. As indicated in his 1891 and other papers, he became involved in a side issue, the possible immunizing effect of one or two bites by his yellow fever contaminated mosquitoes. Also, as in the case of other investigators, he isolated a bacterium, in his case, *Micrococcus tetragenue febris flavae,* from his mosquitoes that had fed on cases and from blood obtained directly from cases. With cultures of this organism, he inoculated many rabbits producing hemorrhagic lesions in the internal organs. He conceived this to be a modified yellow fever, but the organism was subsequently shown to be a common skin inhabitant, *M. tetragenus,* with no specific relation to yellow fever.

We must remember that bacteriologic experience was meager in those early decades of the science; always, then, today, and tomorrow, the choice of a suitable animal for the production of an experimental infection is difficult.

In 1898 the Spanish-American War came suddenly upon us, and with the capture of the Philippines we were forced to assume a responsible position in the Orient and, willy-nilly, we became overnight a world power. Microbiologically speaking, we were far from ready, as shown by the morbidity and mortality records of preventable infectious diseases in our rapidly collected army. Of 280,564 troops in camp, 20,904 contracted typhoid fever and of this number, 2,188 died. The storm aroused by these appalling casualties from a disease in which modes of infection and methods of prevention were moderately well known can well be imagined. At once a board of investigation was appointed with Walter Reed as chairman associated with Victor C. Vaughan and Edward O. Shakespeare. Their report, a landmark in the study of enteric disease, will be considered later. At the moment, we must proceed with the yellow fever story, noting only that the part Walter Reed played as chairman in the typhoid investigations gave him prominence and was doubtless a factor in his yellow fever appointment.

OUR SECOND YELLOW FEVER COMMISSION

As yellow fever had been endemic in Cuba for several centuries, it soon began to take its toll among our troops on the island. Because of this and because of his own years of work in the disease, Sternberg, then surgeon general of the United States Army, appointed our Second Yellow Fever Commission comprised of Walter Reed, chairman, James Carroll, Jesse Lazear, and Aristides Agramonte.[13]

In the two decades (1880–99) between the appointment of the first and the second United States Yellow Fever commissions, the young science of bacteriology, or more properly microbiology, had grown explosively. From infant proportions with a few proved specific causative agents, such as the cholera vibrio (Koch, 1876) it had become a bursting, crusading, scientific field with new methods, many demonstrated etiologic organisms, including those of such vital importance to man as the tubercle bacillus (Koch, 1882), *Bacillus diphtheriae* (Löffler, 1884), and the demonstration of the specific microorganism and modes of insect (or other arthropod) transmission of malaria, elephantiasis, and Texas fever. Microbiology had been rewritten, and with this had come an astounding revolution in our thinking about disease and the means of prevention on the basis of sources and modes of infection.

For a century, competent observers had pointed out that nurses and attendants closely housed in yellow fever hospitals rarely acquired the disease so that direct contagion seemed unlikely, yet fomites, the clothing and bed linen from patients, were still a source of fear. The careful observations on the noncontagious nature of yellow fever by Cathrall (1800) and more especially the courageous self-inoculation and contaminated fomite experiments by the young medical student, S. Ffirth, carried out as a basis for his M.D. thesis at the University of Pennsylvania (1802–3) had been frequently overlooked. They were, however, cited by La Roche (1855) and by Carlos Finlay. In spite of this, however, fears of fomites from yellow fever cases were so deeply imbedded that the commission felt it necessary to test this means of spread under well-controlled conditions.

Their efforts were first directed to determining the part that *Bacillus icteroides* of Sanarelli played in causing yellow fever; this organism because of some recent investigations by Wasdin and Geddings seemed to be implicated. However, careful blood cultures from 18 cases, 11 severe with 4 deaths, 3 well marked, and 4 mild, were all negative for this organism, and cultures taken from the organs of 11 cases at autopsy were also negative. Furthermore, Reed and his colleagues found that *B. icteroides* and the so-called hog cholera bacillus, *B. cholerae suis*, were highly similar and that similar lesions could be produced in experimental animals by injecting cultures of either organism. So this bacterium went the way of the others, merely a secondary invader or a contaminant.

Carter (1898 *et seq.*) in Mississippi, with especially favorable conditions for determining the interval between the arrival of infective cases and the occurrence of secondary cases in the houses, had found that this period was consistently between 2 and 3 weeks. With an incubation period in man of 2 to 6 days, rarely a day shorter or longer, a lapse of 9 to 16 days for development in some intermediary host such as the mosquito seemed not improbable. Others, notably Hosack (1824) and La Roche (1855) had made similar observations, but Carter was the one whose voice became convincing. This possible extrinsic incubation period, and the fact that the disease was not immediately contagious tied in beautifully with Finlay's mosquito theory. These points, together with the failure of everyone in attempts to infect the common laboratory animals and the several similarities between the epidemiology of malaria and yellow fever, led Reed and his colleagues to make the difficult decision to experiment with mosquitoes and human volunteers. Carlos Finlay immediately and with gracious enthusiasm placed his papers, his findings, and his experience at their disposal. He provided them with eggs of his preferred species of mosquito; with these the commission began their mosquito colony.

General Leonard Wood, the military governor of Cuba, himself a physician, gave encouragement, the necessary permission, adequate funds to help persuade some of the volunteers, and the military authority to make the essential quarantine complete. An isolation camp was set up; two vestibuled mosquito-proof buildings were constructed with complete screening. During the succeeding month, the experiments were carried on in one building with mosquitoes that had bitten yellow fever patients, and in the other building experiments with filthy clothing and bedding heavily contaminated by vomitus and discharges from acute cases, but completely free from mosquitoes of any kind. Rigid military discipline and quarantine were carried out, and during the whole period from June 25, 1900, until September, 1901, not one case of yellow fever occurred among the nonimmunes of the camp save in those that had given their full consent for experiments on themselves.

In order to justify the exposure of the volunteers, the commissioners also volunteered; Reed was excused for medical reasons and Agramonte was an immune. Early in August Reed was called back to Washington to complete the army typhoid fever report, and Carroll and Lazear went ahead as determined with inoculations by means of the possibly infected mosquitoes. Of nine such inoculations, including Lazear who, because of his experience in Italy with malaria mosquito studies was assigned the duty of breeding and infecting the insects, *all were negative.* The causes of these failures became clear later, but at the time, confidence in the Finlay theory fell to a low ebb.

Decision to continue, however, was made and on August 27, 1900, Carroll was bitten at 2 P.M. by a mosquito (the species now named *Aedes egypti*) that had fed on a severe case of yellow fever on the second day of the disease, 12 days before. This mosquito had also bitten three other cases on the first or second day, with a lapse of 6, 4, and 2 days respectively before August 27, the date of the possible inoculating bite. Subsequent studies showed that a growth period within the mosquito of at least 12 days was essential for transmission, so that it was actually only the first mentioned bite that was significant. On the fourth day after the mosquito had bitten him, Carroll became ill; he gradually developed a severe case of yellow fever with jaundice and albuminuria—the first successful experimental case.

Lazear's own first experimental inoculation proved, as has been noted, a failure. On September 13, while on a visit to Las Animas Hospital (the yellow fever institution of the area), he deliberately allowed a resident mosquito to satisfy her hunger from his hand. Five days thereafter he had a chill and rapidly developed high fever, jaundice, and albumen in the urine. The case became one of progressive yellow fever, and he died on September 25. These two cases had tremendous impact, but neither could be accepted completely as without an experimental flaw. Carroll had visited Columbia Barracks during the incubation period (a most unlikely yellow fever contact, but one must maintain scientific scepticism), and the mosquito that had bitten Lazear was a chance wanderer in the yellow fever hospital and had no defined history. Also Lazear had had hospital contacts with cases. The first case with a completely clear-cut history was that of William H. Dean, of Grand Rapids, Michigan, private, Troop B, Seventh Cavalry. On August 31, the day when Carroll developed fever, Lazear applied the same mosquito that had bitten Carroll four days before and also three other mosquitoes to William Dean. He was taken sick on September 6, and developed a well-pronounced case of yellow fever. The history of the mosquitoes was complete; the case was typical with an incubation period of six days; Dean had not been off the military reservation for fifty-seven days; he made an uneventful recovery. He never received any financial reward.

The next series (paper read at Medical Congress, Havana, Feb., 1901) gave additional evidence in support of mosquito transmission with six positive cases. One of these (Moran) gave a negative result the first time, apparently too short a period for development in the mosquito, but developed yellow fever on the second attempt. In this as in all the series, the patients were put to bed immediately and the diagnoses were confirmed by a board of physicians with long experience in yellow fever. Another portion of this series included seven nonimmunes who went through the disgusting experience of intimate contact with grossly soiled bed clothes, underwear, etc., for twenty nights under strict quarantine. All of them remained in perfect health. Still a third part of this remarkable series was the demonstration that blood from acute cases, drawn during the first two days of the disease, produced yellow fever in nonimmunes when small amounts were injected subcutaneously.

In several papers (1900 and 1901) the successful Yellow Fever Commission expressed sincere thanks to Finlay for his courteous aid and advice. In a summary address at Baltimore (1901) Reed, in giving some of the history of speculation and experiment in mosquito transmission said: "To Dr. Carlos J. Finlay of Havana must be given, however, full credit for the theory of the propagation of yellow fever by means of the mosquito, which he proposed in a paper read before the Royal Academy in that city at its session of the 14th day of August, 1881. From that date to the present time, Finlay has made a number of valuable contributions to the origin and mode of transmission and the prevention of yellow fever." He continued with a consideration of some of Finlay's changing views during the two decades, stressing the lack of control over the individuals on which Finlay's experiments were made, the prolonged incubation period of some of his cases, and the too short period of possible development in the body of the mosquitoes.

In February, 1901, before the Cuban academy, Finlay summarized all his inoculation attempts, 104 in all, made from 1881 to 1900 with the aid of Delgado. Of the several cases diagnosed as yellow fever, most of them abortive or with ephemeral signs and symptoms, only two showed albuminuria, and these had longer incubation periods than commonly accepted, 14 and 25 days, respectively. In neither of these cases were the mosquitoes applied to the infecting case during the first three days of the disease, and the period for possible growth in the mosquitoes was only two days in each instance. Under these conditions, others have been unable to produce the experimental disease.

In August, 1901, Carroll returned to Havana to carry out one more series suggested by William Welch, who had taught both Reed and Carroll. (For reasons adequate to the military mind, Reed was not permitted to return to Cuba for this last series.) In his constant search of the literature, Welch had noted that the recent reports of Löffler and Frosch (1898) stating that the infectious agent of foot and mouth disease would pass through Berkefeld infusorial earth or unglazed porcelain filters which hold back ordinary bacteria. This observation was similar to earlier findings of Iwanowski (1892) and Beijerinck (1898) with reference to a plant disease, the mosaic disease of tobacco. Following this newly conceived idea and method, Carroll demonstrated that the diluted blood serum from acute cases on the second and third days of the disease passed through a Berkefeld filter would incite yellow fever when injected subcutaneously into nonimmunes. This observation has been confirmed, and places the causative agent of the disease in the filterable virus group. It explains the many failures to obtain a cultivable bacterium from cases of yellow fever.

In the summer of 1901 Guiteras with the aid of Finlay and Gorgas carried out a well-controlled mosquito transmission series partly to follow up Finlay's idea that a controllable immunization might be obtained. In this they did not succeed, but after a discouraging number of failures (many variables in such experiments), eight successful mosquito-to-man cases were obtained. Most unfortunately, however, three of these cases, two Spanish volunteers and one lovely American nurse (Miss Clara Louise Maass), resulted fatally, putting an abrupt stop to further human experiments with yellow fever in this area. The demonstration was tragically complete.

I cannot present the details of all the well-controlled, step-by-step experiments that built up our knowledge of the transmission of yellow fever. Never has so much of a complete medical riddle been cleared up in so short a period—approximately a year. A summary of the reports of the United States Commission and that of Guiteras will bring these exciting successes sharply in focus. We must always have in mind the background of the period, the ignorance, the fears, and the devastating epidemics of three centuries.

1. Thirty cases were successfully transmitted by the Stegomyia mosquito (now *Aedes egypti*) through the man-mosquito-man route. The average incubation period was about 4 days; the shortest, 2 days, 13 hours; and the longest, 6 days, 2 hours.

2. Of the instances of unsuccessful transmission, the chief basis was found to be too short a period of growth in the mosquito; in these successful experiments, 12 days proved to be the shortest period at summer temperatures and 18 days in the cooler winter months. Some of the failures proved to be due to immunity to the infection.

3. Yellow fever can also be produced experimentally by a less natural method, the injection of blood drawn on the first or second day of the disease.

4. An attack of yellow fever produced by the bite of an infective mosquito confers immunity against the subsequent injection of blood from an acute nonexperimental case.

5. Repeated bitings by mosquitoes that had fed on yellow fever cases during the first three days of the disease with a period in the mosquitoes of 2 to 11 days were ineffective in producing the disease and also ineffective in inciting immunity.

6. The germ of the disease is sufficiently minute to pass through a bacteria-proof filter; it is destroyed by a temperature of 131° F. for 10 minutes.

7. Neither filth nor fomites are responsible for the transmission of yellow fever.

8. As Finlay suggested, a disease spread by a certain mosquito can be prevented by eliminating the mosquitoes and their breeding places. The greatest obstacle in the control of yellow fever is the failure to diagnose the first, frequently mild, case.

One wishes intensely that Carlos Finlay, the lone investigator, so persistent for two decades, the one who pointed the way, could also have been successful with his inoculations. One regrets the hurt feelings and the clash that developed between Finlay and the United States Army Commission. But the task was too large for one man with a single disciple, Delgado, and, as Finlay himself stated in his first paper, opportunities are needed "outside the epidemic zone . . . under decisive conditions." He did not have authority to create such a zone as did the United States Commission through use of military discipline.

A careful reading of the literature will persuade all, I believe, that Dr. Finlay's son, Dr. Carlos E. Finlay, of the Havana Yellow Fever Commission (1902), has stated the matter correctly and with appreciation (p. 233, U. S. Senate Document No. 822):

In the light of our present exact knowledge of the length of incubation of yellow fever in man and the considerable period of incubation in the mosquito between the time of biting and when she becomes able to transmit the infection, and also the very brief period (three days) at the beginning of the disease during which alone the patient is able to infect the mosquito, it must be recognized that probably none of Dr. Finlay's experiments was successful, but none the less, must credit be given for what Col. Gorgas has termed the "scientific clairvoyance" with which he had conceived his theory and the enthusiasm with which he maintained it.

I must not leave the impression that investigations of yellow fever during this period were restricted to those men mentioned. The experiments by the United States Army Commission and by Guiteras were promptly confirmed by a commission of the Pasteur Institute, comprised of Marchoux, Salimbeni, and Simond, collaborating in Rio de Janeiro with Oswald Cruz, Carlos Seidl, L. de Aquino, Antonino Ferrari, and Zephiran Meirelles (1903). Also Barreto, Barros, and Rodriquez (1903) in Sao Paulo and a commission of the United States Public Health Service, Rosenau, Parker, Francis, and Beyer, working in Vera Cruz, Mexico, gave additional support, so that the main findings as to the mode of spread of yellow fever could no longer be doubted even by the most obstinate adherents of the older notions.

With the establishment of the mode of transmission of yellow fever, control and prevention became a matter of early diagnosis and isolation of patient and education both of the physicians and the people: in a word, effective administration. By such procedures, Major Gorgas succeeded in clearing up Havana, one of yellow fever's oldest and favorite haunts, and later in freeing the Panama Canal Zone from the clutches of yellow jack, so that the failure of the brilliant de Lesseps was not repeated when the United States undertook to build the canal.

EPILOGUE

Although the next dramatic advance in our knowledge of yellow fever came after my announced terminal date, I am impelled to give a brief epilogue to the triumphant Finlay-Reed drama.

In 1928 Stokes, Bauer, and Hudson,[14] at the Rockefeller Foundation laboratory in Nigeria, after failures with African monkeys, successfully transmitted yellow fever to rhesus monkeys (*Macaca mulatta*) both by inoculations of infective blood and by *Aedes egypti* mosquitoes. This made it possible to study the disease anywhere in the world where laboratory facilities and trained personnel could be provided. In several countries inoculations were made from these monkey sources into mice, and subsequently into chick embryos, and into a variety of tissue culture media.

These new methods in turn gave us more accurate means of diagnosis, and of determining the incidence of the disease by measuring the virus-neutralizing antibodies in the blood of persons and other animals. Such studies in the endemic areas in central Africa and the northern half of South America gave another climax or rather an anticlimax to the always stormy history of yellow fever. Especially in South America, through the fostering aid of the Rockefeller Foundation, the campaign against *Aedes egypti* had so markedly reduced the black areas on the incidence maps from 1900 to 1930 that even good sceptical scientists thought hopefully of the complete elimination of this pestilence in our western hemisphere.

In the 1930's and 1940's, however, to the consternation of everyone, Soper and associates found that far from a wiping out of the disease, a previously unrecognized endemic form "jungle fever" existed in uncounted square miles of the forest areas. It has been found also in a great band across the middle of Africa. This jungle disease was transmitted not by the household *Aedes egypti*, but chiefly by mosquitoes of another genus (Haemogogus) with quite different breeding habits. The disease, endemic in monkeys, marsupials, and other wild animals, is spread to foresters of the area by mosquitoes that breed in water-containing hollows of the trees in the rain forest. The overwhelming impossibility of controlling the disease by antimosquito measures was a shocking blow.

With the transmission of yellow fever to mice and the cultivation of the virus, a method of control, other than antimosquito measures was sought, namely a possible vaccine for active immunization. Of the several that have been produced, the two in broad use at the present time are living attenuated viruses, since killed vaccines have proved of little value (Hindle, Findlay, *et al.*).

The Dakar neurotropic mouse-adapted strain, studied extensively by Peltier and associates, has been employed in over 20 million vaccinations in French African colonies from 1939 to 1948 with resulting successful antibody formation and reduction in incidence of the disease. Unfortunately a number of severe reactions have developed following use, some of them fatal. A safer vaccine is the 17D relatively avirulent, mutant virus developed by Max Theiler of the Rockefeller Foundation.[15] This vaccine was tested severely during World War II when thousands of troops, British and others, were vaccinated and subsequently exposed to possible infection, with exceedingly few cases of the disease developing; also in South America in the general population and among yellow fever workers where the incidence was formerly high, they now work with safety. This vaccine, too, has had its serious difficulties with 20,585 cases of jaundice, some of them fatal, occurring among about 2.5 million American troops vaccinated. Subsequent studies showed that these reactions were not due to the mutant yellow fever virus, but to the fact that some lots of the supposedly normal human serum used as a diluent in the preparation of the vaccine contained contaminating serum hepatitis virus. Since the omission of this human serum, the serum jaundice has not followed the use of the aqueous base 17D vaccine.

Manifestly there is no royal road in establishing control of any disease. As Theobald Smith has well said: "Important devices to protect community health such as vaccination against smallpox are set aside because the accidental death rate resulting from their application may be in the second or third decimal place of a percent." In the case of the widely distributed jungle fever in Africa and in South America the only method available for protecting exposed persons is vaccination. Fortunate we are that such has been developed. Jungle yellow fever still marches on, and late reports indicate that it has extended its boundaries northward into Guatemala. Yellow fever is not conquered; I know of no communicable disease of which that can be said. They may be confined, but never conquered. Like the struggle for liberty and justice, the battle is never ending.

Asiatic Cholera

Asiatic cholera, next to yellow fever the most feared of the epidemic killers of the nineteenth century, was common in the days of Hippocrates. He described the signs and symptoms, including suppression of urine and severe cramps of the limbs. Indeed, the disease was known by most of the classical writers (Galen, Rhazes, Avicenna) and was clearly described by the encyclopedist Celsus (A.D. 7). The disease then as now was endemic in India and spread sporadically and in repeated epidemics down through the centuries to nearby lands.

About 1817 it began to spread from its home among the people along the Ganges until it had encircled the world in its deadly march five times within the century. The sudden onset of the disease, with a brief incubation period (1–3 days, rarely over 5 days), rapid dehydration from profuse diarrhea, prompt collapse, and many deaths, aroused universal fear. The death rate is exceedingly variable from 20 to 85 per cent, depending on many factors, including accuracy of diagnosis of milder cases. The disease is spread chiefly by man as he moves in his daily life, for religious purposes to Mecca or the Ganges, and in search of trade to Cairo or Samarkand, or to California in forty-nine in search of gold. Wars, crusades, and pilgrimages have been ideal distributors of pathogenic microbes throughout history, save that for those organisms restricted to man, eventually in the great epidemics, few susceptible hosts remain and the microbes are deprived of fresh "meal tickets." Then the epidemic dwindles to the vanishing point, leaving only a few latent foci for future wars and new generations to repeat the cycle.

The usual explanations for the rise of cholera in India in 1817 and later were based on the conception that miasmas were the responsible causes. That year was important, however, for the great twelfth yearly festivals or religious pilgrimages. "These festivals are held every year in all parts of India, and increase in sanctity every third, sixth, and ninth year, and still more every twelfth and sixtieth year. This will account far better than the monsoon theory for the greater prevalence of cholera in India every third or fourth year, and its immense spread every twelfth year."[16] Eighteen hundred thirty to thirty-two were years of epidemic disaster in Asia and in Europe with the cholera causing frightful illness, mortality, and possibly worst of all, overpowering panic. In 1831 some 20,000 of the 50,000 Mohammedan pilgrims at Mecca came down with cholera and, as the faithful dispersed to their homes, many carried the disease with them along the trade routes of the world. It spread, both the direction and speed of progress matching those of human travel eastward to Japan, north and west to Mongolia and Russia, thence to Poland, England, and Ireland, and in the spring of 1832, to this hemisphere.

FROM THE FAR EAST TO OUR CITIES AND ACROSS THE CONTINENT

The immigrants from cholera-stricken Ireland were the chief means of bringing the disease to this country; mostly they entered by the Canadian ports of the St. Lawrence River, destitute and fearful; some died during the crossing and others soon after arrival. Survivors, before struggling on to their hoped-for destinations, spent their days and their nights in the streets, fields, and temporary sheds, because the fear of the cholera, which had been announced reluctantly by the health officers, had closed most doors to them. Cholera in this hemisphere as elsewhere struck with such sudden violence and with such high mortality rates that it has left its tragic trail in the professional journals, public reports, and in the popular press. Citing a few figures only, in Montreal, to the eighteenth of June, 1832, the reported cases numbered 1,635, while to the same date there had been 1,622 burials in Quebec. On the river most of the boats were tied up and their crews had fled; one boat with a crew of seven was found floating with six men dead and the lone survivor ill.[17]

The fact that cholera did arrive at New York in 1832, was suppressed so effectively that no records of arrivals at quarantine during the months of April, May, and June, 1832, can be found while the records of preceding and succeeding months are perfect. The emigrants who were well enough to travel were dispatched rapidly upon their journey from that city, and thus, upon the rapid diffusion of the disease over the Atlantic and Western States a new light is thrown.[18]

As in other countries the disease traveled along the trade routes, down the Champlain-Hudson River Valley, down the coast from New York to Philadelphia, Baltimore, and Washington, westward along the Ohio, north and south by men on the river steamers of "old man river," and from New Orleans along the coast.

After the cholera visitations of 1832 and 1835, America enjoyed a cholera immunity of nearly thirteen years, during which time various portions of the continent were still subjected to the same miasmatic influences as during all preceding years. Cholera did not, however, recur in America in this period for the simple reason that those nations with whom the inhabitants of North America had commercial intercourse had no cholera to transmit. The advocates of the pythogenic origin of the disease were still spreading that doctrine. "The medical journals team with cholera-literature of the period, but the vast majority are but labored attempts to prove that mal-aria, improper food, excessive overcrowding in badly-ventilated apartments during warm weather, can and do produce the disease known as Asiatic Cholera."

In 1848 the cholera again came to our shores from the far east through Europe. The ship *New York*, from Havre, docked at New York on December 2 having lost seven passengers en route. Somewhat successful restriction of the spread of the disease was achieved by the clinical type of quarantine of the period. About one hundred cases had occurred at the quarantine station, fifty of which were fatal. Only two cases occurred in New York City, however, and the disease did not spread there.

Another ship, the *Swanton*, leaving Havre about the same time, docked at New Orleans on December 11, having lost thirteen of her passengers during the voyage. Here *no* quarantine was enforced; the ship went at once to her wharf and proceeded to discharge passengers and cargo. Shortly thereafter, cases of cholera began to appear in the city. "During the month of December, 400 cholera deaths were reported at New Orleans, in January 600 and the number increased each month until June when the epidemic culminated in 2500 and odd deaths." Panic seized the city. The Mississippi River and Valley provided routes of passage and therefore routes of spread of the disease to the interior of the country. Apparently every boat on the river was infected. Whereas the tales lend themselves to exaggeration and doubtless some deaths were incorrectly ascribed to cholera, the reports tell a grisly story.[19] At St. Louis, early in April, the disease was again epidemic and during May and June, the mortality was high. Seventeen physicians died. But the reports of gold in California were so compelling and gold fever so virulent that in spite of possible death from starvation and exposure and in spite of the hazards of the cholera some 35,000 persons pressed on across the continent by land, while other thousands went by sea to the Isthmus of Panama, re-embarking on the western coast for San Francisco. Some persons arrived at St. Joseph by steamers sailing up the Missouri River after many deaths had occurred among the passengers. But the living pressed on, over the Platte route, so that despite the distance and the time elapsing, the cholera reached Sacramento overland in October, 1850, at almost the same time that it was brought into San Francisco by the *Carolina*, carrying gold seekers from Panama. After the arrival of this vessel, a few cases occurred in the city; but it was not until the first week of November that the explosion occurred after fresh arrivals from Panama. The epidemic lasted until about Christmas, when it disappeared. The total number of deaths was about 250. In Sacramento the disease spread more rapidly, and all who could fled the city. Out of a population of 8000, less than 4000 remained and of these, before December when the disease subsided, over 1000 had died. "It is also a point of utmost significance that at each of the *malarial localities* that *produced* the disease in North America, according to Dr. Wynne, at none was this malarial influence exercised or apparent until *after* the arrival of individuals previously infected by the cholera."

Life was vivid and violent in these early California days although the Shirley letters written by the wife of a physician in a mining camp to her sister in the East show a general desire for rough order and manifest kindliness. Prices were excessive, waste was rampant, family life impossible for most, as only 8 per cent of the population were women, 2 per cent in the camps. The rush to the mine fields was incredible; 80,000 persons poured into the gold fields in 1849, and in July, 1850, 500 ships were reported deserted by their crews in San Francisco Bay. Gradually, however, vigilance committees and popular courts took the place of no law or of lynch law. Endemic disease carried on in the place of the epidemics.

In 1865 and again in 1873 the cholera leaked through the ineffective quarantine barriers of our ports. The history of this and the other cholera epidemics in this country as well as those in Europe and in Asia where the disease is endemic are best presented in tragic detail by J. M. Woodworth, J. C. Peters, and Ely McClellan—a thousand pages of personal and public tragedy, appalling sudden death, and panic. In the 1873 epidemic, "of the first eighty deaths in New Orleans, forty-six received certificates of death by cholera morbus."[20] "As a résumé of the results of my inquiries, it may be set down as the unqualified opinion of all the physicians with whom I have consulted in the city of New

Orleans, that the cholera of the spring of 1873 in that city and vicinity was native in origin; that is, it was not brought here from abroad." In the minds of most, decomposing organic matter was still the paramount cause; anticontagionism was still powerful. If the disease was caused by epidemic miasmas in the Sydenham tradition, it was therefore non-contagious and almost unavoidable. The putrid miasmas and epidemic constitution of the air were the primary causes, a feeble constitution was a predisposing factor, and irritating foods, such as corn, cucumbers, and cherries, were exciting causes.

THE ANIMALCULAR HYPOTHESIS

JOHN CRAWFORD

J. K. MITCHELL, AND DANIEL DRAKE

The animalcular hypothesis brilliantly developed by Fracastorius in the sixteenth century was deeply buried as the centuries rolled on, with only an occasional suggestion or bit of evidence to exhume it. On this side of the Atlantic, Henle's notable paper (1840)[21] seems to have made little impression, and manifestly only the development of bacteriology in the 1870's and 1880's and laborious microscopic studies could give definite evidence. Phyllis Allen[22] (1947) cites John Crawford of Baltimore (1807) as the first American proponent of the animalcular theory. He drew his ideas by analogy especially from insects such as the ichneumon fly that lays its eggs (as parasites) in the body of other insects. The growing larvae live upon and eventually destroy the unwilling host. A few other American observers were also dissatisfied with the prevailing conceptions. J. K. Mitchell, father of S. Weir Mitchell of more modern fame, maintained the animalcular theories in six delightful essays, published in a book entitled *Cryptogamous Origin of Malarial and Epidemic Fevers* (1849).[23] His writings had considerable influence on his contemporaries, including Daniel Drake, frontier physician of the Mississippi Valley.

Drake will be remembered as the most famous physician of his period in what was then the West of America; he was a prolific writer and an acute observer; he was deeply interested in the Hippocratic concept, and in the relation of environment to people and their diseases. Drake founded two schools, the Medical College of Ohio and the Medical Department of Cincinnati College, and held at different times nine professorships in five different medical schools. He published his celebrated essays on the improvement of medical education in the best medical periodical of the region—a journal that he had founded. The most noteworthy of his many contributions, resulting from his wide travels throughout the St. Lawrence and Mississippi valleys, is the thousand-page exhaustive and exhausting treatise, *Principal Diseases of the Interior Valley of North America*. Rising from poverty and harsh pioneer conditions largely through his own ambitious efforts, Drake remained gentle, simple, and humorous; he possessed distinct literary ability.

As early as 1832 Drake had considered it possible that epidemic cholera was caused by factors other than miasmata. He suggested that eggs of minute insects, smaller than mosquitoes, could conceivably float in the air and following inhalation or swallowing by man could subsequently develop in the body, thus producing the disease. Drake maintained, however, that cholera was not contagious, that quarantine procedures had proved a failure, and that persons should not flee from their homes to parts unknown in the hope of avoiding the disease. He advocated strict sanitation, clean housing, and even mosquito bars to keep out night germs.

Some years later, after some familiarity with Ehrenberg's monumental work on infusoria (1838) and his experience in the epidemic of 1848–49, Drake developed his ideas further. Under the heading vegeto-animalcular hypotheses in the first edition of his *Principal Diseases of the Interior Valley of North America* (1850),[24] he considers visible plants and animals known to have deleterious effects in the animal body and by analogy suggests that some microscopic organisms might satisfactorily explain the origin of autumnal fever and of cholera. He effectively maintains, however, the hypothetical character of these ideas and that microscopic observations must come to the aid of our bewildered minds.

By 1887 and more especially in 1892 when cholera again knocked menacingly at our ports, the miasmatic errors had been largely laid to rest by Koch's successful demonstrations (1883–84) of the cholera vibrio. This gave us a bacteriologic method of detecting ambulatory cases of the disease and a means of effective specific quarantine.

Cholera, like typhoid fever and the dysenteries, is a disease of defective human excreta disposal, with feces from cases and from carriers via food (including water), fingers, flies, and fomites as the means of transmission. Major difficulties in control are the passage of the infecting organisms in the stools from the apparently well persons in the brief prodromal period and intermittently from convalescent cases for periods up to ten days or more. Although chronic carriers have not been demonstrated as they have in typhoid fever, we do have the problem of passive carriers up to 6 or 7 per cent of the population in some epidemic areas.[25] Water-borne epidemics, such as that of the Broad Street pump in London (1854), are commonly explosive in character. A fulminating outbreak, that of Hamburg, 1892, is a perfect demonstration (the bacteriologic gods must have arranged it) of the transfer of the disease by a contaminated water supply, the Elbe River. High death losses occurred in Hamburg, 1344 per 10,000 inhabitants, while the same river worsened by the entrance of the Hamburg sewage with its additional load of cholera vibrios was rendered relatively safe for the neighboring town of Altona (23 deaths per 10,000 inhabitants) by means of a slow sand-filtration plant. The towns were separated only by political boundary, and many Altonians worked during the day in Hamburg.[26] Cholera was once called by Koch "our best ally" in the fight for better hygiene. Its dramatic effects frightened legislators into taking progressive measures far more rapidly than the creeping death resulting from tuberculosis or typhoid.

The specific relationship of the *Vibrio cholerae* and Asiatic cholera has by a number of laboratory cases, some accidental and some purposeful, been proved beyond any doubt. By the time of the 1892 epidemic, laboratory methods for isolating and identifying the organism had been sufficiently perfected so that very few infected persons penetrated our quarantine barriers. The disease remains, however, a problem in the Orient, and any considerable break in public health services may bring it to our ports again. With our well-controlled public water supplies and methods of sewage disposal, any cases entering the country can hardly seed an extensive epidemic. Although the enteric disease problem has for our country been greatly minimized, the increasing use of water for industrial purposes, air conditioning, and irrigation, with the consequent lowering of our water table is providing new and serious problems for our heavily populated areas as well as for our desert and semiarid regions.

Greater Importance of Endemic Disease

LEMUEL SHATTUCK,
J. M. NEWMAN, AND HENRY I. BOWDITCH

These appalling epidemics, that have dropped from the unknown, raged for a long period, destroyed the daily life of the family and community, and left "the dead to bury their dead," have brought panic to all peoples. Pestilence has through the ages clutched the hearts, awakened drowsy legislators, torn open the purse strings, and created a powerful urge to do something. All too frequently, even as late as the ruinous influenza epidemic of 1918–19, we have not known what to do, but we have always done something, wise or foolish. We have prayed to saints, to the gods, or to one God, we have made burnt offerings of sheep, of incense, gunpowder, or sulphur, and of man himself; we have built exquisite plague churches, such as the Church of the Redeemer in Venice, and our artists have painted gorgeous pictures such as an altar piece by Titian with the two great plague saints San Sebastian and San Roch on the right, the two medical saints Cosmas and Damian on the left, and Saint Mark as a representative of Venice enthroned high in the center. Centuries later we worked with better results, but with less beauty, through the building of sewage-disposal and water-filtration plants and through different vaccination programs. Preventive measures have necessarily varied, depending on the prevailing ideas as to the cause and mode of spread of the disease; always, however, emotional responses have influenced the procedures.

Quoting from the pungent essay of a recent author, Shryock (1929), on the "Origins and Significance of the Public Health Movement in the United States,"[27]

It is difficult to discover any cases of reforms in health administration, from those traditionally ascribed to the Emperor Sigismund, in 1426, to the Massachusetts sanitary survey of 1850, not occasioned by the threat of epidemics. This role of epidemics in making reform possible is interesting, in view of the fact that such diseases are not usually so serious a threat to public health as are the endemic ones. This is realized by pioneer American sanitarians, . . .

The principal causes of death, even during the periods of the great epidemics, were not cholera and yellow fever, but the so-called zymotic or fermentation diseases, those that we now place among the common communicable diseases. From Lemuel Shattuck[28] and his associates in the *Report of the Sanitary Commission of Massachusetts* (1850),

We find that dysentery, typhus fever, [this term included also typhoid fever] consumption, and other fatal diseases are common in nearly all parts of the State. They are the constant visitors. In some periods and places more so than in others, but in all, they have become familiar to us, and cease to excite notice or alarm. . . . Consumption, that great destroyer of human health and human life, takes first rank as an agent of death.

In J. M. Newman's report on the sanitary police of the cities[29] (1856), he summarizes earlier sanitary surveys of the American Medical Association's committees on hygiene dating from 1848, and gives mortality tables from several areas over a period of years. These show the ratio of deaths to population, the deaths due to zymotic diseases compared with total deaths, and the considerably greater death losses in the cities as compared with the adjacent country districts.

Newman states:

This report will be an effort to tabulate the effects of disease, and to exhibit by figures the ravages that preventable disease is committing in our midst, and especially in our cities. The havocs of epidemics and the deductions therefrom will occupy less attention than the slow, continuous, unceasing inroads of diseases less rapid and alarming, but as certain and fatal as they are insidious. The public mind has been accustomed to view the matter of sanitary reform too much, if not alone, by the light of epidemics. They lose sight of the less violent, slower, but no less certain causes of sickness and death with which they are continuously surrounded. Death reaps a yearly harvest to the grave, and when it exceeds not the usual annual number, it is not heeded, and the inquiry is not made whether a part of his trophies might not have been snatched from him; it is only when his victims are largely in excess that public attention is arrested and alarm excited.

. . . .

The deaths by cholera in the United States, for the year ending June 1, 1850, which nearly if not quite covers the epidemic period of its second visitation to our shores in 1849, were 31,506, as returned by the census report of that year. As large as is this aggregate, it is exceeded by the sum of the other forms of disease of the alimentary passages.

We gather from the same source, that during the same period there were from

Cholera infantum	3,960 deaths
Cholera morbus	1,568 deaths
Diarrhea	6,366 deaths
Dysentery	20,566 deaths
Thrush	424 deaths
	32,884 deaths
Add by cholera	31,506 deaths
	64,390 deaths

And it is seen we have a total of 64,390 deaths from diseases of the alimentary passages, being 19.93 per cent of all the deaths reported for the year.

. . . .

Fever in its varied forms, is also one of the mighty agents in the constant destruction of life witnessed on every side. Too little care, as a general thing, is paid to accuracy of type in diagnosis to insure uniform correctness of classification, and no doubt the name of one form of the disease is frequently substituted for that of another, and there cannot consequently be that minuteness of detail arrived at, desirable to assign to each distinct type its true percentage of mortality. But enough can be learned to prove the destruction annually caused by the diseases bearing the general names of fevers.

. . . .

In the "Mortality Statistics of the Census of 1850," we find the number of deaths caused by fever in its various forms, for the year ending June 1, 1850, returned as follows:

Fever	18,108
Fever, Intermittent	964
Fever, Remittent	148
Fever, Ship	240
Fever, Typhoid	13,099
Fever, Yellow	785
Total number of deaths by fever	33,344

It will be seen that the number of deaths by fever was greater than those by cholera, during the same year in which the latter raged as an epidemic. It is perhaps not too much to say with these figures before us, that we had two epidemics abroad through the country, doing the work of death side by side. One was spreading consternation and alarm wherever it appeared; the other was silently, unnoticed, and unheeded, but just as certainly, filling the grave as the dreaded cholera.

Bowditch in his study of *Public Hygiene in America*, begun as part of our centennial celebration of 1876,[30] also affirms that "Hitherto, little or no attention has been paid to it [hygiene], except, when, under the influence of some frightful epidemic, the panic-struck nations have been aroused from their usual apathy, and have then vainly tried to resist the pest by drugs, by appeals to the gods whose laws they have never studied or finally, by legal enactments, after the days of suffering have passed." In the slow growth of the public health movement in this and other countries, leaders have come to realize these facts. The emotions provide energy but direction must come from knowledge and wisdom.

MALARIA

DANIEL DRAKE, TIMOTHY FLINT, W. G. MAC CALLUM

And on every day there,
As sure as day would break,
Their neighbor, "Ager" came that way,
Inviting them to shake.

Malaria was introduced early into this country chiefly in the southern states in the blood of the unfortunate slaves from Africa (1619 *et seq*). By the time of the Revolution, the disease had become endemic from

Georgia to Pennsylvania; it marched slowly north and west along the coast and the river valleys. By the middle of the nineteenth century, when the disease reached its peak, it had spread even into New England and northern New York and was especially serious along the Mississippi River and its tributaries. Contemporary writers of that century placed malaria high on the list of endemic disabling as well as fatal diseases.

Although the method of transmission was discovered by Ronald Ross in 1897–98, and Gorgas started large-scale antimosquito campaigns as early as 1901, first in Cuba, then in Panama, few active measures in the continental United States were begun before 1912.

To us malaria is a disease clearly ascertainable by the presence of plasmodia in the thick blood smear. To 19th century physicians malaria was and could be but that mysterious emanation of swamps and "decaying vegetable matter" which caused "malarious" or "estivoautumnal" disease. . . . Particularly under frontier conditions, there was no official and very little unofficial recording of diseases, and to make things worse, just at its height, malaria [or fever and ague, the chills, intermittent, remittent, bilious fever or whatever it was called] was so common that by many it was no longer regarded as a disease at all and therefore, of course, not recorded as such.[31]

Chills were part of the inevitable "acclimatization." He ain't sick, he's only got the ager, was the common reaction. "Especially the malaria of small children, which constitutes the bulk of malaria cases in highly endemic sections, went unnoticed, at least by medical men. What Hippocrates and Aristotle had known was forgotten. There was even a widespread belief among doctors that malaria only attacks adults. Laymen sometimes seem to have been better observers of infantile malaria." Daniel Drake, our leading epidemiologist of the interior valley of North America, leaves no doubt of the extensive prevalence of "autumnal fever," although one is forced to admit confusion among the intermittent, remittent, and bilious fevers. Timothy Flint, the Massachusetts missionary and herald of the frontier, in his early study on nineteenth century frontier conditions, makes the following significant statement: "The Valley of the Arkansas, with very little exception, is sickly. Remittents and intermittents are so common, that when a person has no more than a simple fever and ague, he is hardly allowed to claim the immunities of sickness. . . . The autumn that I was there, it appeared to me that more than the half the inhabitants, not excepting the Creoles, had the ague."

In our awareness of the confusion among early physicians in the diagnosis of malaria, typhoid fever, and the dysenteries, and that the official statistics are of little value, "We cannot forget, that this was a time when many doctors were not trained in medical schools, when even a medical school training did not amount to much." Buley in his study of medical practices in the Old Northwest cites the action of the Supreme Court of Michigan: "a doctor is any person calling himself such; a rule valid until 1883."[32] Would not the modern physician be at a loss in many cases without the blood smear for the plasmodium in malaria and the several microbiologic methods as aids in diagnosis of typhoid fever and the diasastrous "flux," the dysenteries? Indeed, the deadly dysentery was "the American disease" of the period, and typhomalarial fever was the confusing term perpetrated by J. J. Woodward, co-author of the *Medical History of the War of the Rebellion;* on that basis it was introduced into the census statistics. The Spanish-American War report stated that 100 per cent of the "malaria" cases in the military camps were typhoid.[33]

The story of the slow retreat in our country of this world disease has been told by many, most completely by Mark Boyd and sixty-five contributors (1949).[34] It is commonly agreed that many factors aided in this decline. In Ackerknecht's revealing study of *Malaria in the Upper Mississippi Valley 1760–1900,* he concludes that

the eradication of malaria from the Upper Mississippi Valley was to a large extent the work of indirect measures undertaken without sanitary intentions: better agricultural methods, cattle breeding, better housing, screening, more prosperity, education, etc. But it is most likely that this progress was only realized, and only realized so quickly, because of the help of quinine. Quinine kept the "invasion army" of the settlers fighting in a decisive period. . . . Quinine, the "direct antimalarial" paradoxically enough acted in the most indirect way: in making possible the indirect, unconscious socio-economic achievements. Without quinine the economic development of the whole region and therewith the decline of malaria would most probably have been at least considerably retarded.[35]

The decreasing size of the black areas on maps of malarial incidence in this country tell a story, complex in the many factors involved, but an achievement of major proportions.

ENDEMIC TYPHOID FEVER

Although typhoid fever has not had the lurid fear-inciting history of epidemic cholera, it continued in some areas with a high endemic rate, and has been a notorious hazard because of the chronic and well carriers that excrete the organism intermittently from as many as 2–3 per cent of recovered cases. We continued to have a distressingly high typhoid rate until well into the twentieth century. As always, it took an epidemic to shake us out of our lethargy. That came with shocking force as the result of our unpreparedness for the handling of large groups of men during the Spanish-AmericanWar.

TUBERCULOSIS

LEMUEL SHATTUCK AND THEOBALD SMITH

Hippocrates, in the fifth century B. C. wrote, "The greatest and most dangerous disease and the one that proved fatal to the greatest number, was consumption."[36] Save in the severest epidemics, this has continued throughout the ages, with the Four Horsemen of the Apocalypse providing conditions ideal for its spread. But as to the modes of spread they were enigmas until yesterday.

In the histories of our colonies, consumption is only occasionally mentioned (Packard). As always, the more acute and violent diseases attracted the attention rather than a slow wasting disease with a long incubation period and without startling visible lesions.[37] By the nineteenth century the identification of tuberculosis in its many forms and the correlation of lesions at autopsy with clinical symptoms was gradually, but so slowly, changing professional and public attitudes. This reformation was instituted by men of the French school in the early days of the century chiefly by G. P. Bayle and René Laënnec, brilliant young leaders in the new knowledge of lung pathology. Both of these men died of pulmonary tuberculosis, Bayle at forty-two years and Laënnec at forty-six years of age. Laënnec, who was also the father of stethoscope and mediate auscultation, followed in over two hundred autopsies the early tiny translucent seedlike lesions through their growth into irregular cheesy masses with subsequent softening and cavity formation. He correlated these lesions with symptoms in the living and the sounds he heard in listening through his "little trumpets." He went as far as was possible with the technics available in showing the unity of tuberculosis. Manifestly that could not be proved until decades later when Villemin, Koch, and Theobald Smith provided us with methods for demonstrating the infecting bacterium.

Shattuck gave "consumption the first rank as an agent of death." He cites many figures from American and foreign cities and their neighboring rural areas which tell the tragic story of the many deaths from tuberculosis in the early decades of the century compared with total deaths. We shall take a few cities only as samples:

	Years	Periods	Deaths from All Causes	Deaths from Consumption	TB % of Total
Portsmouth, N. H.	19	1800–11 1818–25	2,367	471	19.81
Providence, R. I.	5	1841–45	3,032	718	23.68
New York City, N. Y.	10	1811–20	25,896	6,061	23.40
Philadelphia, Pa.	10	1811–20	23,582	3,629	15.38
London, England	8	1840–47	397,871	57,047	14.33
Paris, France	4	1816–19	85,339	15,375	18.01

From the wealth of material on tuberculosis, a mass of similar figures for the last half of the nineteenth century and subsequently could be added to our complete exhaustion. Esmond Long,[38] competent student of this disease, has reiterated that it "waxes and wanes in different countries" with industrial revolutions, and the consequent rise and fall in living conditions. "In this period not less than a fifth of all deaths in Boston, New York and Philadelphia were due to tuberculosis. . . . Tuberculosis was undoubtedly under-reported in official records, a fact that makes the recorded high rates all the more impressive."

One of the more personal recent accounts of the White Plague is that by René and Jean Dubos. They were able to get away from the "it was observed" style and yet retain a scholarly point of view with emphasis, too, on the losses to society through the early death of such brilliant men as Keats, Chopin, and Paganini.

"Early statements concerning deaths caused by tuberculosis are very inaccurate."[39] But by using only figures from the more readily identifiable pulmonary tuberculosis and from various sources, it becomes apparent that in England and the eastern United States, the decline in such deaths began early in the nineteenth century before the birth of bacteriology. The improvements in living conditions, nutrition, etc. that have been factors in reducing the incidence of several communicable diseases were active also in tuberculosis. In the United States a marked temporary rise occurred between 1850 and 1875 due to the disastrous overcrowding in our eastern cities because of the large influx of immigrants.

With the rise of bacteriology, the active campaign of prevention based on case finding, compulsory reporting, and isolation of patients in sanitariums, the mortality rates have gone steadily down. Around 1920 tuberculosis lost its primary position in the mortality tables, giving that place to cardiovascular diseases. The mortality curve has continued its downward trend, but the incidence remains appallingly high, especially among young adult persons. Rather discouragingly also, the drop in number of new cases has not followed the decline in deaths. Doubtless some of this is only apparent and is due to early and more accurate case finding. No doubt exists that tuberculosis continues to be the great endemic White Plague.

2

THE ATLANTIC SEABOARD

CHAPTER V

Early Sanitation and Public Hygiene

*And other [seed] fell on good ground, and
sprang up, and bare fruit an hundredfold.*   LUKE 8:8

As has been stated, early medical and public hygiene, both precept and
practice, were closely interwoven with the religion of the people, the
epidemic constitution of the atmosphere, some malign conjunction of
the stars, and a little later with gaseous emanations from decomposing
organic matter. About this last problem it was possible to do something,
so in the last half of the nineteenth century, this public nuisance became
the major point of attack for our public and private health organizations.
City populations, far removed from the necessity of rebuilding depleted
soil with animal manure and vegetable compost, became obsessed with
the idea of danger from decomposing organic matter from any source.

In ancient times the sanitary codes of the Jews as described in the
Old Testament had much of wisdom. In the time of the Tarquins,
sixth century B. C., Rome built a large sewer, *Cloaca Maxima*, designed
initially for drainage of swamps, but later when abundant water was
provided by the successive construction of some fourteen aqueducts,
this was used for the water carriage of household wastes. Outside of
Rome, the Pont du Gard at Nimes, built under Agrippa (A.D. 18), is
the most beautiful of the surviving aqueducts, exquisitely strong and
graceful with its triple arcade, one surmounting the other; it now
serves admirably as a traffic bridge. The destructive invasions and wars
that brought about the fall of Rome, caused a break in many sanitary
regulations and the ruin of many aqueducts.

Modern interest in sanitary reform and human welfare became more
active about 1845. Improvement of the external environment became

a moving precept of the age. This concept stemmed from many sources, with epidemics of yellow fever and cholera supplying the emotional compulsion. Richard Shryock stated: "The public was from time to time terrified into being good."

Great Britain was the forerunner in public health and was especially influential in this country because of the common language. Edwin Chadwick (1800–1890), barrister, published in 1828 an "Essay on the Means of Insurance against Casualties of Sickness, Decrepitude and Mortality." Stimulated by finding that a lengthening in life expectation followed the improvement in living conditions in the middle class in England, and aided further by a legacy from the English philanthropist Jeremy Bentham, he continued his studies, published in a series of papers, the most notable, *A General Report on the Sanitary Condition of the Labouring Population of Great Britain.* The Chadwick reports,[1] those of Sir John Simon, as the administrator who began application of Chadwick's advice, and the epidemiological work of Southwood Smith gave encouragement to those in this country who were struggling for increased support of public hygiene.

In the Boston area, Lemuel Shattuck,[2] another farseeing layman, quoted the British authors liberally in his history of the movement; his sanitary survey with its fifty specific recommendations is an outstanding landmark in the forward march of public health in this country. It took nineteen years, however, for the seed sown by Shattuck and his associates to sprout into the Massachusetts State Board of Health; New England soil is full of rocks. As a bit of realism, we should note that the Sanitary Commission, of which Shattuck was chairman and leading spirit, was authorized because of fear of a cholera epidemic, and the actual establishment of the State Board of Health nineteen years later "had its inception," according to Dr. Wolcott, "because of an outbreak of typhoid fever in a girls' school, in which the wife of a prominent state official was interested." This does not mean that humanitarian motives are unimportant.

In England, we find John Howard (1728–90) in prison reform, Elizabeth Fry (1780–1845) in nursing and reform of the "Hell upon Earth," Newgate Prison, Florence Nightingale in nursing reform in the British Army of the Crimean War, and William Wilberforce (1759–1833) in the abolition of the slave trade. In this country, we find Dorothy Dix (1802–81) pressing for hospitals for the insane, Horace Mann, shouting, "Be ashamed to die until you have won some victory for humanity"; also, William Lloyd Garrison and the anti-slavery movement with all of its ramifications, the authors, Emerson, Whittier, Longfellow, and Harriet Beecher Stowe, and the Unitarian movement with William Ellery Channing as leader—all were significant. But these, too, had compelling human suffering, if not a rampant infectious disease, to furnish emotional drive.

In colonial America, as already indicated, temporary boards of health and a variety of quarantine regulations came into being when fears of epidemics gripped the people, only to lapse as the disease and fears waned. The history of these and later efforts is interestingly told by many, including Bowditch, Chapin, Whipple, several authors in *A Half-Century of Public Health*,[3] and the recent *History of American Epidemiology*.[4] As the nineteenth century grew older, one may observe an increase in national voluntary groups such as the American Medical Association (1847) and the American Public Health Association (1872) and in public organizations such as state boards of health, Louisiana (1855) and Massachusetts in 1869, with some eighteen more such state agencies in the next decade.

Smillie cites a report as early as 1806 by a citizens' committee on the sanitary conditions of New York City. On a national basis, the efforts of the Medical Department of the National Institute in Washington in 1845 give an inkling of the situation over the country. In their report to the newly formed American Medical Association, they state:

The United States may be considered as a country in which no legislative enactments exist, regulating its sanitary condition, for with the exception of some municipal regulations, forced from the necessity of circumstances upon the large cities, and a few of the first steps of legislation in one or two of the States of the Union, each individual is permitted to exercise his own free will in regard to hygienic measures, too frequently either from ignorance of its laws, or cupidity, at the expense of great sacrifices of human life.[5]

They made two recommendations, first, the establishment of a permanent committee on hygiene, and second, a uniform system of registration of births, deaths, and marriages through enactments by the various state legislatures. This first aim was accomplished almost immediately and the sanitary surveys of this committee in the succeeding years present clearly the lack of public hygiene in the larger cities. Much of this is gathered together in a summary report by James M. Newman.[6] In these surveys great emphasis is placed on ventilation, the evil influence of emanations, the high incidence of zymotic diseases, and the need of improving external environment. The second recommendation involved prolonged education of many legislators in many states; not until 1930 did all of our states (save Texas) meet with the registration standards set up by the United States Bureau of the Census.

Following the Sanitary Conference of Paris in 1851 which affirmed the medical tenets of the day that "even epidemic diseases of contagious character are never spread from person to person and that epidemics are always the result of cosmic conditions," several such conventions were held in this country beginning with one in Philadelphia in 1857. In spite of the enforcement of quarantine regulations, the great epidemics of yellow fever, cholera, and smallpox, as well as the more important endemic diseases continued to take their toll. These failures, especially in yellow fever, were important in the continuing adherence of the medical profession to the doctrine of anticontagionism. Increasingly, sanitary surveys became an important mode of studying the distressing facts of life in our cities. *The Sanitary Condition of the Laboring Population of New York City* by John H. Griscom in 1845, a world picture of these problems by Bell of Philadelphia in 1859, or the more extensive study, "The Sanitary Conditions and Hygienic Wants of New York," by a citizens' committee with Stephen Smith as a major influence in 1865, all tell much the same story.[7] A few extracts from the Smith report will show the dismal scene.

Death rates had markedly increased, crowding in small filthy quarters with several families, men, women, and children, in one room, much-abused privies, seldom emptied, an estimate of 18,000 persons living in cellars, typhoid fever, typhus fever, and infantile diarrheas prevalent, refuse of all sorts thrown into the narrow streets or courts, saloons, and brothels intermixed; "in some cases, it seems questionable whether the alley was intended as an entrance-way to a rear house or a sewage ditch for the slops, water, garbage, human excrements, and urine. . . . About twelve of the privies were found full to the floor timbers or within one foot of them. . . . Twenty-five persons are expected to use one seat-opening."

Overwhelmed by the startling revelations of this report, a Metropolitan Board of Health was created in 1866 with Dr. Smith as commissioner of the board. The American Public Health Association has continually fostered sanitary surveys and with the publication of the excellent text on *Preventive Medicine and Hygiene* by Milton J. Rosenau of Harvard Medical School[8] (1913), the practice of requiring each medical student to make a survey of his home town was adopted by Harvard and some other schools.

Medical Education

> The lame in the path outstrip the swift
> who wander from it. FRANCIS BACON

In addition to the low state of public hygiene in our cities in mid-nineteenth century, medical practice had also sunk to low depths.

In a pioneer country, with a rapidly increasing population and the continued westward migration, the demand for doctors, and therefore for medical schools, was great. There were virtually no legal restrictions on the establishment of medical schools. Many were decidedly inferior and were established primarily for the financial gain of the promotors and the faculty. The operation of a medical school was often a profitable enterprise and there was an intense competition for students. Besides the so-called medical schools and the apprentice training in physicians' offices, there arose "diploma mills" in all sections of the country. These sold diplomas with no pretense whatsoever of providing medical training of any kind.

The multiplication of medical schools was such that, by the end of the nineteenth century there were about as many medical schools in the United States as there were in all the rest of the world. A few of these institutions were of good quality: . . . but chaos was the rule. . . . Admission requirements were usually non-existent. Often ability to read and write was not essential.[9]

Sigerist states that "wherever a few doctors were gathered together, they could found a school, get a charter, call themselves professors, give medical instruction in some rented building, deal out diplomas, and pocket the tuition fees."

The Council on Medical Education of the American Medical Association, derived from the earlier committees with similar functions, worked for twenty-three years from 1904 under the guiding hand of Arthur Dean Bevan with substantial aid from the other members of the Council and George H. Simmons, long-time editor of the *Journal of the American Medical Association*. After the first decade the Council reported some successes but because of the personal resentment aroused by their studies and efforts, because of aversion to publicity on the part of some institutions, and because our constitution and states rights could not permit national action, they were pessimistic about continued progress.

The struggle for advancing requirements continued, however, and in 1908 the desire of the council to obtain aid from an outside body received the approval and co-operation of the Carnegie Foundation for the Advancement of Teaching. Abraham Flexner with N. P. Colwell of the Council and four years of intensive work on the part of many interested in medical education brought forth in 1910 Bulletin number 4, *Medical Education in the United States and Canada*, and in 1912, Bulletin number 6, *Medical Education in Europe*.[10] The results of these Flexner reports were amazing. With no legal powers on the part of the Carnegie Foundation or of the American Medical Association's Council on Medical Education, merely by pertinent, sharp statements of facts showing the grossly inadequate conditions in many of our schools, the striking differences among our institutions, and even greater differences when compared with the major institutions in European countries, the rapidity of progress was astounding. The nonacceptable Class C schools disappeared shortly, Class B schools came up to Class A rating, enormous sums of money from private philanthropists, from foundations, and from public sources were poured into medical schools and associated hospitals. Co-operation overcame inertia and opposition, standards were advanced first to the requirement of a high school diploma for admission, and later to two and now to three years of college work to include courses in biology, physics, and chemistry. The medical course has been immeasurably strengthened and lengthened from one or two years of a few months each, in the middle of the nineteenth century, to four years of nine months. Each state has its licensing board for the right to practice with a minimum requirement of one year of internship in an approved hospital beyond the regular medical course, and each specialty now has extensive standard requirements for its board exminations. This has been an astounding evolution.

Meantime, the field in which we are immediately interested had been cultivated chiefly in Europe with a harvest especially in improved understanding of communicable disease. Responding to the new knowledge, some of our medical schools and a few colleges and universities began in the late 1880's to give lectures and a few demonstrations of the diphtheria and tubercle bacilli and the malarial plasmodium; by the time of the great advance in medical education during the first decades of the twentieth century, all schools gave attention to the all-powerful parasites.

CHAPTER VI

Johns Hopkins University
The Medical School

Joy, *temperance and repose*
Slam the door on the doctor's nose.
CODE OF HEALTH, SALERNO, TWELFTH CENTURY

"Although still a young institution, the Johns Hopkins is the oldest university in the United States"; so wrote Shryock in a well-documented essay, "The Unique Influence of the Johns Hopkins University on American Medicine." Charles William Eliot, who became the reforming president of Harvard University in 1869, declared that the Harvard Graduate School "started feebly in 1870 and 1871, did not thrive until the example of Johns Hopkins forced our faculty to put their strength into the development of our instruction for graduates." And what was true of Harvard was true of every other university in the land which aspired to create an advanced school of arts and sciences.

Shryock continued,

The results were as anticipated: Hopkins products were soon in demand all over the country. Within twenty years, over sixty American colleges or universities had three or more professors holding Hopkins degrees on their staffs. There were, for example, ten at Harvard, thirteen at Columbia, nineteen at Wisconsin, and twenty-three at Chicago. By that time other graduate schools were in operation, but in many places it had been the impact of Hopkins men which first made for truly higher education.[1]

Johns Hopkins University was founded in 1876 with Daniel Coit Gilman, as President. Not until 1889 was the Hospital opened and the Medical School not until four years after that. Many were the difficulties. It is not easy to think of the present thriving Johns Hopkins Uni-

versity as it was three quarters of a century ago, when it was in swad-
dling clothes. This institution, particularly the Medical School, had a
long and painful period of gestation and labor. There were objections
to a hospital by the owners of nearby real estate and by the physicians
of the other medical school in Baltimore, the University of Maryland.
In view of the almost complete lack of entrance requirements in many
schools, the proposed standards for admission were thought by most to
be impossibly high. A bachelor's degree or its equivalent, a reading
knowledge of French and German, and designated courses in physics,
biology, and chemistry were the requirements set by Gilman, Welch,
and Billings. Would a sufficient number of students meet these requirements? Osler remarked, "Welch, we are lucky to get in as professors,
for I am sure that neither you nor I could ever get in as students." He
might also have queried whether the freer methods of instruction, the
placing of more responsibility directly on the students, and the grossly
inadequate facilities would hold even a highly selected group.

Of the first graduates of the school, five were from Baltimore and gladly accepted the
opportunity the school obviously offered them. For graduates of distant colleges, it
took no little imagination, enterprise, and courage to enlist in an undertaking which had
no precedent in this country. Two of those admitted were from Harvard, two from
Yale and of the other graduates one was from each of six colleges: . . . Aside from the
Johns Hopkins Hospital in which medical students would have no work for two years,
there were literally no medical school buildings, and classes were conducted in the old
pathological laboratory of the hospital and in the distant biological laboratories of the
University. Instruction seemed so casual that about half the class decided to leave and
go elsewhere for medical work. Dr. Welch, the dean, learned of this dissatisfaction
and invited them to come to his room to talk things over. He is said to have offered
them cigars but I suspect that as usual, he was smoking one himself, with a well-filled
box on the table before him. He explained the difficulties of starting a new school and
asked for the cooperation of the students. He persuaded them to stay. Needless to say,
in after years they were profoundly grateful for the advice they had received and often
later somewhat appalled by the memory that once admitted they had to be persuaded
to remain.[2]

The Baltimore and Ohio Railroad stock that Hopkins had given to
found the university had fallen to such a low level that what had seemed
ample proved to be not nearly enough. After many begging letters and
ringing of door bells, a strong committee of dedicated women with Miss
Mary Garrett of Baltimore as the chief donor provided the necessary
$500,000 for the opening of the Medical School with the stipulation
that the suggested high entrance requirements should stand and furthermore that women should be admitted on the same basis as men. This
was still the Victorian era, and reluctance is a mild term for the atti-

tudes of Gilman and the board of trustees towards coeducation in the medical school. But they finally capitulated, and history tells of the success of all of these requirements.

The reasons for the outstanding success of Hopkins are not far to seek. With a few notable exceptions even the Harvard faculty, as President Eliot states, was not interested in graduate instruction. And the medical schools were admittedly in a far weaker state, supported largely by student fees. With emphasis on men, not buildings, Gilman sought advice widely, selected unusually competent productive young scholars (average age of the medical faculty was about thirty-three years), and the institution provided each with freedom to blaze his own trail. Welch, for example, was appointed in 1884 at the age of thirty-four, nine years before the medical school was opened for regular classes, and Osler was the oldest, appointed in 1888, at the age of forty. The ferment of the scientific revolution was bubbling up in spots throughout the country, but nowhere else was such a yeasty mass, so large a group of productive scholars working in the different but related fields. The example of the German universities, the research scientists in other countries, and the expansion of our country in industry and wealth were most important for this development.

William Welch—The Heroic Age of American Medicine

It is also difficult for me to think of the assured, rotund William Henry Welch (1850–1934), the most brilliant star in the sky of American medicine during this heroic age, always ready with his flowing sparkling phrases, as an indecisive young graduate of Yale with a teaching career in Greek as his first choice. Since no position in classics offered itself, he accepted a teaching job in a private school. The school folded up at the end of the year, so even this opening disappeared, leaving Welch at loose ends once more. In this contingency, he decided to follow in his father's medical footsteps and to spend the year at Sheffield Scientific School studying chemistry; there were no laboratory courses in the academic departments of Yale. Then, in 1872 he entered the College of Physicians and Surgeons in New York where he followed the didactic lectures for three years rather than the required two for the M.D. degree. He reports that the work was easy, no entrance requirements, no laboratory courses, and nobody failed because the school was supported by student fees.

Bright spots in Welch's medical course were the winning of a microscope as a prize for the best report of Sequin's lectures on diseases of the nervous system and in the final year the thesis prize for an essay on goiter. Welch's indecision seems now to have left him, and he stood out in his classes both as a student and as a leader. After graduation in February, 1875, Welch received an appointment as intern at Bellevue Hospital where in addition to other facilities he came in contact with Delafield, the pathologist, and had more experience in post-mortems. Again at loose ends at the end of his internship and with no positions whatever in New York and a dislike of the practice of medicine, Welch persuaded his father that a period of study in the active laboratories of Germany was necessary for his further advance.

In April, 1876, he sailed for Europe for the first, the longest, and the most eye-opening of the many trips to the older countries that he was to make during his long life. He knew little German and had never had laboratory courses in normal histology or in physiological chemistry, so he spent a portion of the year taking courses that the present-day student completes in his first year in medical school. He enjoyed histology with Waldeyer, physiological chemistry with Hoppe-Seyler at Strasbourg, then went to Leipzig where his most valued opportunity was working under Ludwig in the physiology laboratory. He was astounded at the high level of the courses and the quality of investigation in all the laboratories, "nothing like it in America." In Breslau he worked in pathology with Cohnheim, then back to Strasbourg to study under von Recklinghausen, previously denied to him because of his lack of preparation. With Cohnheim he did one of his best experimental pathological studies showing that pulmonary edema is caused by disproportion (*Missverhältnis*) in the action of the two cardiac ventricles.

The excitement over Koch's experimental production of anthrax with pure cultures of *Bacillus anthracis* ran through the laboratories, but did not at this time impress Welch, although he must have been aware of the demonstration in Cohnheim's laboratory. He did not refer to bacteria in his letters until von Recklinghausen called his attention to their probable importance. Then he wrote to his father that "for the last six or eight years there has been strong and increasing evidence that infectious diseases are due to the presence in the blood or body of microscopical organisms."[3] The active minds and laboratories of the German leaders of the period convinced him that he must have another year in Europe, and in spite of some financial difficulties, it was finally arranged. Meantime he was absorbing the delights of life in Europe through each sense organ and every pore—the art museums, he spent days in the Louvre; the theatres, opera was his special devotion, and Lohengrin in Berlin was beyond criticism; walking trips in Switzerland and Bavaria; discussions with other students in the Stadtpark over his "eight pints" of beer, the *Gemütlichkeit* of Munich and Vienna.

Back in New York early in 1878 after his two exciting years, Welch desperately sought a job to earn his living without going into medical practice. He was blue and lonesome. "There is no opportunity in this country and it seems improbable that there ever will be." After climbing many stairs, he did obtain several odd jobs that gave him minor chances and contacts with successful men in medicine, especially the elder Janeway and Austin Flint, at Bellevue Hospital. There he was finally granted three small rooms with kitchen tables devoid of microscopes and everything else so common in Germany, whereupon he opened what was probably the first pathological laboratory in this country. He had clung to his ideals, he had brought the spirit of the German laboratories with him, and he attracted students from the several schools of medicine in the city. Delafield now offered him a small post at the College of Physicians and Surgeons, but Welch could not forsake the institution that had made a place for him. Instead, he recommended a junior colleague of some of his European adventures, T. Mitchell Prudden, who received the appointment.

Welch received increasing recognition, but he realized that he was splitting his efforts; always he had in mind the possibilities he dreamed about at the new Johns Hopkins University. He did for a while engage in a little medical practice, never lucrative; he appreciated that it took him away from his métier. One would like to know more about the man at this period, his life and thoughts during these six crucial years of discontent and disillusion, failure from his point of view, battling with the meager conditions for medical education in the metropolis, New York. All the while he carried on, taking each small task as it came his way, building up experience and facing his world with dignity and enjoying occasionally the theater, opera, and a bit of gaiety. Even the definitive biography by the Flexners, father and son, passes over this important period in a few pages.

In March, 1884, came the long-hoped-for opening at Johns Hopkins. He thought the matter over for three weeks and then, although his New York friends told him he was making the mistake of his life and tried to make a suitable place for him—they had waited too long—Welch accepted the proffered chair in pathology. But financial difficulties were to make it impossible for the medical school to open its doors for regular classes for nine long years, so in September, Welch again sailed for Germany to prepare further for his new adventure. It would be inappropriate for this history to follow Welch through this or his numerous other European trips, his wanderings, his visitings, his studies and experimental work. Never, I imagine, has anyone been a guest in so many laboratories. He met all the leaders in biological and medical sciences. All, that is, save one; he never met Pasteur.

By this time (1884) a dozen microorganisms had been proved, with varying degree of completeness, the causative agents in specific diseases. The anthrax bacillus (Koch, 1876), the typhoid bacillus (Eberth, 1880), the *Bacillus tuberculosis* (Koch, 1882), and the *Vibrio cholerae* (Koch, 1883) were causing a sag in anticontagionism. Welch wrote President Gilman from Leipzig, "I am convinced that for some years the relation of microorganisms to the causation of disease is to be the most important subject in pathology." He was eager to work with Koch, the leader in this "brave new world." When the laboratories were opened in July, 1885, Welch became a student in the first public course given by Koch. He greatly enjoyed the close daily association with the master.

On the way back to Germany from England to take this course, Welch apparently did not stop off in Paris. He wrote his stepmother, "There is nothing especial of a scientific nature to lead me there." How could he have been so unaware of the two decades of important achievements of Pasteur and his associates, including the successful vaccinations against chicken cholera and anthrax and the recent studies on rabies? Probably because his German masters were so parochial.

In October, 1885, Welch began his life in Baltimore, plunging with enthusiasm into the activities of the city, and into his most productive experimental period. Although the Hopkins Hospital was not completed for almost four more years, he with Gilman, Billings, and others laid plans for the medical school and the closely associated hospital. To us at this distance, the prospects for the institution seem pale indeed. But Welch was jubilant over the free hand he had in the plans, over his associates of the moment, and in prospect. He was assigned three small rooms in Newell Martin's laboratory, "a commodious two story building originally designed as a dead house," quarters that seemed to Welch "a great contrast to the so-called laboratory in New York." Assuredly only persistent faith in their vision of a unique *university medical school* could have given the blithe spirit, courage, and a sense of future achievement to Welch and his pioneer associates. In February of the next year (1886) Welch gave nine public lectures in bacteriology, and in the autumn formal instruction in pathology was begun for graduates in medicine. Since many of his bacterial cultures brought from Koch's laboratory had died in the meantime, and this had also happened with those brought over by Prudden, he sailed off to spend a month in Berlin to retrieve similar treasures.

By the following May, Welch reported a tremendous renaissance with twenty-six medical graduates working in the laboratory, eight of them carrying on original investigations:

Sternberg—had studied thermal death points of bacteria;
Booker—the bacteriology of stools from children with summer diarrhea;
Abbott—the behavior of bacteria in drinking water;
Councilman—the malarial parasite of Laveran;
Herter—experimental production of myelitis;
Welch—had begun his own work on experimental glomerulo-nephritis, and with Mall on hemorrhagic infarction.

In those years of the bursting of bacteriology on an amazed world, Welch gave weekly lectures to all comers on medical subjects of outstanding contemporary interest. One year it would be diphtheria, another, cholera, and then the pneumococcus and the pneumonias. Subsequently these would become major addresses before a conference of health officers, the Congress of American Physicians, or other organizations. The physicians of the country were still a bit dubious about the importance of microbes that they had never seen, but no one could marshal the facts more effectively and be so urbanely persuasive as Welch. Although he became a major contributor during the early days of bacteriology in this country and a leader in stressing the microbic origins of infectious diseases, yet he commonly regarded bacteria and other microorganisms chiefly as agents in pathology. Only occasionally did he seem to sense the broader aspects of microbiology.

The first bacteriological problem that Welch tackled was hog cholera, a disease then (1887, *et seq.*) prevalent in Maryland. Along with many other investigators, including Salmon and Smith in this country, Pasteur, Metchnikoff, Schültz, and Koch in Europe, Welch failed. Like the others, he became confused by the similarity of many of the lesions produced by secondary invaders. The immunologic tests for specific relationships had not been discovered.

EARLY BACTERIOLOGIC METHODS

We must keep the times in mind and realize that the methods of bacteriology in the eighties, nineties, and even later were primitive and inexact. Bacteriology and its kindred branch immunology remained among the weakest of the descriptive sciences until well into the twentieth century. Technics were simple and special skills were not needed; only slowly did bacteriology become a highly detailed science.

To obtain pure cultures of a single species for study, the progressive dilution method of Pasteur and of Lister gradually gave place to the solid gelatin media of Koch on glass plates; the messy liquefiers of this method were eliminated when the relatively indigestible agar-agar,[4] still unbelievably valuable, came into use. The continuing boon of the cotton plug for tubes and flasks and the circular petri dish for pouring dilutions are to this day our simple universal aids. Common dyes and special stains such as the Gram and acid-fast gave evidence of differences in chemical structure. Differences in physiology as shown by the action of a microbe on a single carbohydrate with the production of acids or acid and gas, when this ingredient is added to the medium, led us almost at once into biochemistry, where Pasteur started. Since bacteria as disease-inciting agents were the prominent ones in the awakening of our minds, experimental animals were used early both as a means of eliminating contaminating organisms (pneumonia sputum into mice) and as the models in determining etiology by fulfilling the Henle-Koch postulates.

This mode of study immediately took the bacteriologist over into pathology; soil, dairy, and industrial bacteriology opened still other doors. Calibrated pipettes of the chemist fostered quantitative methods, and physical and chemical agents such as steam in autoclaves under pressure and toxic salts such as those of mercury were employed for sterilization and disinfection. Artificial means of building up active resistance, so-called vaccination, came early as in smallpox by Jenner, 1798, and in rabies by Pasteur, 1883–85. Artificial passive immunity by developing the active process in the body of another animal, as for example by the injection of repeated doses of the exotoxins of *Bacillus diphtheriae* into a horse and the use of the antitoxin produced by the horse as a therapeutic agent in the sick person, came in 1890 and later.

The antigen-antibody reactions that have proved so valuable in establishing specific relationships between a given microbe and a particular disease also became available later, 1888–1901. From 1888, when Nut-

tall described bactericidal properties of blood serum, through the discovery of specific bacteriolysis by Pfeiffer (1894), the quantitative
study of the influence of serum-opsonins on phagocytosis by Denys
and LeClef (1895), agglutination by Grüber and Durham (1896), the
precipitin reaction by Kraus (1897), the allergic-anaphylactic reactions
by many observers from 1898 on, and complement fixation by Bordet
and Gengou (1901), we have been provided with remarkably sensitive
and specific methods.[5] The stage was set for the rapid advances that
came in the twentieth century.

But we were immature and dependent on Europe in many of the
natural sciences in the Welch period and indeed to a high degree until
after World War I. The all-important compound microscopes in
our colleges and universities came chiefly from Austria and Germany
(Reichert, Leitz, and Zeiss); we were dependent on Kahlbaum for
pure chemicals and on Witte for our bacteriologic peptones. We used
Jena resistant glassware in all-important chemical technics and Grübler
stains in our histologic and bacteriologic procedures.

Gage and others give Charles A. Spencer the credit for the manufacture in this country of the first compound microscopes of superior
resolving power (1851). Later, Spencer joined his son Herbert R.
Spencer and Robert B. Tolles in forming the Spencer Lens Company
beginning the independence of our country in the production of microscopes. Tolles produced homogeneous immersion lenses as early as
1874. Bausch and Lomb developed microscopes under an arrangement
with Zeiss and when World War I broke the lines of contact, they
made optical glass of high quality, completing our freedom in this
respect. The production of Pyrex glass by the Corning Glass Company
and the development of the manufacture of pure chemicals and dyes
by several American companies only gradually gave us a large degree
of laboratory independence.

We fail to realize the importance of methods, either a new one
devised for a particular purpose or more commonly one adapted from
a neighboring science. Obviously, broad generalizations such as evolution, or relativity, or in microbiology, parasitism, chemical specificity
of antigens, or the inheritable transformation of one bacterium by
union with a substance from a different organism are more deeply significant. The need, the vision, and the ingenuity precede and underlie
the development of a method. But if reasonably successful and general,
a method can be applied in other areas, and we recognize its ever in-

creasing usefulness. One could, for example, write much on the development and uses of the microscope or the centrifuge and on the wide employment of stains. We cannot think harshly of anyone in this early period for failing to search for a possible filterable virus, since such parasites were unknown until 1892, when Iwanowski, a Russian botanist, reproduced the mosaic disease of tobacco with bacteria-free filtrates of leaves from diseased plants. And not until 1898 was the first animal disease, foot and mouth disease, shown by Löffler and Frosch to have a similar type of etiologic agent.

CLOSTRIDIUM WELCHII

Welch's major contribution in bacteriology, with G. H. F. Nuttall, was the isolation (1892) of a previously undescribed Gram-positive, anaerobic, gas-producing, capsulated, nonmotile bacillus from the blood and tissues of a case that had died of a ruptured aortic aneurysm. They did not observe spores because of their failure to employ media that remained alkaline, as for example, Löffler's blood serum. Subsequent studies, especially during World War I, have shown the importance of this and six or seven related bacteria in causing gas gangrene from wound infections. Bull and Pritchett in this country (1917) and Weinberg and Séguin in France (1918) did noteworthy work in these diseases, producing antitoxins against specific toxins of several of these organisms and demonstrating the complexity of the polymicrobic infections.

Although the name suggested by Welch, *Bacillus aerogenes capsulatus*, is suitably descriptive, it was discarded later because by international agreement (1904) trinomials are ruled out unless they are varieties. The term, *Bacillus*, or preferably, *Clostridium welchii*, came into general use in this country and in Britain, while the term, *Fränkel bacillus* (described in 1894), has been used in Germany. In 1908 the French scientists Veillon and Zuber used the name, *Clostridium perfringens*, and to avoid some confusion in France during World War I, this term was frequently employed and was adopted as the species name in 1931 by the Permanent Standards Commission of the Health Organization of the League of Nations. Taxonomic rules do permit, however, the retention of long established names, so that both by priority and by usage the scientific name should, it seems to me, be *Clostridium welchii*.[6]

The papers on this organism represent the last considerable experimental studies that Welch carried out. Running his department even by his casual laissez-faire methods, training a succession of younger men, the increasing public claims on his time, such as membership in the Maryland State Board of Health for thirty-one years, and the broad problems of medical education drew him away from the insistent daily demands of laboratory work.

Welch was a confirmed bachelor; a lover of books, plays, cigars, and good conversation; a devotee of good eating to the sacrifice of any girth control. He ignored his correspondence, was not interested in being on time save possibly for a baseball game (he knew all the batting averages); he had no intimates of either sex, but hosts of admiring students and friends, who smiled with appreciation at his foibles, and gradually made him a legendary hero. But he was not 24 carat, which is much too soft; he knew who was king and the "the king can do no wrong." Welch continually advised for others a strict hygienic life and provided a list of rules for health, but "I break every one of them and am perfectly well although my anterior-posterior measurement is large."

While Welch was traveling in China with the Rockefellers for the dedication of the Peking Union Medical College, Mr. Rockefeller was shocked one day to see him eat a persimmon purchased from a street vendor.

"Why, Dr. Welch," Rockefeller cried, "you should not do that."
Welch looked up with benign surprise, "Why not?"
"You might get some disease."
"What for instance?"
"You might get cholera."
"Yes, but what else?" Welch asked calmly; continuing to eat the fruit.

Flexner tells also of Welch's failure to show up for his class lectures, so that he had always to be prepared to give them. "If he had not arrived by fifteen minutes after the hour, I would begin, but sometimes after I had got well started, I would hear his quick, short steps as he ascended the stairs. I stopped, and walking to the front of the room, he began the topic all over." Certainly we should consider this outrageous treatment of a competent younger colleague.

Welch's capacity to sweep down through the years in medical history showing both trends and high spots; or in other fields as Osler stated "from bridge to baseball, from Horace to Herrick," or the latest work on the pneumococci, or medicine in the Orient, was truly remarkable. Whether he was holding his so-called quiz (largely a fascinating monologue on the history of pathology), that he continued to give long after he had delegated most regular teaching duties to others, writing one of his masterly survey articles, or after a social stag dinner, entrancing his associates, appropriate adjectives fail.

Years ago, when I was quite young professionally, I read a paper before a national society holding its annual meeting at the Johns Hopkins Medical School. Dr. Welch discussed it briefly and asked me a question that I could not answer. He must have noticed that I was embarrassed because he immediately jumped up again saying that anyone could ask a question that might take years to answer. Of course everyone loved him.

The designated period of this history suggests that I should leave Welch at this point, but I feel compelled to continue briefly. The years following the turn of the century saw in this country the outpouring of enormous private fortunes to the public weal, especially in the field of medicine. This was Welch's great opportunity which he used with consummate skill. The excellent expending of the funds of the Carnegie, the Rockefeller, and other foundations, and of private philanthropists calls for universal approbation. Welch aroused the approval of these groups; through his wise advice, excellent medical institutions were developed in many parts of the world.

When Welch retired from the chair of pathology in 1916 at the age of sixty-six, moneys were provided largely through the Rockefeller Foundation for the achievement of one of his dreams, the founding of the School of Hygiene and Public Health as part of Johns Hopkins University. Welch became the guiding spirit and Dean of this institution from 1918 to 1925. A second retirement brought another long-hoped-for opportunity, this time, a chair in medical history. Welch suggested that Fielding H. Garrison, the leader in that field in this country, would be the appropriate appointee. But Welch was their man. So at seventy-five he began anew, aided in planning a medical library building, went again to Europe, this time to purchase more books for the library, established an Institute of the History of Medicine, which he turned over as a productive organization to Sigerist when he retired for the third time at the age of eighty-two in 1932.

After his death in 1934 (also the year of Theobald Smith's death) the medical and lay press equally sang his praises. The brief summary in the *Lancet* is characteristic, "His fame was literally world-wide," and Flexner wrote, "Popsy, the physician who had been so greatly loved, died as he had lived, keeping his own counsel, essentially alone."[7]

Early Microbiologists at Hopkins

W. T. COUNCILMAN, G. H. F. NUTTALL,

EUGENE L. OPIE, W. D. MAC CALLUM,

W. W. FORD, T. C. GILCHRIST,

AND R. B. SCHENCK.

Reverting to the early days at "The Hopkins," malaria was prevalent in the whole Baltimore area, so that Laveran's discovery of the parasites in human blood (1880) and Ronald Ross's demonstrations of transmission by anopheles mosquitoes (1881–97) gave incentive to the investigators for years of patient study. In the encyclopedic work on malaria edited by Mark Boyd,[8] credit is given to Councilman and Abbott (1885) as "perhaps the earliest to verify Laveran's observations in the United States, while Sternberg (1886) fresh from studies under Marchiafava and Celli, also demonstrated the parasites in the blood of an American patient in the laboratory of William H. Welch." Thayer and Hewetson (1895), Welch and Thayer (1897), and Osler (1897) are given credit for "aiding materially in bringing order out of chaos" of our misunderstanding of the intermittent and remittent fevers. In distinguishing the different fevers on the basis of causative organism, Welch gave the name *Plasmodium falciparum* to the parasite of estivo-autumnal fever. Most importantly, although Laveran had described exflagellation earlier, MacCallum (1897) gave the first description of actual fertilization of a female gamete by a single flagellated male organism. Opie[9] (1898) and MacCallum were the first in this country to follow Ross in the study of the hematozoa of birds, a thorough investigation.

Aside from malaria, the paramount infectious diseases in Baltimore at this period were the pneumonias, tuberculosis, and the enteric diseases, including typhoid fever and both bacillary and amoebic dysentery. Studies on all of these diseases were carried on in the pathological laboratory by Welch and his associates. Of the great numbers of amoebae known to zoologists, most of them are free living, a few are parasitic in various animals, and certain forms infect man. The important parasitic genus, endamoeba, was established by Leidy (1879, see Chap. XI);

to those interested in human pathogens, the studies of Councilman and Lafleur[10] (1891) in the early *Johns Hopkins Hospital Reports* present in scholarly detail the history and literature on amoebiasis, methods of demonstrating *Entamoeba histolytica*, and reports on their fifteen cases. This stands as one of the best early investigations of this disease, found throughout the world, but more numerous in the tropics and subtropics.

Prior to the opening of the medical school, a regular course in bacteriology was announced with Welch in charge and a course in public hygiene under John Shaw Billings from the United States Army in Washington. The assistant announced for both courses was A. C. Abbott, who had been working with Welch for several years, especially on experimental diphtheria and also on the relation between water supplies and epidemics. Welch was eager to emphasize the broad problems of public health, so in 1886 he sent Abbott to study with von Pettenkofer and with Koch. Upon Abbott's return, progress was hoped for along these lines, but in 1891 he became assistant director, under Billings, of the newly established Hygienic Institute of the University of Pennsylvania. So G. H. F. Nuttall, who had been working with Welch as a fellow in pathology, fell heir to Abbott's mantle. He wrote an interesting paper detailing methods of his devising for the quantitative estimation of tubercle bacilli in sputum and the next year (1892) was co-author with Welch in the publication already referred to on the gas-producing organism, *Bacillus aerogenes capsulatus*.

Earlier (1888) Nuttall, working in Flügge's laboratory in Göttingen, had first described bactericidal properties of normal blood serum and while at Hopkins, becoming interested in animal parasites, he published (1900) an extensive critical essay on the role of insects, arachnids and myriapods, as carriers in the spread of bacteria and parasite diseases of man and lower animals. Recognizing Nuttall's general interests, Welch sent him as his second emissary to Germany for further experience with the intent to build up public hygiene. But Nuttall was diverted to Cambridge University, became a Fellow of Magdalene College, the Quick Professor of Biology, and the director of the Molteno Institute of Parasitology. His comprehensive monograph *Blood Immunity and Blood Relationship*[11] (1904), for which he used the resources of the whole British Empire, and the precipitin reaction as the basis of tracing animal relationships, was his major contribution. He was a highly productive scholar, long-time editor of the *Journal of Hygiene* and the *Journal of Parasitology*, deeply interested in the history of science and the personalities of the men involved, a bibliophile, urbane, and altogether charming, hospitable, and cordial to Americans and others working in his laboratory.

Following Nuttall at Hopkins, W. W. Ford took over much of the bacteriology and the public hygiene. He contributed to a clearer understanding of the involved water and sewage problems of Baltimore, but more important was his demonstration that glucosides, nonprotein substances from poisonous mushrooms (*Amanita phalloides*) and poison ivy (*Rhus toxicodendron*), were definitely antigenic, thus giving a foundation for allergic reactions (1906–7).[12] Although a number of observers since that time have not obtained antibodies following the injection of rabbits with synthetic glucocides, this work stands out as an early example of a principle now well recognized, namely, that simple compounds may combine spontaneously with proteins and act as determinant groups giving a new and different specificity to the original protein.

The poison ivy findings of Ford and his associates have been supported by later observers, although more than one simple substance seems involved. The so-called poisonings are cases of hypersensitivity similar to drug sensitivities. Both sensitization and desensitization have been accomplished. We should bear in mind the period of Ford's experiments; this was long before the days of the residue antigens of Zinsser (1923) and the antigenic polysaccharides from pneumococci (Heidelberger and Avery, 1923). Obermeyer and Pick (1906) had begun chemical studies of antigens and had reported the antigenic alteration of certain proteins by the addition of simple chemical radicles, but the term hapten was unknown and the detailed chemical studies of Landsteiner in Europe and in this country and Marrack in England were decades in the future.

Stanhope Bayne-Jones followed Ford, but he, like so many of Welch's capable young associates, did not stay long at Hopkins. He became professor of bacteriology at the newly formed University of Rochester Medical School, but after a few years, wandered from the path into administrative positions.

J. Howard Brown, a student of Theobald Smith from Harvard, succeeded Bayne-Jones, but his period at Hopkins is beyond the limits of our self-imposed restrictions.

Especially interesting is the example Baltimore provides of the importance of the succulent oyster and typhoid fever in compelling public health measures. In spite of Welch's membership on the Maryland

State Board of Health and the presence of two medical schools in the city, Baltimore long had had polluted water supplies, grossly defective means of sewage disposal (Wynne, 1850; Ford, 1911; Howard, 1920 and 1924), and high typhoid and enteric fever rates.[13] Successive sewerage commissions were appointed and competent engineers were employed who made adequate plans and recommendations; then the whole matter was dropped because the people refused to approve a bond issue to pay the cost of the work. Cesspools increased with frequent connections with the storm sewers. While white marble or white wooden front steps gleamed along miles of Baltimore streets, gray smelly household wastes wandered slowly in the gutters even along Monument Street by the Hopkins Hospital, and raw sewage flowed into the bay not far from the oyster beds.

In 1905 a third commission made recommendations. With pressure from the oyster industry the plans were adopted, money was provided, and at long last, a sewage-disposal plant and sanitary sewers to carry both domestic wastes and human excreta were undertaken. Not until 1915 was the plant completed, and not until 1918 were the necessary connections made. By this time also (1918–19) a single adequate source of potable water (Gunpowder River) with an extensive filtration plant near Lake Montebello was in use (saving Lake Roland for emergencies) and "during these two years the percentage of B. coli determinations in both laboratories (at the filtration plant and the city laboratory) was relatively low." It is worth stressing that it was not until the end of World War I that the great city of Baltimore was forced to provide safe potable water and adequate sewage disposal to its highly mixed population. Salutations to the humble oyster! "Even as late as 1922, the system was not fully completed and over 20,000 houses remained unconnected."[14]

As with other microorganisms, most of the early observations on the Hyphomycetes (*Fungi imperfecti*) that cause disease were made in Europe. Quite remarkably, however, three primary studies may be credited largely to work done in the pathology department at Hopkins. T. C. Gilchrist, who was trained in Great Britain, described in 1896 a case of "blastomycetic dermatitis in man." He gave excellent details, photomicrographs, and drawings of the lesions and the budding yeast-like organisms that he named *Blastomyces dermatitidis*. In 1898 with W. R. Stokes he published more completely the findings in a second case from which pure cultures were grown on all ordinary media.

With these organisms, experimental transfer of the disease was success-ful in several species of animals. The disease is frequently called North American blastomycosis or Gilchrist's disease.[15]

In 1893 Emmet Rixford of San Francisco sent material from two cases of protozoan (coccidioidal) infection of the skin and other organs to Welch for investigation. This was studied simultaneously by Gil-christ in the pathological laboratory of the Johns Hopkins Hospital and by Rixford in San Francisco resulting in an extensive publication in 1896. Clinical histories, post-mortem findings, clear descriptions, ex-quisite plates with photomicrographs and drawings were presented, including also several moderately successful inoculations of the tissue into rabbits, but there was no success with cultures. Consultation with C. W. Stiles of the Bureau of Animal Industry in Washington led the authors to suggest that they were dealing with a protozoan parasite. (See Ophüls, Chapter XVI.)[16]

Another excellent early paper (1898) by B. R. Schenck of the pathol-ogy department reports a case of refractory subcutaneous abscesses caused by a fungus possibly related to the Sporotricha. Pure cultures were readily grown from the abscesses on all ordinary media, and with them local lesions were produced in dogs and a pyemia in mice. Photo-graphs and drawings of the organisms and the lesions completes the report.

A few years later (1903) two French observers, de Beurmann and Ramond, described a similar organism from abscesses in a similar single case (no photographs or drawings were published), but they were unable to reproduce the condition in experimental animals. Since then, such cases have been described and reproduced experimentally in many parts of the world and gradually the disease, though rare, has been recognized as one to be differentiated from syphilis, tuberculosis, and coccal infections. The organism has been found growing on vegetable tissues, and most human cases are wound infections; it is best diagnosed by culture methods. Now it is commonly acknowledged that the slight differences in the organisms from different parts of the world are within the limits of species variation, and *Sporotrichum schenckii* is the pre-ferred scientific name.

CHAPTER VII

Massachusetts, Boston, and Public Hygiene

> *Knowledge is proud that he has learned so much*
> *Wisdom is humble that he knows no more.*
>
> WILLIAM COWPER, *The Task*

> *Solon, asked how justice could be secured*
> *in Athens, replied, "If those who are not*
> *injured, feel as indignant as those who are."*

A long nineteen years elapsed between Shattuck's masterly sanitary survey of Massachusetts (1850) with his emphasis on vital statistics, the bookkeeping of life, before the State Board of Health was established by act of June 21, 1869.[1] Henry I. Bowditch, first chairman of this board, was highly influential in continuing the stress on sanitary surveys and epidemiological studies. His report on consumption in New England (1862) emphasized this major disease and his own lifelong interest. His investigation of public hygiene in America, a request study presented at the International Medical Congress at our Centennial Exposition in Philadelphia (1876) was eye-opening in exposing our almost complete lack of awareness of public responsibility for the health of the citizens. Twenty pertinent, reasonably specific questions were sent widely to appropriate physicians, authorities, and college leaders, with responses (1876–77) largely negative or indefinite in character.[2] In the meantime Griscom's excellent study, "*The Sanitary Condition of the Laboring Population of New York City*"[3] (1845), the repeated surveys of some of our larger cities by members of the Committee on Hygiene of the American Medical Association (1847 *et seq.*), and gleanings from the growing European literature, especially that from England, had been slowly seeping down to the people. In 1870 the strong anti-contagionist attitude, especially among physicians, even in the enlightened commonwealth of Massachusetts, is shown in a sixty-nine page inquiry into the, "Causes of Typhoid Fever as it Occurs in Massachusetts."

In summary the Board stated:

The single continuous thread of probability which we have been able to follow in this inquiry, leads uniformly to the decomposition of organized (and chiefly vegetable) substance as the cause of typhoid fever as it occurs in Massachusetts.

Whether the vehicle be drinking-water made foul by human excrement, sink drains or soiled clothing; or made foul in enclosed places by drains, decaying vegetables or fish (Swampscott) or old timber (Tisbury) or in open places by pigsties, drained ponds or reservoirs, stagnant water, accumulations of filth of every sort, the one thing present in all these circumstances is decomposition.

And may not the influence of soil charged with vegetable remains, in the season of heat and of drought, be also referred to the same cause? Although not yet proved, it is exceedingly probable that a rich and fertile soil in which decomposable substances are retained near the surface by any cause, whether a clay subsoil or a ledge of rock, or a protracted drought, is a soil favorable to the production of this special disease.[4]

Let us bear in mind that this statement, emphasizing rotting vegetation rather than "excreta containing the specific exciting agents" from cases of typhoid was the opinion of the majority of physicians of Massachusetts, fifteen years after Budd's convincing evidence to the contrary, and seventeen years after Snow's Broad Street pump papers showed how cholera was spread.

With primary emphasis on the public nuisance and general cleanup campaigns, attention was gradually drawn to the pollution of our streams, wastes from factories, and sewage from villages and cities, although the causal relation with enteric diseases was not discerned until later.

But the bacteriologic era was dawning; in 1884 the Massachusetts Drainage Commission began a study of the pollution of the rivers of the state, and two years later this function was turned over to the State Board of Health. Associated in this work were competent men, many of them on the staff of the Massachusetts Institute of Technology; Hiram F. Mills, engineer; Thomas M. Drown, consulting chemist; W. T. Sedgwick, biologist; Allen Hazen, chemist and engineer; Harry W. Clark, chemist; and several younger assistants such as Edwin O. Jordan and George W. Fuller, both of whom later climbed the ladder of distinguished service in our country. In 1887 the Lawrence Experiment Station for the study of public water supplies and the scientific treatment of sewage was established. This station, planned by an engineer with vision, Hiram F. Mills, developed methods and provided initiative for similar studies in this and other countries. Its contributions will be discussed in greater detail under Sedgwick and the Massachusetts Institute of Technology. The establishment of a publicly supported food and drug laboratory (1891), compulsory reporting of deaths in towns over 5,000 (1894), a diphtheria antitoxin and bacteriological laboratory (1895) with Theobald Smith, admittedly America's most distinguished bacteriologist, as director, the beginning of tuberculosis control by the state (1895), distribution of smallpox vaccine (1903), and the employment of divisional state health inspectors, and other public health activities put Massachusetts well in the van in this country, so that the annual and special reports of the State Board of Health are a requisite in any library covering the field of preventive medicine and public health.

Massachusetts Institute of Technology

> Does science leave no mystery? On the contrary,
> it proclaims mystery where others profess knowledge.
> There is mystery enough in the universe of sensation
> and in its capacity for containing those little
> corners of consciousness which project their own
> products, of order and law and reason, into an
> unknown and unknowable world. There is mystery
> enough here, only let us clearly distinguish it
> from ignorance within the field of possible
> knowledge. The one is impenetrable, the other we
> are daily subduing.
>
> KARL PEARSON, *Grammar of Science*, 1892

The Massachusetts Institute of Technology, now so widely honored as the outstanding educational and research institution in engineering and underlying sciences, opened its doors hesitantly in 1865 in rented rooms to fifteen students. Emphasis was placed then and always on the laboratory method of instruction. The early years of the "Boston Tech"[5] under the leadership of William Barton Rogers were those of the rapid expansion of this country after the horrors of our Civil War and of the phenomenal growth of bacteriology through the startling discoveries of Pasteur, Koch, and many others delving into the microbic world.

WILLIAM THOMPSON SEDGWICK

Sedgwick (1853–1921), who contributed so largely to the advancement of public health, had a hard time financially working his way through Sheffield Scientific School at Yale, but was graduated with an honor record in 1877. He then entered the Yale Medical School, but was disheartened by the didactic teaching. He expressed regret that he had been born too late; there was nothing under debate, nothing to be discovered. During his last year in Sheffield, he had assisted Chittenden in physiological chemistry and while he was registered in the medical school for the second year, Chittenden went off to Europe. The young Sedgwick was at once drafted as instructor in the course. The laboratory and problems susceptible to experimental approach rather than dictum from on high proved highly attractive to him, so that when both he and his intimate friend E. B. Wilson (later distinguished professor of biology at Bryn Mawr and at Columbia) were offered fellowships in the new pioneering Johns Hopkins University, they jumped at the chance to work under the stimulating leadership of Newell Martin. From that time on Sedgwick became fundamentally a biologist and even later when his major endeavors were in public health, he approached all problems from that broad point of view.

In 1883 after earning his doctor's degree under Martin and working as associate for two additional years, Sedgwick was appointed assistant professor of biology at the Tech. Although his major graduate work had been in zoology, Sedgwick had studied yeasts and molds while at Hopkins and had become excited by the startling microbiological discoveries. The year after he came to Massachusetts Institute of Technology he began a brief lecture course on germs and germicides for senior students who were preparing for medical school. From this humble "germ," although there never has been a named department of bacteriology at the Institute, the culture medium and the wise inoculating enthusiasm of Sedgwick have been such that public health officials, influential sanitary engineers, bacteriologists, and productive leaders in other important institutions have spread widely from this source.

Sedgwick was a warm-hearted leader, president of his class at Yale, head of his department at Tech for thirty-eight fruitful years, a truly remarkable teacher, stimulating to all who came under his sway, chairman of the administrative committee of the Harvard–M.I.T. School for Public Health Officers, influential throughout the country, first president of the Society of American Bacteriologists (1899–1900), president of several other national societies of note including the American Public Health Association (1914–15), the recipient of honorary degrees, and an active member in so many local and national boards that a listing would confuse the reader. Yet he moved with serenity through his many duties, never appearing hurried; friendly, fertile in ideas, buoyant in spirit, wise in counsel; he loved teaching and human beings. He wrote innumerable letters to "his boys" throughout the world. His home on Bremmer Street, presided over by his gracious wife, gave generous welcome to his students and other friends. Sedgwick was a master of English and the art of gripping an audience, a coiner of the catching title or phrase. "Shall we infect or shall we protect the waters of our lakes, harbors, and estuaries." "The so-called germ theory of disease is the child of fermentation and grandchild of the microscope." "A sand filter is more than a mechanical strainer, and more than a chemical furnace, it is a breathing mechanism." His longtime friend, E. B. Wilson of Columbia University, describes him as "a cheery and even jovial companion, endowed with a keen sense of humor and with that equally precious and saving gift of fortune which he himself was fond of calling horse sense." Mrs. Sedgwick emphasized that his religion was one of service, that they were both wishful agnostics, that he was impatient even angered with occultism, as a belief in the breaking of natural laws. He loved to travel (as did Mrs. Sedgwick) and enjoyed reading aloud biographies and poetry, Keats and Arnold especially. Of his many honors, he especially appreciated the exchange professorships in the Universities of Leeds and Cambridge. Walking and amateur botanizing were his chief recreations and summers on his "2 stony acres" on Mt. Desert Island gave him treasured opportunities.

The long list of exceptionally loyal, competent men trained in his department and the graduates of the Harvard-Technology School of Public Health are his living monuments. Listed in the appreciative biography, written by three of his more prominent disciples, E. O. Jordan, University of Chicago, G. C. Whipple, Harvard University, and C-E. A. Winslow, Yale University, are 124 titles of his writings that portray the breadth of his scientific and cultural interests.[6] Many of these are general in character, as was true of the papers of other leaders in this period, when the germ theory was still in doubt and the findings of foreign investigators had to be verified in this country before we could be convinced.

Massachusetts State Board of Health
Lawrence Experiment Station and Sewage Disposal

H. F. MILLS, HARRY M. CLARK, AND S. DE M. GAGE

Throughout his life, Sedgwick's major interest was public health and the supporting microbiologic sciences in which such dramatic advance was being made. He was, however, primarily not a laboratory investigator, preferring to work with ideas. His pioneering spirit was given increased opportunity through active co-operation with the Lawrence Experiment Station, through his position as consulting biologist of the Massachusetts State Board of Health (1888), and later through the Harvard-Technology School of Public Health (1913–22). This institution worked efficiently under the direction of a triumvirate, consisting of M. J. Rosenau and George C. Whipple both at Harvard and Sedgwick as chairman from Massachusetts Institute of Technology, until the separate Harvard School of Public Hygiene was established with Rockefeller funds. Although textbooks, in spite of the immense amount of labor involved, are all too frequently of ephemeral value only, Sedgwick's *Principles of Sanitary Science and the Public Health*[7] (1902) went through many editions and was used and appreciated widely through decades.

The prevention of typhoid fever and other enteric diseases by the adequate treatment of sewage and by the provision of potable water became the chief lines of Sedgwick's work. Here was a public nuisance that was not an imaginary windmill. Modes of spread now universally recognized were still in doubt in the 1880's and the 1890's, and all the engineering problems, mechanical, biological, and biochemical, had still to be worked out. The Lawrence Experiment Station was far from impressive in appearance, but the excellent quality of its reports was widely acclaimed. All tests were made on a quantitative basis with many types of tanks and varying grades of sand, earth, gravel, and rock, always with appropriate gauges, measuring and sampling devices, and day and night attendants to handle different time intervals. A long series of competent younger associates of Mills and Sedgwick carried out an immense number of analyses under varying controlled conditions. By 1909 more than 50,000 chemical and 150,000 bacteriological analyses had been made and more than 400 filters tested.

The results of these studies to determine the underlying principles of the so-called filtration of sewage and other wastes have been brought together in illuminating reports by Harry M. Clark and S. DeM. Gage. These voluminous papers have been further summarized by George C. Whipple in his masterly long-range review of the achievements of the Massachusetts State Board of Health[8] (1917). Laboratories in other lands, notably Germany and England, were also studying these problems, but there is common agreement that many of the results of the Lawrence Station combined with laboratory studies made at the Tech until 1896 and after that at the State House were major contributions. First of all the biochemical and bacteriologic studies made it clear that the essential process, whatever the type of bed employed and however the sewage was applied, was biologic and not merely a sifting. Indeed the term filtration for most of the processes developed is largely a misnomer; digestion, whether aerobic or anaerobic processes predominate, is a better term. Coarse rock and the organisms collected thereon were found fully as effective as fine sand, and less likely to become clogged. This idea was taken up in England because sand areas are not readily available for intermittent filtration, so the contact and trickling beds, both of which use coarse material, were frequently adopted there. The British generously have given credit to the Lawrence Station for initiating this method. The two-story septic digestion tank commonly ascribed to Imhoff has had an interesting history of litigation. This process was used experimentally at Lawrence in 1899. Imhoff himself at the International Congress of Hygiene and Demography (1912) attributed the idea of separate sludge digestion to Harry M. Clark of the Lawrence Experiment Station, although the more complete applications were made in England and in Germany.

In 1911 compressed air was used at Lawrence with consequent increased growth of aerobic sporeformers and rotifers as digesting agents. Fowler of Manchester, England, as a visitor at Lawrence, was impressed with the results, developed the method practically and named it the activated sludge process, now being used widely both here and abroad. Again the British have been generous in granting priority to the Lawrence Station. Interesting and strange is the fact that contrary to most scientific advances, many of the ideas seem to have appeared first in this country and the practical applications in Europe.

In reviewing the studies from the Lawrence Station one is impressed both by the variety and the detail and with the importance of this type of work in the development of bacteriology and public health procedures at this period. Examples may be cited as follows: methods of disposal of different trade wastes; the improvement of sand filters in water purification (1904); the use after 1898 of the now universally employed quantitative tests for *Bacillus coli* to determine the effectiveness of filtration of potable water; the testing of shellfish from polluted and unpolluted waters (1900); the use of germicidal agents such as bleaching powder in water; the microscopic examination of water for microorganisms other than bacteria such as diatoms, algae, and infusoria that at times give disagreeable odors and tastes to filtered waters (1901); and the development of the so-called American or mechanical filtration of water by using a coagulant such as sulphate of alumina, followed by a period for settling and rapid filtration through a small bed of fine sand.

In all the biological aspects of this work one finds the wise enthusiasm of Sedgwick and the quantitative experiments of his associates at the Tech. Many of these studies consisted of improvements of methods developed in European laboratories with additional data, and Sedgwick was always careful to give credit to earlier investigators and to his own younger colleagues. With Tucker he developed an improved method for the quantitative biological examination of air, with Rafter the Sedgwick-Rafter filter for the quantitative collection of microorganisms other than bacteria in drinking water, with Prescott and Winslow methods of bacteriological examination of water and foods, and with Jordan and Richards he worked on studies on nitrification. All aided materially in the advancement of microbiology in this country.

Typhoid fever was widely prevalent in Sedgwick's time with little appreciation of the public responsibilities. In Massachusetts epidemics occurred especially in the industrial areas, Lowell, Lawrence, and other cities along the Merrimac River. With H. F. Mills, engineer for the city of Lawrence, Sedgwick began epidemiological studies here as early as 1890. They found raw sewage flowing into the river from villages upstream and the diluted but untreated river water used for drinking purposes in Lawrence and Lowell with the inevitable results. In succession, Sedgwick made similar surveys of the causes of high enteric fever rates in Chicago with Allen Hazen (1892), in Somerville, Massachusetts (1893), Marlborough, Massachusetts (1894), and Pittsburgh and Allegheny, Pennsylvania (1899).[9] By now, the basic facts are so well known as to make the story tedious; in those days, it was shocking, dramatic, and just beginning to be understood. Each epidemic was a variation on the same theme; from cases and from carriers, or from either, feces via water, milk, and other foods, and sometimes by flies, were carried to the alimentary tract of susceptible individuals.

In fact, it took a war and the shock of the astounding number of cases and deaths from typhoid fever in our army camps during the Spanish-American War of 1898 to awaken the public from its lethargy. In response to the general indignation, Surgeon General Sternberg appointed an excellent investigating board consisting of Walter Reed, Victor C. Vaughan, and Edward O. Shakespeare. Their thorough studies in two large tomes with overwhelming detail appeared also as an earlier extensive abstract of the report in 1900. The excellence of this report is outstanding, one of the most complete ever made, and its influence on the health officers and people of our country was strong. A few quotations will give point.

"Among 107,973 officers and men in the 92 regiments carefully studied, in camps in this country, the estimated number of typhoid cases was 20,739 or about 20%. Of these cases, 1580 men died." We should bear in mind that vaccination against typhoid and paratyphoid fever was not made compulsory in our army until 1911, and that most of the volunteer medical officers had had no military experience.

All the recognized sources and modes of infection for typhoid were noted as factors, with contaminated water playing only a small role and flies a larger part than commonly.

Flies alternately visited and fed upon infected fecal matter in the latrines and the food in the mess tents. More than once, it happened when lime had been scattered over the fecal matter in the pits, flies with their feet covered with lime, were seen walking over food. . . . In our histories of the different regiments we have had too frequent opportunity to call attention to the fearful pollution that existed in many camps. As we have stated, fecal matter was deposited on the surface about the camps at Chicamauga. . . . Camp pollution was the greatest sin committed by the troops in 1898.[10]

Of great interest to a microbiologist is the fact that, as late as this 1900 period, the board felt it essential to investigate the obsolete theory that some poison or miasma given off from the earth in gaseous form was a responsible factor in causing typhoid. Needless to say the evidence controverted this idea, but old superstitions are difficult to down. Man seems to prefer to cling to some mystical emotional notion rather than cold, demonstrable, frequently disagreeable facts.

The public reaction to this epidemic and the report, the investigations

Upper left   WILLIAM HENRY WELCH, 1850–1934
                   Photograph taken about 1900, at the age of fifty.

Upper right   EUGENE LINDSAY OPIE, 1872——
                   Photograph taken about 1909, at the age of thirty-six.

Lower left   WALTER REED, 1851–1902
                   Photograph taken about 1900, at the age of forty-nine.

Lower right   JAMES CARROLL, 1854–1907
                   Photograph taken about 1902, at the age of forty-eight.

Upper left   WILLIAM THOMPSON SEDGWICK, 1855–1921
Photograph taken about 1900, at the age of forty-five.

Upper right   HERBERT WILLIAM CONN, 1859–1917
Photograph taken about 1905, at the age of forty-six.

Lower left   THEOBALD SMITH, 1859–1934
Photograph taken about 1900, at the age of forty-one.

Lower right   CHARLES-EDWARD AMORY WINSLOW, 1877–1957
Photograph taken about 1935, at the age of fifty-eight.

of the Massachusetts State Board of Health, the Lawrence Experiment Station, and the Massachusetts Institute of Technology were vital in bringing the water supplies, sewage disposal, and typhoid fever rates of our cities from a deplorable state, far worse than in major cities of Europe, to a high standard of excellence. Nowadays the microbic origin of many transitory cases of gastroenteric disease seems to me (after a long life in microbiology) almost too completely accepted, especially by the traveling public. They are commonly ready to blame the water or food, a virus, "something I ate," rather than gross overeating and overdrinking. How ready we are to place the onus on a scapegoat and to seek a remedy in a pill!

Sedgwick's mantle was so ample that liberal portions fell on many of his students, especially on the shoulders of Samuel C. Prescott (1872—), who succeeded the master as chairman of the department at Massachusetts Institute of Technology, and of C-E. A. Winslow (1877–1957) who went far and wide, to New York, to New Haven, and even to foreign capitals to build further the international character of public health. Prescott was a rugged citizen and indefatigable. Throughout his long, active life, he continued to study the problems of potable water, prevention of food spoilage by adequate storage and by dehydration, and industrial microbiology. Besides detailed studies, he wrote valuable texts in each of his chosen fields.

In an unpublished essay, "The Rise and Early Development of Bacteriology in New England," Prescott writes the following on the canning of food in France.

In 1819, William Underwood brought to America and to Boston the Appert Process of food preservation by sterilization and thus the beginnings of a great industry. Although he was ignorant of the true reasons for its success, he actually accomplished the destruction by heat of living microbes responsible for the deterioration and spoilage of food materials. I think this may be regarded as the first bacteriological procedure operated in New England or in America, although carried out in ignorance of the fundamental facts. Thus an empirical process long preceded exact knowledge or sound theory.[11]

Prescott enjoyed tracing the development of dehydration methods from prehistoric cave woman, who hung wild grapes in the sun to become raisins and the cuts of reindeer to dry.

World War I forced Malthus to the front once more; production and conservation of food became a major element of life, both at the front and in the home. Efforts were made on each side of the battle line to increase production, to ration food, and to prevent waste and spoilage. In Germany commercial dehydration of foods, especially potatoes and other root vegetables, had a rapid expansion from 1900; this became a large factor in feeding the people during and after the war.

Prescott records in some detail the findings made during the war. Several different methods of dehydration, four types of storage, and a variety of containers of the foods were studied. After initial examinations for moisture content and microbes, they left sample lots undisturbed for two, four, and six weeks with re-examination at these periods. Not only were bacterial counts made, but also isolation and identification of the bacteria of seven genera and a number of species of fungi. With the storage conditions employed, bacterial counts of the dehydrated foods gradually diminished while mold spores remained practically constant.

Harvard University

> *Without further argument it will, we think, be*
> *admitted that the sciences are none of them*
> *separately evolved—are none of them independent*
> *either logically or historically but that all of*
> *them have, in a greater or less degree, required*
> *aid and reciprocated it. . . . No facts whatever are*
> *presented to our senses uncombined with other*
> *facts—no facts whatever but are in some degree*
> *disguised by accompanying facts: disguised in*
> *such a manner that all must be partially understood*
> *before any one can be understood.*
>
> HERBERT SPENCER, *The Genesis of Science*, 1854

In 1869, the same year in which the Massachusetts State Board of Health was finally instituted, Charles William Eliot (1834–1919) was appointed president of Harvard University. His influence in the upbuilding of that ancient institution to its present outstanding position can hardly be exaggerated. The classics, although still recognized as important, were demoted from their omnipotent position, the sciences were brought into their own, the rigid curriculum was abolished, new faculty appointments were made on the basis of proved productive scholarship and, in the profession most closely allied to our subject, it is said that Eliot found the medical school in bricks and he left it in marble. Bacteriology has had its opportunities at Harvard University chiefly in the Medical School. As already indicated, public health problems, especially those concerned with water purification and sewage disposal, were studied and taught in various combinations with the Massachusetts Institute of Technology.

HAROLD C. ERNST

In 1885, nine years after Koch demonstrated the anthrax bacillus as the cause of that disease, Harold Clarence Ernst (1856–1922) having acquired for himself a small closet as a laboratory, began, in spite of protests by certain members of the faculty, an elective course of six lectures in bacteriology at the Harvard Medical School. After graduating from Harvard College (1876), where he was noted especially as a baseball pitcher, he obtained his medical degree in 1880, and practiced medicine briefly in Jamaica Plain. Stimulated by the advances in bacteriology, especially the cultivation of the tubercle bacillus by Koch, Ernst went to Germany, as did most of our young leaders, to learn the new techniques in Koch's laboratory. With the growth of bacteriology and the recognition of its importance in human disease, Harvard Medical School increased its support, creating a department in 1891, making Ernst professor in 1895, a position he held until his death. Ernst established a diphtheria antitoxin laboratory (1894) in association with the city board of health; he worked actively for public health regulations such as improvement of vaccination laws, tuberculin testing of cattle, and better registration laws for physicians, and was prominent in founding the American Association of Pathologists and Bacteriologists, of which he was the capable secretary for fifteen years save for the year of his presidency, 1909. From its first number in 1897, he edited the *Journal of the Boston Society of Medical Sciences* that in 1901 became the *Journal of Medical Research*, which he owned and edited. He continued this arduous task until his death in 1922; forty-three volumes were produced under his skillful direction, a time during which both the *Journal* and the society that fostered it achieved high distinction. In 1925 the name of the journal was again changed to the *American Journal of Pathology*, which became the official publication of the American Association of Pathologists and Bacteriologists.

Many of Ernst's published papers dealt with tuberculosis: the use of tuberculin in diagnosis, the occurrence of the bacilli in milk from cows manifesting no lesions in the udder (7 of 14 tested in one series, 1889), and morphology of the organisms from human and from bovine sources (1903). He wrote a number of papers on the microscopic diagnosis of diphtheria and the use of diphtheria antitoxin; he confirmed Pasteur's studies on the infectivity of the brain from rabid animals; he also contributed a number of general survey papers such as, "Recent Advances in Bacteriology," "Development of the Microscope," "A Review of Phagocytosis," and papers on medical education. He loved gadgets and took excellent photomicrographs. Active both in body and in mind, Ernst was one of our early leaders and editors in bacteriology, especially impressive in controversies before legislative committees. His baseball record did not hurt him in these public relations. He is described as austere and taciturn, but by the time I came to know him slightly, he had become mellow and was gracious, even loquacious.

Milton J. Rosenau, the second member of the Harvard–M.I.T. committee in charge of the combined school of public health, spent a far longer period of his productive life with the United States Public Health Service than he did in Boston, so I shall consider him and his contributions to microbiology when we look at Washington and the federal services. The third member, George C. Whipple (1866–1924), one of the early (1889) graduates from Tech, left three dimensional monuments to his successful career in sanitary engineering in different parts of the country, but since he worked more than a decade during his formative years in the Boston area and a similar period in his maturity, this seems a suitable place for a brief sketch.

Whipple organized two of the early water-control laboratories, one at Chestnut Hill outside of Boston (1889–97) and the Mount Prospect laboratory of the New York City system (1897–1904). These led him to study the organisms, chiefly certain diatoms and protozoa, that occasionally give objectionable odors and flavors to otherwise excellent potable water. From this work came the fine *Microscopy of Drinking Water* illustrated by many of his own drawings; this went through several editions and is still a standard aid in this field. His investigations of typhoid fever gave us a book with exceptionally broad coverage, with many charts, tables, and figures, not readily available elsewhere, showing death rates from this and other diseases in many cities and the marked lowering of these rates following the installation of suitable filtration systems.[12] We are also grateful for his two volume review of a half-century of the Massachusetts State Board of Health, making available to all the treasures of public health research and control previously buried in the heavy annual reports. Whipple was a modest, well-balanced, kindly man with a quiet sense of humor and wide interests; he was devoted to his work, his friends, and his family. He was unusually generous to his minor subordinates.

THEOBALD SMITH

> *With all deductions, the triumphs of sanitary*
> *reform as well as of medical science are perhaps*
> *the brightest page in the history of our century.*
>
> W. E. H. LECKY

In the fields of these chronicles, the luring of Theobald Smith[13] (1859–1934) by President Eliot from the Bureau of Animal Industry in 1895 and the arrangement of his joint appointment with Harvard and the Massachusetts State Board of Health were conspicuous successes. Bacteriology was still young, and the work of the Antitoxin-Vaccine Laboratory brought Smith into immediate contact with practical difficulties, while the professorship in comparative pathology allowed his mind and hands freedom to investigate in many directions. Smith was admittedly our most notable productive scholar in the broad fields of "Parasitism and Disease," the title of his last essay written after his official retirement. He was the son of Philip and Theresa Schmidt, German immigrants, who came to this country in 1854 and settled in Albany. His father, a tailor, established a small shop, and Theobald grew up in humble surroundings, went for a while to a school where German was the language, then to the public school, and in 1877 won by competitive examination a state scholarship to Cornell University.

Mathematics and biology were his chief academic interests at Cornell, with music and tramping the woods as an amateur botanist, his strong hobbies. The piano, indeed, was a delightful relaxation throughout his life and he earned a good bit of his living expenses in college by playing the organ ("pedipulating," he called it) or by pumping for others to play. Had a teaching opening in mathematics appeared at the end of his college course, he would have accepted it gladly. As none came, his second choice was followed; he entered the medical school in 1881. (Is it not interesting that neither great leader, Welch nor Smith, was initially interested in medicine?) During the two-year course for the degree, Smith spent one spring semester in the biological laboratory at Johns Hopkins University with Newell Martin. At the end of the two short years of a few months each, Smith realized that he was unprepared to practice medicine, As he did not relish the restrictions of an apprenticeship in a country practice, he returned to Cornell for graduate work in biology with Simon Henry Gage, professor of histology, his most valued teacher and his warm lifelong friend.

Almost immediately following his return to Cornell, came the opening with Daniel E. Salmon, chief of the Bureau of Animal Industry at Washington. Because of Smith's persistent industry and the skill he had shown in carrying out two small pieces of histological research, Gage recommended him and at the age of twenty-five years (1884) Smith began his professional life in Washington, in a stuffy little attic laboratory, insufferably hot in the summer. He continued his work with the Bureau for eleven highly productive years. His active professional life divides itself readily into three periods, each with a different geographical center and differing types of opportunity and responsibilities.

1. 1884–95, Director of the pathology laboratory in the United States Bureau of Animal Industry, Washington.
2. 1895–1915, Director of the antitoxin laboratory of the Massachusetts State Board of Health and professor of comparative pathology in Harvard Medical School.
3. 1915–29, Director of the Division of Animal Disease at the Rockefeller Institute for Medical Research at Princeton, N. J.

As his longest period of service was in Boston and Harvard, I shall consider all of his work at this time, although the research on unraveling Texas fever with Kilborne during his Washington period is commonly considered his magnum opus; his researches at Princeton and the development of the Rockefeller Institute there were also major achievements. Many regret the passing of this division of the Rockefeller Institute that he built up so wisely, and passed on to his able successor, Carl Ten Broeck, although we can appreciate the difficulties in maintaining what amounted to two institutions with similar purposes.

When Smith went to Washington in 1884, he knew no bacteriology, little pathology, and essentially nothing of the infectious diseases of domestic animals, a field into which he was immediately plunged and in which, within a very few years, he was to make outstanding contributions. May we try to glimpse that period once more? Just shortly before, following investigations of Davaine, Pollender, Pasteur, and others, Koch had for the first time demonstrated a causal relation between a bacterium and anthrax, an important disease of lower animals and of man. In 1881, Pasteur in a dramatic, fortunate experiment at

Pouilly-le-Fort, France, had shown successful resistance to the injection of fully virulent cultures of *Bacillus anthracis* in a group of 24 sheep, 1 goat, and 6 cows. This protection had followed a series of injections of attenuated organisms. Of the test animals, all but one survived, while an equal number of control animals all died of anthrax. Artificial vaccination or immunization, which had hitherto been thought peculiar to smallpox, immediately assumed broad general biological possibilities. The earlier emotional clashes (1859) over the *Origin of Species* were partly forgotten in the excitement over hoped-for control of disease.

Plagues of Hogs

When D. E. Salmon was called to the Division of Animal Industry in 1879 (in 1884 this became the Bureau of Animal Industry, and Salmon was made chief), diseases of domestic animals were causing uncounted losses, dire disaster to farming communities, and the general fear that these little understood diseases would spread to man. Hog cholera was, and for that matter still is, one of the great menaces with which the livestock industry has had to contend. So when young Smith became director of the pathological laboratory of the Bureau, he was promptly assigned to work with his chief on this rapidly fatal epizootic of hogs. Such a difficult tangle he found. As a matter of fact, he never did succeed in unraveling the snarl of problems. In that respect he joined a goodly company, Pasteur, Metchnikoff, Schütz, Welch, and others, even Koch, too, as far as he entered into the problem. I shall merely indicate some of the quandaries rather than the halting progress of the work; it was more than a dilemma, it was a trilemma in which and around which Smith continued to work as occasion presented during most of his life. There were at least three diseases that were being studied in different lands with nine or ten confusing names in the three languages most used at that time.

These diseases with their common English names are hog cholera, swine plague, and swine erysipelas, but names, clinical pictures, causative agents, and investigators were all well mixed. The study of the outbreaks gradually led to an understanding of hog cholera and swine plague, the two that were present in this country. In 1885 Salmon and Smith isolated and described a motile, Gram-negative, easily cultivable bacillus from a number of cases of hog cholera and reproduced what seemed to be the disease by feeding the organisms to experimental hogs. Their experimental animals showed parenchymatous degeneration of the viscera, some focal necroses in the liver, and inflammation of the intestinal mucosa chiefly in the colon, just as had been the case with the sick animals in the field, and they recovered this organism from the experimental animals at autopsy. It was therefore called the hog cholera bacillus or *Bacillus cholerae suis* (now *Salmonella cholerae suis*).

Sometimes however and in some outbreaks, they found another bacterium, a very small bipolar staining, nonmotile rod which they isolated readily from the blood, from the spleen, from pneumonic areas in the lungs, as well as from the intestines. Earlier experiments with this organism by Löffler had placed it as the probable cause of a pneumo-enteritis, swine plague, or *Schweineseuche* of the German literature. The two diseases run together; sometimes one, sometimes the other is the primary infection. Although the two diseases have been so confusing, the two bacteria are readily differentiated in the laboratory. At times Salmon and Smith found typical cases of hog cholera from which they could isolate *neither* the so-called hog cholera bacillus nor the organism of swine plague. This confusion in hog cholera was not cleared up until 1903 when de Schweinitz and Dorset, of the Bureau of Animal Industry, successfully transmitted a disease indistinguishable from hog cholera by means of bacteria-free filtrates of diseased animals. They completed their proof by finding that serum from animals that had recovered from hog cholera would neutralize the virus, rendering it harmless when injected into susceptible hogs. The hog cholera bacillus proved to be merely a pathogenic secondary invader.

How then shall we estimate the value of the long studies of Smith and his associates in these hog epizootics?

1. They added to our knowledge of the large and confusing group of bacteria now named *Salmonella* in honor of Dr. Salmon.

2. They aided in differentiating swine plague from hog cholera.

3. Several excellent instances of serendipity stem from these studies in the *Salmonella* group and should be considered in rendering judgment. The first was by Salmon and Smith in 1886; they found that active artificial immunity could be incited against these hog cholera bacilli by several injections of heat-killed organisms. Similar procedures have been used rather widely both in veterinary and in human medicine, notably in the preparation of antityphoid vaccines.

4. Smith and Reagh (1903) were, I believe, the first to demonstrate the essential antigenic differences between the bodies of bacteria and the flagella. This gave further evidence of variations in bacteria, motile

and nonmotile strains of the typhosus bacillus for example, and has altered materially both the understanding and practices in bacteriology. The large number of named types in the *Salmonella* genus and the many types of pneumococci and streptococci are based on different but comparable subtle differences in antigenic structure.

Texas Cattle Fever

Most medical historians agree that Smith's four-year detective search in solving the baffling problems of this severe anemia of cattle was his outstanding achievement. I am inclined to give equal prominence to other studies built up year after year, one fact upon another, such as his contributions in tuberculosis, his progressive studies in diphtheria, especially the active immunization with toxin-antitoxin mixtures, the important investigations in blackhead of turkeys, the experimental production of scurvy, and his seventy-five or more papers establishing methods and modes of thought in general bacteriology.

Many who have emphasized the tick-fever work as the first proof of the biologic spread of disease by an arthropod carrier have overlooked the observations of Patrick Manson who ten years earlier (1877–79) detailed the metamorphosis of Bancroft's filaria, the causative agent in elephantiasis, with drawings of the different stages of the nematode in certain mosquitoes, especially *Culex fatigans*. He showed that it is only in those mosquitoes that had fed on filariated blood that the metamorphosis occurs. Later he described the nocturnal swarming in man. Manson was aware that he had not carried out the important experimental transmission to man. He stated that he had not had the hardihood to attempt the *experimentum crucis* by filariating a man by means of filaria metamorphosed in passing through the mosquito. In this respect Smith and his associates had the advantage that always obtains in studying diseases of lower animals. They could and did carry out the crucial experiment of experimental transmission of the disease by infected ticks. In working with infectious diseases of man, we are always faced with the choice of a model, more or less successful, usually less. We may use small laboratory animals, dogs, monkeys, and even anthropoid apes to lay our foundations, but the final test must be in man whether it is labeled an experiment or not.

Just as Jenner followed the folklore suggestions of the dairymaids in experiments which resulted in successful vaccination against smallpox, so Smith and associates followed the notions of the cattle ranchers that ticks were in some obscure manner at the bottom of their troubles with Texas fever. Smith's first paper, a brief preliminary one, appeared in 1889, then a paper of 191 pages in 1891 and the complete report of 301 pages in 1893 by Smith and Kilborne. This is a masterpiece of orderly reasoning, experiments to answer specific questions, and complete details of each animal used; it is a recognized classic in medical literature.

Before 1868 the following facts about Texas fever were well known:

1. Southern cattle bearing the latent infection were free from signs of the disease.

2. Infection was commonly transmitted only during warm months of the year; in depths of winter, the cattle were harmless.

3. The disease was not communicated directly from southern to northern cattle, but the ground over which the former had passed was contaminated by them and thence in some unknown manner the disease was transmitted to susceptible cattle.

4. Southern cattle after remaining a short time on northern pastures lost the power to infect those pastures and remained harmless. Similarly cattle that had been driven considerable distance lost the power to infect pastures.

5. When pastures and trails had been traversed by southern cattle, the disease did not appear at once when northern cattle were exposed to the land; a period of not less than thirty days elapsed before the cattle began to die.

6. The disease occurred either in an acutely fatal form during the hot months, appearing suddenly and as a rule in all the animals of a herd at the same time, or in the autumn as a mild nonfatal or chronic type.

What an enigma! It is possible only to suggest, in our rapid survey, the variety and detail of the experiments performed in the "four years of slavery," as Theobald Smith called it. The manifest red blood cell destruction caused him to examine the cells from the blood and organs of sick animals and at autopsy. He was soon able to describe a pyriform parasite which he found in varying numbers in the red blood cells. He referred to early work of C. W. Stiles who in 1868 had been the first to lay stress on the changed condition of the blood corpuscles. He concluded from Stiles' description that he had actually seen the same organism which Smith named *Piroplasma bigemina*. He referred also to Babes' finding of inclusions in the red cells of Texas fever cattle (1888), but since that author succeeded in cultivating these as bacteria, Smith concluded that Babes was in error. The organism is now, however, commonly named *Babesia bigemina*. In Smith's studies, it was found in fourteen outbreaks of the disease, two of them experimental, and not in normal northern cattle.

Tick Experiments

I wish I could picture the laborious persistence of Smith and his associates, hot summer after hot summer, in field and in laboratory, as they whittled away at the known facts and gradually dug out the answers from northern and southern cattle and from myriads of ticks. Each year for four years the farm land of the Bureau was divided into well-separated areas with "buffer states" between them, and in these were separately enclosed the different experimental animals, until the evidence was beyond doubt.

(1) Northern cattle on which young ticks from southern cattle were placed became ill; (2) well cattle injected intravenously with blood from sick cattle became ill; (3) northern cattle kept in fields in which infected ticks had been scattered became ill; (4) well cattle were placed with sick native cattle from which ticks had been laboriously hand picked each day for several days until one could be certain that no ticks remained and the well cattle remained well. *Sick cattle are harmless when the cattle tick is absent.*

Quoting from a summary in the 1893 monograph,[14]

(1) Texas cattle fever is a disease of the blood, characterized by a destruction of red corpuscles. The symptoms are partly due to the anemia produced; partly to the large amount of debris in the blood, which is excreted with difficulty, and which causes derangement of the organs occupied with its removal.

(2) The destruction of the red corpuscles is due to a microorganism or micro-parasite which lives within them. It belongs to the protozoa and passes through several distinct phases in the blood.

(3) Cattle from the permanently infected territory, though otherwise healthy, carry the micro-parasite of Texas fever in their blood.

(4) Texas fever may be produced in susceptible cattle by the direct inoculation of blood containing the micro-parasite.

(5) Texas fever in nature is transmitted from cattle which come from the permanently infected territory to cattle outside of this territory by the cattle tick (*Boophilus bovis*).

(6) The infection is carried by the transovarian passage through the progeny of the ticks that matured on infected cattle, and the organisms inoculated by them directly into the blood of susceptible cattle.

(7) Sick natives may be a source of infection (when ticks are present).

(8) Texas fever is more fatal to adult than to young cattle.

(9) Two mild attacks or one severe attack will probably prevent a subsequent fatal attack in every case.

(10) Sheep, rabbits, guinea pigs, and pigeons are insusceptible to direct inoculation. (Other animals have not been tested.)

(11) In the diagnosis of Texas fever in the living animal the blood should always be examined microscopically if possible.

Tuberculosis

Smith's first independent paper (1884) was on tuberculosis. The series of some thirty papers on this disease by Smith and his several associates exhibits an outstanding quality of the man, namely, his persistence, his clinging to a problem even though interrupted by other pressing duties. In this instance nine years elapsed between his first two papers on tuberculosis and his third; in the interim appeared his significant papers on hog cholera and the contributions which cleared much of the confusion of Texas cattle fever.

In 1894, after giving definite recognition to Cooper Curtice, F. L. Kilborne, and E. C. Schroeder for their parts in the study, Smith records tests of the recently introduced tuberculin reaction in a herd of sixty cattle, with careful clinical, pathological, and bacteriological examinations. The almost overwhelmingly detailed histories of each cow and the subsequent guinea pig and cultural studies provide a typical example (178 pages) of the step-by-step painstaking method which Theobald Smith used throughout his life. As one of the final statements in this paper, he approves the tuberculin test in cattle as *good* but *not perfect*. In a later paper (1906) in which Smith reports autopsies on 350 cattle with positive tuberculin tests, he expressed his consternation at finding so large a percentage of our milk cattle to be tuberculin positive.

In 1896 and again in 1898 came papers, at first tentative and later more assured, on differences in virulence in tubercle bacilli from several sources. Quoting from his 1898 paper: "The absolute identity of tubercle bacilli infecting mammals has been so generally assumed and the assumption used as a basis for the enactment of sanitary measures, having for their object the prevention of any transmission of the tubercle bacilli from animals to man, that any one who would attempt to question this identity must be prepared to meet considerable scepticism."

Tubercle bacilli which Smith isolated from the udder or other affected organs of tuberculous cattle and cultivated on artificial media were definitely more pathogenic for rabbits, as well as for cattle, than were organisms isolated from human sputum or affected human lungs at post-mortem. For example, an appropriate measured dose of the bovine strains injected into the ear vein of rabbits produced death commonly in 17–20 days, while a similar dose from human sputum strains caused only a slowly progressive infection, commonly with a gain in body weight. The gross and microscopic examination of the organs at autopsy confirmed the differences. He described cultural characteristics correlated with this difference in virulence. Smith was again impressed, as he had been in his hog cholera studies, with variations among organisms from similar sources. He continued to stress variation in microorganisms throughout his life, long before dissociation and mutations became a part of our daily microbiologic conceptions.

As to the importance of bovine tuberculosis in human disease, Smith (with E. C. Schroeder) had shown back in 1893 that certain tuberculin positive cattle without obvious signs of tuberculosis of the udder shed tubercle bacilli in the milk. In a review of this subject nine years later (1902), Smith concluded:

1. There is no evidence to show that bovine tubercle bacilli may indiscriminately infect the human subject. A few bacilli are harmless but the flooding of the digestive tract with bacilli from tuberculous udders is dangerous.

2. There is some evidence that bovine bacilli have been isolated from human beings, that the successful transfer is uncommon and that it depends on certain conditions that need careful clinical and pathological study.

3. The evidence that transmission takes place must be based on the isolation of tubercle bacilli having the characters of the bovine variety.

The clash of opinion with reference to types of mammalian tubercle bacilli gradually diminished as the evidence from many different cases came in from laboratories in several countries. In 1901 at the International Congress on Tuberculosis in London, Koch startled his audience by reversing his earlier position, stating that the bovine tubercle bacilli were sharply different from the human. He based this change of mind, he stated, largely on his experiments with his co-worker Schütz that showed that tubercle bacilli from human cases did not cause progressive tuberculosis in cattle. He gave no credit to the earlier and much more complete studies of Smith. By 1908 at the International Congress on Tuberculosis in Washington, Smith was able to say, "The designation *human* and *bovine* which I applied tentatively to these types in 1898 has been generally accepted." With minor modifications our present position agrees with his.

Smith's absorbing interest in bovine tuberculosis and its relation to human disease led him to amplify (1898, 1899) the work of Sternberg (1887), Yersin (1888), and others in determining the thermal death point of tubercle bacilli in milk and other media. His conclusions, which are especially important in the pasteurization of milk, run as follows.

1. "Tubercle bacilli when suspended in distilled water, normal salt solution, bouillon and milk are destroyed at 60° C. in 15–20 minutes. The larger number are destroyed in 5 to 10 minutes.

2. When tubercle bacilli are suspended in milk, the pellicle that forms during the exposure at 60° C. may contain living bacilli after 60 minutes."

Yet another phase of Smith's work in tuberculosis ties in with his interest in active immunity and also with the work of Koch, Behring, *et al.*, who recommended and used for a while certain strains of human type bacilli for the vaccination of calves. Experiments reported by Smith in 1911 showed "that not every strain of tubercle bacilli, clearly belonging to the human type, is adapted for the vaccination of calves against tuberculosis under ordinary conditions." Strain XXIV, for example, below rather than above the average virulence of human type for rabbits was fatal for four of nine calves on first injection. In a later paper (1915 with Marshal Fabyan), the authors cite a number of cases from the literature, as well as their own, in which the injections of human type tubercle bacilli into calves "may in rare cases lead to subsequent shedding of such bacilli in the milk." "Bacilli lodging in the undeveloped udder appear to be less promptly destroyed there than in other organs and tissues." "The hazard unless the treated herd is inspected by a competent person or unless the milk is pasteurized seems to make the procedure impractical."

In weighing the more unusual portion of the contributions of Smith in the field of tuberculosis, namely the differentiation of human and bovine types, by how much does he stand alone and how much did he derive from others? In his two earlier papers (1896, 1898) he refers to a number of authors who had been injecting tuberculous material and pure cultures into experimental animals. Especially he names Arloing of Lyons, who published a monograph in 1892, and states that the sources of Arloing's organisms are not well established. In a later review paper (1908) Arloing states that his early work had been devoted chiefly to distinguishing between the avian and mammalian tubercle bacilli. He gives Smith the credit of differentiating the bovine from the human types *"plus près de nous."*[15]

One must bear in mind, however, that the infectivity of the tubercle had been clearly demonstrated by the French military surgeon Jean Antoine Villemin in a series of startling papers published between 1865 and 1869 and amplified in a book of over six hundred pages, *Etudes de la Tuberculose*, in 1867. Even in his first communication (1865), Villemin stated:

1. "Tuberculosis is a specific affection.
2. The cause lives in an inoculable agent.
3. Inoculation is readily made from man to rabbit.
4. Tuberculosis belongs then to the class of virulent diseases, and should take its place in classification besides syphilis but more closely to the disease of glanders."

Later he reported that bovine tuberculous material was more virulent for rabbits than human tubercles. "We have observed that none of the rabbits inoculated with human tubercles exhibited a tuberculous process as rapid and completely generalized as that which we have obtained by inoculation of tubercles from the cow."[16] These discoveries were soon confirmed and extended by many investigators, notably by Cohnheim and Salomonsen (1878) and by Hänsell (1879). All of these studies formed the basis on which both Koch and Theobald Smith built.

Smith does not mention the work of Villemin, although he certainly knew something of it since the beginning sentence of Koch's first article on the tubercle bacillus (1882) refers to the demonstration by Villemin that tuberculous tissues inoculated into experimental animals will reproduce the disease. Koch, however, gave no specific references either in his 1882 or the more complete 1884 paper. Something of the commotion that Villemin's "heretical findings" produced can be learned from the fact that he was asked to withdraw from the French Academy of Medicine because of his radical views on the transmission of tuberculosis, and by the fact that, although he continued to experiment and publish, he was not sufficiently recognized to receive an obituary (Oct. 6, 1892) in the Paris medical weekly, *La Presse Médicale*. The quality of his work has now been fully recognized; indeed it is gratifying to find it referred to favorably in this country in the formerly well-known textbook *Flint's Practice of Medicine*, as early as the third edition published in 1868.

Other Noteworthy Contributions by Smith and Associates

The investigation in these three subjects, tuberculosis, hog cholera, and cattle fever, are typical of the problems and the methods of Theobald Smith. So many other lines of successful study are found among his more than 250 articles and monographs that one wishes one could write a more complete story, a definitive biography.

Hardly had the major riddles of cattle fever been answered, when Smith's attention was called in 1893 to another economically important disease, infectious enterohepatitis, or blackhead, of turkeys, which at that time was causing heavy losses, especially in Massachusetts and Rhode Island. He spent August, 1894, at the Rhode Island Experiment Station at Kingston working on the disease; after a number of autopsies he concluded that he was probably dealing with an infectious process. In 1895 he published a description of a new species of protozoan that he found in the caeca and in the liver of the sick birds and named this *Amoeba meleagrida* (n. sp. 1895); it was later reclassified as *Histomonas meleagridis.*

After his move to the Rockefeller Institute at Princeton, this was the first disease Smith again studied. In a critical survey, he refers to the experiments of Moore, who in 1895 transmitted the disease by feeding liver and caeca of diseased birds to healthy stock. Similar experiments of this general type in the hands of Smith and Graybill gave inconsistent results. In four well-controlled experiments they showed that a small threadworm, *Heterakis gallinae*, commonly found in the caeca of turkeys and chickens, was "an accessory weakening agent, preparing the way for the specific agent of blackhead." "Eggs of *H. gallinae* were fed to turkeys and *then* the 'amoebae' produced the disease, but without the nematode only a few cases of blackhead occurred." These observations of the constant association of the nematode with the disease led to further studies by Tyzzer and Fabyan (1922), two of Smith's early associates; they demonstrated a remarkable parasitic cycle, finding that the protozoan was actually carried along in the infected embryos of the nematode worm.

The parasitologist, Maurice Hall, says that "this work alone would have insured Smith a permanent and high place 'as a student of disease.'"

Theobald Smith's appointment as Director of the Massachusetts Antitoxin and Vaccine Laboratory involved him in public health problems and important tasks of preparation and standardization of smallpox vaccine and diphtheria and tetanus antitoxins. This more or less routine work, which many would have scorned, provides an example of the excellent use which Smith and his associates (Herbert R. Brown and E. L. Walker) made of material that just came their way.

a) The beautifully complete study of parasitic amoebae of the intestinal tract of man and other animals by E. L. Walker, from Smith's department, was a major contribution to our knowledge of these confusing parasites, so widely spread in nature.

b) Smith and his associates studied and emphasized the variation in capacity of different strains of diphtheria bacilli to produce toxin and the variability of families of guinea pigs to react to diphtheria toxin and to produce antitoxin.

c) They studied passive immunity with guinea pigs *in utero* confirming the observations of Ehrlich and others, and determined the duration of this immunity.

d) The young suckled by immune mothers acquired a passive immunity.

Later, in the Princeton period, Smith returned to these problems and with Ralph Little found that colostrum with its high antibody content against members of the *Bacillus coli* group would prevent scours, the highly fatal diarrhea of new born calves.[17]

e) A more notable contribution arising from the Board of Health work was the finding (1907–10) that neutral mixtures of diphtheria toxin-antitoxin would incite antibody production in guinea pigs and protect them against fatal doses of toxin. Smith suggested that a similar procedure might be effective in man. In reviewing the literature he found that Dreyer and Madsen (1901) had reported somewhat similar studies, using mixtures of toxin-antitoxin with a toxon reaction, effective especially in rabbits, goats, and horses. Smith also reported that after completion of their researches, he found a preliminary paper by W. H. Park (1903) with similar results in horses. Behring's work along these lines came later, from 1913 and subsequently, but for all that, he usually gets the credit rather than his predecessors.

f) The peculiar hypersensitivity of guinea pigs to a second injection of horse serum after an interval of some days was described by Smith to Ehrlich while he was visiting the Frankfurt institute. Ehrlich gave the problem to Otto, one of his associates, who investigated the phenomenon extensively and generously published his findings under the title of *Das Theobald Smithsche Phaenomon* (1905).

We all know how important and involved allergy has proved to be. In biographical sketches of Smith and his work, it is recorded that he made no published statement, but his discussion of an important paper on the subject by Rosenau and Anderson in 1906 was published. This so clearly reveals the confusion of the period that I have cited it rather completely under Rosenau. Paul A. Lewis of Smith's laboratory did, however, publish an excellent article in 1908. He referred to earlier observations in the laboratory using guinea pigs in the titration of diphtheria antitoxin, but gave no details. He confirmed and advanced many of the findings then current and raised appropriate questions in regard to the nature of the injury in anaphylactic shock. These studies led to the later experiments of Auer and Lewis (1910) in which they demonstrated that anaphylactic death in guinea pigs was caused by asphyxia due to the tetanic contraction of the smooth muscles in the bronchioles.

Smith's investigations in contagious abortion of cattle yielded some twelve papers including a critical monograph (124 pages, 1923) with R. B. Little, describing especially the work on active immunization. His first publication (with Marshal Fabyan) was in 1912, and he continued actively interested throughout the rest of his life with a final publication in 1933. Much of this work was along lines also studied by others in several countries. I would point out that Smith, because of his experience with latent udder infections in tuberculosis, early (1912) expressed his fear of possible brucella infections in man through the milk from cows infected with these organisms.

When Smith reviewed his study of brucellosis in 1917 at the Princeton Rockefeller Institute, the disease was regarded as the most serious menace to the dairy industry. His efforts played a considerable part in the reduction of brucellosis. One point which he noticed in the pathology of the disease deserves attention, namely the intracellular location of *Brucella abortus* in the epithelial cells of the chorion and his appreciation of the importance of the multiplication of bacteria in cells lacking the enzyme systems of active phagocytosis.

Smith and his associates also described with accuracy another organism *Vibrio fetus* (n. sp. 1918) which they found in some outbreaks of contagious abortion in which the presence of *Brucella abortus* was carefully ruled out. With the gradual reduction in *B. abortus* infections, *V. fetus* has become proportionately more important.

Theobald Smith—The Man

Now that we have glimpsed, all too briefly, the productive career of Theobald Smith, and can agree, I believe, with Professor Bulloch, the British historian of bacteriology, that he ranks alongside the greatest masters of bacteriology, we can learn something of the man and how he achieved his phenomenal successes.

He was long, lank, and lean, a shy man, an introvert who kept a personal diary of some length during the formative years, using English, German, or French as the spirit moved him. In later years the diary dealt largely with the weather and obvious occasions. His son Philip tells me that the diary shows considerable indecision and doubt. Unlike many of his contemporary American bacteriologists, Smith, because of lack of funds, did not have the privilege of foreign study, but he did have an unusual facility in foreign languages. German was almost his native tongue and with French he was only somewhat less at home. Through the printed page then, he communed with Koch, Pasteur, and the other European scholars. Later, when he was exchange professor from Harvard to Berlin, he delivered his lectures fluently in the vernacular.

All agree that Smith was a perfectionist and impatient with less, both in his family and among his laboratory associates. He had come up without any silver spoon and felt that hard work and economy of time and money were necessary. Throughout his life he maintained the methodical, well-ordered day with long hours at the task, *ohne Hast, ohne Rast*. He planned carefully, took complete notes, the articulated work of the several decades, and always his mind was alert for the beckonings of important bypaths. With Pasteur, Smith showed, "In the field of experimentation, chance favors only the mind prepared for discoveries, by patient study and persevering effort."

A few items learned from his son will enrich the picture. Father was extremely methodical. He routinized his life; he planned the use of his time far ahead; he was regular in his habits. He greatly objected to hurrying, for that betokened poor planning. He rarely suggested lack of time as a basis for refusal. He commonly arrived at the station 15–20 minutes before traintime. But once he was late. He had been showered with many honors and had a trunk full of honorary degrees and their respective hoods, but was delighted when Yale informed him that they would be happy to honor him with an LL.D. degree. But, he missed the train by one week. He was terribly mortified and chagrined. Smith drank coffee sparingly, taking only that portion of a cup after dinner that would aid in keeping him alert long enough to complete the planned reading or writing. He measured this amount quite exactly, a quarter-, a half-cup or more as the case demanded. Once while walking together in Switzerland, Smith and his son drank beer. The father became ill, attributed his illness to the beer and thereafter abstained entirely from alcoholic beverages. Almost every evening, after playing the piano until 8 o'clock when the young Philip went to bed, he worked later into the night. He especially enjoyed his summers in the family cottage on a point of land which they bought on Silver Lake near Chocorua, N. H. His life there included botanizing, wood-chopping, some rowing, no swimming, and reading and writing. He always had a microscope and slides along for further study.

He had few intimates; the one man with whom Smith did unbend was his old professor and chief at Cornell, Simon Henry Gage. Great preparations were always made in the home when Gage was about to pay a visit. Much backslapping and free and easy conversation prevailed.[18]

One of his close associates states:

He was a very gentle, courteous, and considerate person in his home, and was really a wonderful host. However, he wanted the party to break up by not later than 10:00 P.M. Dr. Smith was careful of everything to a degree which is almost inconceivable to the average person. It permeated his entire life, both in his home and in his laboratory. He would not tolerate any waste of time or material. One example: he had four jacks for his automobile—small lever type—and would jack his car up every night to take the weight off the tires. He never used antifreeze in his radiator, but drained the water every evening and filled the radiator in the morning with heated water in order that the engine would warm up more gradually before starting. These tales are typical of the many true stories about Smith's foibles, stories that show his impatience with any form of waste, a thrift that was at times extreme.

Is it not strange that, even now, twenty-three years after his death we have no definitive biography of our most noteworthy microbiologist?[19] The sketch by the French parasitologist, F. Mesnil (1935), is important, especially since it came from another land. He cites many of Smith's contributions and stresses his foreign honors; he is both critical and laudatory. He summarizes the Texas Fever work.

"It is the first time that the physiologic cycle of a protozoan pathogen has been traced. It belongs in the history of our knowledge beside the work of Patrick Manson who discovered ten years earlier the development of the blood filaria in the mosquitoes."

Of the many sketches published after Smith's death (1934), the memoir written by Hans Zinsser for the National Academy of Sciences is by far the best, being both critical and appreciative. I shall quote his farewell paragraphs.

To the younger bacteriologists whose lives overlapped his own, Theobald Smith was a hero to be emulated and whose approval was a mark of distinction. He illustrated to them the dignity of austere devotion to scholarship and the modesty of wisdom. But always they stood a little in awe of him. He, with Welch, were the two greatest individual influences that helped to hold the younger men working in the medical laboratories steadfast in the faith of the worthiness of honest effort. But Welch was loved instinctively for the warmth of his heart and for the urbane benevolence with which he encouraged younger men and commended them often beyond their deserts. Of Theobald Smith they thought as the dispassionate critical mind by which they were impersonally, though justly, appraised.

In following his career and studying his work a warmer current flows into one's thoughts of him. One feels that he was lonely in the restraints by which reason disciplined him. One wishes one had been more intimately his pupil. And in realizing the great debt our science owes to him, one begins with admiration and ends with affection.

From quite another division of Harvard University, the laboratory of cryptogamic botany, Roland Thaxter[20] published in 1892, a major contribution to bacteriology, a detailed study of a "new order, the *Myxobacteriaceae*." While collecting fungi in the neighborhood of Kittery, Maine, he observed a bright orange-colored growth, apparently amorphous, occurring on decayed wood, fungi, and similar substances. By further study, this material was found to consist of motile rodlike organisms multiplying by fission and secreting a gelatinous base. Thaxter's careful investigations of this and similar organisms laid the foundations of our knowledge of the fruiting myxobacters; he regarded these organisms as representatives of the Schizomycetes. They have gone through several taxonomic vicissitudes and were given only scant attention even by Migula in his *System der Bakterien*. They now seem safely classified as *Myxococcaceae*, one of the five families in the order of Myxobacteriales; many members of this order have the ability to decompose complex polysaccharides such as cellulose, agar, and chitin.

The thorough investigation of actinomycosis, and the causative agents, the ray fungi or actinomycetes, in 1905 by James H. Wright[21] of Massachusetts General Hospital and Harvard Medical School is noteworthy. His paper was based on a study of 13 cases in man and 2 in cattle; a careful review of the literature was followed by incisive descriptions of the characteristic granules, or "drusen," excellent photographs, cultivation of 13 strains of the organisms, including the 2 bovine, and the experimental production of local but nonprogressive lesions in rabbits and guinea pigs. Although this study was made years after similar researches in Europe, it was a noteworthy contribution that has been widely cited.

We have in Baltimore and in Boston examples of the important emphases in the early development of bacteriology in the United States. At Johns Hopkins, the individual aspects of infectious diseases, their history, pathology, and their causative agents were stressed. In Boston, with the remarkably active State Board of Health tying in with both the Massachusetts Institute of Technology and Harvard University, we find the public health aspects of bacteriology receiving the greater emphasis. Especially through the studies at the Lawrence Experiment Station, methods were developed for large-scale purification of sewage and also for the filtration of polluted waters, thus making our crowded industrial cities possible without a high enteric disease rate. As we travel south and later west on our bacteriologic journeys, we shall find other types of studies that have proved of inestimable value to society. Of necessity I must choose only a few examples from our broad continent with its diverse backgrounds.

CHAPTER VIII

Rhode Island

He who does not go beyond the facts,
will seldom get as far as the facts.   T. H. HUXLEY

Shall we now follow Roger Williams, the nonconformist, who, forced to flee from theocratic Massachusetts, was successful after much clashing and battling in establishing a colony that stressed civil rights of the individual and separation of church and state. But that is not our story, save that the attitude of nonconformity has shown itself in the political history of the colony and the state of Rhode Island and even in its public health history under the leadership of Charles V. Chapin. Religious freedom was emphasized in the eighteenth century in the charter of its major institution of higher learning, Brown University, where representation on its governing boards was provided for all the sects then present in the community. The early life of the inhabitants, a contentious lot, followed rather closely that of its neighbor colonies; with similar endemic and epidemic diseases, with similar difficulties over colonial boundaries, with the mother country, with the Indians, and with struggles towards self-government.

Providence Department of Health

CHARLES V. CHAPIN

Charles V. Chapin (1856–1941), superintendent of health of Providence for forty-eight years, was designated America's greatest municipal health officer by the committee of competent specialists asked by Smillie to evaluate the outstanding pioneers in each field of public health in this country.[1] For much of this period, he worked in close association and sympathy with Frederic P. Gorham of Brown University, the training and qualities of the one aiding and supplementing those of the other. Obviously, Chapin did not gain his pre-eminence without painful growth struggles during the early decades of the bacteriology era, when inconvenient facts were forcing us to change our thinking and our practices in attempts to control communicable diseases. At the beginning of his lifework, the emphasis was on external environment, on cleanliness as the method to achieve municipal health. "A clean city is a healthful city" was the common slogan. Colonel Waring cleaned up Havana, but yellow fever continued to be a serious menace until the modes of spread were revealed by the Reed commission and efforts were directed specifically.

From 1888 Chapin was also Registrar of Vital Statistics,[2] and for the rest of his active life he made weekly examination of the mortality lists of Providence, drawing his own conclusions as practices were altered. In studying these and his limited budget, he began to realize that much of the money spent in the elaborate removal of public nuisances gave relatively slight return in improved health of the community. Not only the statistics in Providence were available to him, but quite early he compiled a study *Municipal Sanitation in the United States* and later a report for the American Medical Association, *State Public Health Work*, thus giving his acute mind an extensive basis for judgment.

In his address, "Dirt, Disease and the Health Officer," he used the yellow fever story as his text and urged the health officers of the country to bury the filth theory with its emphasis on emanations of decaying matter as the cause of disease. He stressed the thesis that Budd had advanced half a century earlier, one that had been largely overlooked. "Do not claim," he said, "more for municipal housecleaning than the facts warrant. Teach on all occasions the true relation of dirt to disease." He continually emphasized the value of proportion in the use of public health funds. "Three or four food inspectors cannot save half as many lives as one baby nurse."

Although there were some important truths in the generalization of the early promoters of public health, and although their projects for civic betterment saved many lives and did much for human comfort and convenience, there were several errors which have had an unfortunate influence on preventive medicine and still have today. One of these is that disease breeds in filth instead of being merely carried in filth. Another is that all kinds of dirt are dangerous, not merely the secretions and excretions of the human body. A third unfortunate hypothesis is that infectious diseases are usually airborne.

In 1906 Chapin shocked the America Medical Association with an address, "The Fetich of Disinfection," building up a strong case that infection through fomites is rare. "Living with a tuberculosis patient is the danger, not his clothes after he is dead. . . . Terminal disinfection is costly and useless and teaches discarded theory." He presented in detail the facts on the survival of the different pathogens outside of the body. On this basis, terminal disinfection for diphtheria was abandoned in Providence in 1905 with no general increase of the disease.

Arguments were bitter. Chapin's colleagues angrily attacked his thesis and called him a traitor to public health. But his reputation for sanity, his repeated gentle insistence at medical meetings, the mortality and morbidity figures from the city where his preachments were carried out in practice gradually caused other health boards and officers to discontinue terminal gaseous fumigation and disinfection. New York City in 1915 and others later, save in special cases, discontinued without consequent increase in the incidence of the several communicable diseases.

Chapin was a prodigious reader and wrote voluminously. His more significant papers and contributions were brought together by Gorham in *A Review of Public Health Realities*. Of all his writings, the most influential and the one that ranks, I believe, among the dozen most significant book contributions in microbiology in this country is his *Sources and Modes of Infection* (1910), which is worth rereading to this day. Of course every text in microbiology and disease whether of man, lower animals, or plants, considers the problems of transmission of each organism or disease, but this study brought together the world literature collected around the viability of pathogens outside of the body and the different paths of transmission. Again and again the facts emphasized the importance of the control of the case and the carrier, the immediate contact rather than transmission through fomites or air.

At the Providence City Hospital, later named for Dr. Chapin, "for the first time in this country, was put into practical application the theory that infectious diseases are not air-borne. Instead of assigning one disease to a ward or separate building, different diseases were cared for in the same ward or even in the same rooms, by employing rigid aseptic nursing technique." Insistence on thorough hand-washing with soap and water, not some irritating disinfectant, after contacts with each patient seemed to be the basis for fewer cross-infections than in most institutions of this kind.

These points were not unique with Chapin, and he gives credit to many, especially to the French as being the first to appreciate that the transmission by air is of little importance. It was neither the results of the practices in Providence nor his skillful marshaling of the pros and cons, but the rather remarkable qualities of this man that gave him so much influence.

Chapin was small physically, short and slender, never weighing over 115–20 pounds. He had an unusually discriminating mind, always a delight, and a capacity like Sedgwick to choose pungent phrases that stuck. But even though the phrases were sharp, he never showed the least bit of venom, and he never shouted. Smilingly he reiterated his analyses of the facts, and smilingly he moved among his associates with a gentle gracious manner. Some of his friends have thought that he was too considerate of the feelings of his subordinates, resulting at times in inadequacy. Possibly so, but those of us who were privileged to associate with him even slightly were encouraged in mind and spirit. Aside from his major position, Chapin was professor of physiology at Brown from 1886 to 1894 and later was closely associated with Gorham and was a lecturer in public hygiene both at Brown and at Harvard.

Brown University

FREDERIC P. GORHAM

Instruction in bacteriology was begun at Brown in 1893, almost a decade after its inception in Massachusetts and several other areas, by George Wilton Field, associate professor of cellular biology. Two years later, Frederick Poole Gorham (1871–1933), as a young instructor, took over this work in association with his courses in zoology; throughout his active life he developed courses and investigative interests in many phases of bacteriology, especially those related to public hygiene.

Gorham was a redhead with a matching personality, buoyant, genial, optimistic, almost jubilant in his reactions. He had a broad background in natural history and was active in the public weal as well as in narrower scientific problems. Bacteriologist of the Providence Board of Health for thirty-four years, in class a compelling lecturer, and in the laboratory fertile with suggestion, Gorham was also an active member on many public committees including those of the Rhode Island State Tuberculosis Sanitorium, the State Shellfish Commission, the Park

Commission of Providence, and the Committee on Mosquito Control. His lectures were broad in scope, sparkling, and well organized; for many years he was in charge of the beginning course in zoology and as one of the old-time members of the football team expressed it "that red haired chap, what *was* his name, kept even us awake and interested."

Gorham's contributions are found chiefly in his graduate students who have subsequently proved competent in commercial, public health, and university positions. His research interests are shown in the early publications of these men, although the name of Gorham, at his own insistence, never appeared. Unfortunately his early studies on phosphorescent bacteria were never published. He was deeply interested in the dangerous distribution of sewage in Narragansett Bay and the possible contamination of the oyster beds. Important studies were made over the years by his graduate students, leading to the improvement of sewage disposal in the towns on Narragansett Bay and keeping the problem alive until federal action was taken.[3]

The water and milk supplies of Providence and the control of preventable diseases common in that period, such as tuberculosis, typhoid fever, and diphtheria occupied his attention and that of his students. He wielded a strong influence in the laboratory section of the American Public Health Association and was one of the more active charter members of the Society of American Bacteriologists. In his presidential address in 1911, he reiterated his constant plea for greater use of synthetic media of known composition with accurate quantitative studies of physiological properties. His sharp distant vision is shown by another portion of this address and the recent developments in microbial genetics with Nobel awards. "Variation, selection, and heredity are factors of evolution in bacteria as elsewhere; they would provide an excellent field for the study of evolution."

Gorham was an early riser, beginning to plow through the literature at about four-thirty, arriving at the city laboratory by eight o'clock for the daily microscopic examination of smears from the throat cultures for diphtheria organisms, and beginning his university work by nine with his first lecture. Then at a leisurely pace, he was ready for a full day of work, accomplished with zest and a friendly gaiety.

CHAPTER IX

Connecticut and State Agricultural Experiment Stations

*The species name has only the value of a name
on a package: we must always be ready to change it
or to do away with it.*

DUCLAUX

Come, we will transform the world by our discoveries.

PASTEUR

In Connecticut we shall proceed at once to the active period of bacteriology in the late decades of the nineteenth century. The more notable sites of growth were in Wesleyan and Yale universities, in the two agricultural experiment stations, at Storrs and at New Haven, and in the city and state laboratories.

Wesleyan University

HERBERT W. CONN

Important in early bacteriology both in Connecticut and in the country at large was Herbert W. Conn (1859–1917), long the professor of biology at Wesleyan (1884–1917), one of the three persons most active in founding the Society of American Bacteriologists, influential in establishing the State Laboratory of Hygiene (1905), and its first director. A native of Fitchburg, Massachusetts, a sickly boy who welcomed the more elastic pace of a private school, he was graduated from Boston University in 1881 and continued advanced study in biology under the stimulating guidance of W. K. Brooks at the young Johns Hopkins University. With his doctor's degree in hand, he was immediately appointed associate professor of biology at Wesleyan, where he remained active for the rest of his life, filling at the same time positions in other nearby institutions.

Conn was a shy, retiring, austere introvert, a typical New Englander, never a good mixer, blunt of speech, impatient with small talk, careless of his clothing, but a successful teacher and public lecturer, not infrequently with somewhat boring reiteration. He described cocci as little round spherical balls. Conn preached personal hygiene, but as for himself he would commonly use the public drinking cup; he roundly condemned the so-called typhoid fly, but so disliked screens that Mrs. Conn was forever shutting the screen doors after him. Another entertaining human weakness was his complete lack of interest in spelling. From his journal during a period in Europe, one finds that "we rowed along a quiet country rode" and on another occasion, "road a boat on a river."[1]

When his convictions were involved, his marked dislike of argument was thrust into the background, and we find him putting up a good fight for clean milk or for a state laboratory of hygiene. In spite of early ill health (probably rheumatic fever), he became an energetic adult, an effective organizer, and a highly prolific writer. From his pen came seventeen books, many of them popular and brief such as *The Story of Germ Life*, a type needed in that period. Of published papers, some thirteen were on zoological subjects and about seventy on bacteriology, including many general bulletins in collaboration with W. M. Esten and W. A. Stocking on the problems of the dairy industry, issued by the Storrs Agricultural Experiment Station. Esten wrote, "His technical accomplishments were at times far from exceptional, but he possessed extraordinary ability in directing work and in organizing factual material already obtained."

Like Sedgwick, Jordan, and others, Conn is an example of zoologist captured by the amazing growth and importance of bacteriology. He also presents another example of the radiating influence of Johns Hopkins in the advance of the natural sciences in this country. The germ theory of disease was still a matter of debate when he began to teach. An instructive article by Conn published in *Science* in 1888 mirrors the state of bacteriology in our medical schools of the period as well as his own probing mind. In response to a questionaire sent to the deans of our medical schools, those of twenty-eight named institutions, including most of the stronger schools, responded. To the first question, "Is the theory that most, if not all, infectious diseases are caused by the growth of microscopic organisms, accepted by the members of your faculty and the physicians in your vicinity," most of the responses were in the affirmative. Seven, however, replied, "No," "Not wholly," "It may be true, but it may not," or with other equivocal answers. Question 5, "To what extent does the subject receive attention in the medical course of the school with which you are connected," brought a wide variety of answers ranging from "Incidentally only," "More than deserved," to "A well-equipped bacteriological laboratory with a special instructor." Most institutions gave bacteriology only slight attention; it being commonly interwoven with other courses. Conn's conclusions run: "It may be said that our medical schools and profession generally have been and are advancing along this line of bacteriology as fast as can be expected. . . . The indications are: that a few years will see bacteriology established as a subject to be taught, either as a branch of pathology or otherwise, in all of the medical schools whose financial condition will warrant it."[2]

Conn's interest in public water supplies was aroused by an outbreak of typhoid fever in 1894, at Wesleyan, beginning eight days after initiation banquets and continuing for about two weeks with a total of 25 cases from three fraternities of which 13 were severe and 4 fatal. Oysters served raw on the half shell were the only common article of diet among the cases. Conn's further detective work showed that the oysters had been placed for a few days on less saline "fattening beds" in the Quinnipiac River, a short distance from a private sewer draining a house where there were two cases of typhoid fever. The same lot of oysters had provided uncooked zest the same evening at a fraternity banquet at Amherst; here six cases of typhoid fever occurred among those who had eaten the raw oysters. The chain of evidence was complete.[3] Subsequently a number of such outbreaks have been traced beyond any reasonable doubt to contaminated oysters eaten raw. This was, I believe, the first epidemiological demonstration of pollution of oyster beds and stimulated much study of this involved problem, especially by Gage and his associates at the Lawrence Experiment Station, Gorham, Fuller, *et al.* in Narragansett Bay and Brown University, and later by Howard, *et al.* in Chesapeake Bay. Control of the situation rested entirely with the several states until Congress passed laws in

1910 prohibiting the sale of polluted shellfish in interstate commerce.

Soon after the establishment of the State Agricultural Experiment Station at Storrs, Conn was appointed (1887) to carry on bacteriologic studies for the station in his laboratory at Wesleyan and to direct the more practical aspects at the station. In studying the organisms important in the souring of milk, Conn and Esten early recommended the use of certain pure cultures as butter starters in pasteurized cream. Similar studies were carried out elsewhere notably at the experiment stations at Geneva, New York, and at Wisconsin, but it was not until 1921 that Hammer showed that at least two organisms were necessary for high quality butter, one for acid production and the other for the aromatic June flavor.

Connecticut State Board of Health and Hygienic Laboratory

C. W. Chamberlain, first secretary of the Connecticut State Board of Health, began to urge the establishment of a state laboratory in 1883, and in 1889 the board voted a sum not to exceed $1200 for purchase of apparatus and $2000 annually for two years for "the payment of scientific, laboratory, and other expert work" on the public supplies of potable water in the state. Ground waters were also studied, the tests being carried out chiefly at Yale, and the normal chloride figures were established for the state. Through the combined efforts of many physicians, health officers, and Professor Conn, a state laboratory of hygiene was authorized by act of legislature in 1905. The laboratory was located in an old building on the Wesleyan campus, and Conn was named first director, with a modest appropriation of $3000 a year. The usual bacteriologic tests of that period, diphtheria throat cultures, Widal tests for typhoid fever, examination of sputum from suspected cases of tuberculosis, were carried out with increasing services as time rolled on. In 1917, after the death of Professor Conn, the State Bacteriologic Laboratory became the Bureau of Laboratories and was moved to New Haven with Charles J. Bartlett as director. In 1924 the laboratories were again moved to their present location at Hartford with F. L. Mickle as full-time director.[4]

Agricultural Experiment Stations

As always in this country, private initiative and organizations have antedated government functioning. Not only in medical fields, but also in the agricultural arts and sciences this has been so. After many years of stormy debate, including a veto by President Buchanan and pressure from many agricultural societies, the Morrill Act establishing Land Grant Colleges was signed by President Lincoln May 15, 1862; a few days later the Homestead Act, also after a stormy debate, opened thousands of acres to pioneer settlers. Not until 1887 did the Hatch Act provide federal moneys for nationwide research in the Agricultural Experiment Stations. Since that date, other bills, such as the Adams Act of 1906, have made additional federal funds available, and the states have also been generous to the great industry that grows most of our food and, until recently, all the materials for our clothing. Before this period, however, without federal aid, through private leadership, agricultural stations had been established in sixteen states. Some thirteen other states had somewhat similar organizations commonly associated with the state college, but not actually designated as the state experiment station. Scientific societies were established by gentlemen farmers; the Philadelphia Society for the Promotion of Agriculture was founded in 1785 with George Washington, the farmer of Mt. Vernon, as an honorary member, and in South Carolina a similar society was founded the same year. A summary *History of Agricultural Experimentation and Research in the United States* has been admirably presented by Alfred Charles True,[5] but with only a few pages dealing with microbiology, necessarily a later development. The microbiological work of several representative agricultural experiment stations will be considered here with the Connecticut stations as examples of their small beginnings and later growth.

In 1875 largely through the initiative of Orange Judd, editor of the *American Agriculturalist* and a trustee of Wesleyan University, a Connecticut Agricultural Experiment Station was started with an appropriation of $700 a quarter for two years. For this station Wesleyan furnished a small room on its campus with Professor W. O. Atwater as part-time supervisor; he will be remembered more especially for the Atwater-Rosa calorimeter and his dietary studies with this instrument. He subsequently became first director of the Office of Experiment Stations of the United States Department of Agriculture.

Two years later, an independent state station was created in New Haven with S. W. Johnson as director, and the Middletown station was discontinued. The work of the new station was directed chiefly to the analysis of fertilizers, the quality of farm seeds, and feeds and feeding;

Upper left   WILLIAM HALLOCK PARK, 1863–1939
                  Photograph taken about 1910, at the age of forty-seven.

Upper right   SIMON FLEXNER, 1863–1946
                  Photograph taken about 1914, at the age of fifty-one.

Lower left   HANS ZINSSER, 1878–1940
                  Photograph taken about 1931, at the age of fifty-three.

Lower right   HIDEYO NOGUCHI, 1876–1928
                  Photograph taken about 1918, at the age of forty-two.

Upper left   Veranus Alva Moore, 1859–1931
                      Photograph taken about 1900, at the age of forty-one.

Upper right   James Morgan Sherman, 1890–1956
                      Photograph taken about 1925, at the age of thirty-five.

Below   Theobald Smith, 1859–1934
                      From Albany, our greatest microbiologist.
                      Low relief plaque by Howard Kenneth Weinman, made for Third
                      International Congress of Microbiology, 1939, New York.

instructive farmers' bulletins were published. Work along these lines was characteristic of all the stations of this early period, with emphasis on the special local problems such as citrus fruit and wines in California, dairy products in New York and Wisconsin, and sugar in Louisiana. Bulletins and reports in large numbers have been issued by all the stations; many of these have been compilations or mainly so and have been distributed widely for educational purposes.

While much credit must be given to German chemists for our early knowledge of the nature of proteins, praise is due Thomas B. Osborne, trained at Yale, who worked for years (1886–1928) as research chemist at the Connecticut Agricultural Experiment Station. More than a hundred papers attest his success in the preparation and study of pure proteins, chiefly from important food grains. Of special interest from our point of view is the work of Wells and Osborne and their use of the anaphylactic reaction to establish chemical identity. This will be discussed further in the chapter dealing with Chicago.

The growing dairy industry and the recognition of the importance of infectious diseases of lower animals and of plants gradually brought microbiological studies into the experiment stations.

Dairying was very important in the work of the stations between 1888 and 1906. Through their work the handling of milk and the manufacture of butter and cheese were put upon a scientific basis, and practical procedures and apparatus were radically improved. Systematic investigations in dairying were carried on chiefly by the stations in Wisconsin, New York (Geneva), and Connecticut (Storrs).

. . . .

The Connecticut (Storrs) Station made a long series of studies on the bacteriology of milk and its products, including a determination of the species of bacteria found in dairies in the state, the organisms connected with the souring of milk and ripening of cream, the relation of lactic bacteria to other species in milk, cream, and cheese, and the conditions necessary to the sanitary production of milk. It then undertook a study of the problems involved in the manufacture of soft cheese, especially of the Camembert type, under bacteriological control.

. . . .

About twenty stations did some work on bovine tuberculosis, especially making tuberculin tests. . . . The Wisconsin Station went further than any other, not only in making tuberculin tests, but in examining milk for tubercle bacilli and in experimenting on the infectiousness of milk from tuberculous cows, the control of tuberculosis by isolation of affected animals, the relation of separator slime to tuberculosis in hogs, and the thermal death point of tubercle bacilli under commercial conditions. The stations in Maine, Michigan, New Jersey, and Wisconsin studied the normal temperatures of cattle under various conditions and the relation of these temperatures to the tuberculin test. . . .[6]

The bacteriological work of the stations included isolation, culture, and description of many species of useful and pathogenic bacteria in air, water, soil, fertilizers, plants, food, feeding stuffs, and other agricultural products, and of those bacteria affecting useful and injurious animals. Among the more important investigations in this field were those on soil bacteria at the Michigan, New Jersey, Delaware, and West Virginia Stations, on dairy bacteria at the New York State and Connecticut Storrs Stations, on silage bacteria at the Wisconsin and New Hampshire Stations, and on the bacteria of legumes and root nodules at the Michigan and Oklahoma Stations.[7]

In plant pathology work on life histories of many fungi and bacteria injurious to cultivated plants was carried on. Tick fever of cattle has been studied extensively in the southern states, hog cholera especially in the Middle West, anthrax in Delaware and the California stations.

Following the passage of the Hatch Act, Connecticut established a second agricultural experiment station at Storrs in association with the state college; here the department of animal diseases had its beginning in 1908 when a co-operative research program on white diarrhea of chickens was begun with Rettger of Yale. The causative agent, *Salmonella pullorum*, the septicemic nature of the diseases in young chicks, and the carrier state in the ovaries of apparently well adult hens, giving possibility of transfer of the disease to the unborn chicks, were all well worked out by Rettger and his associates. On their findings it became possible to prevent the disease and to maintain pullorum-free flocks. Studies on Bangs disease in cattle and the importance of barn-yard fowl as carriers of the blackhead infection to turkeys were also continued here through many years.

Yale

Bacteriology sprouted at Yale[8] somewhat later than at Harvard; 1891 saw Langdon Frothingham appointed assistant in the Sheffield Scientific School with a small laboratory improvised on the second floor of the old Sheffield Mansion, the chief aim being the study of the chemical nature of the products of *Bacillus mallei*, causative agent of glanders. In 1901 a course in municipal and sanitary engineering was given by Herbert D. Pease in a better equipped laboratory, and a year later Leo Frederick Rettger (1874–1954), whom we immediately think of when Yale and the early years of bacteriology come to mind, was appointed instructor and placed in charge.

LEO F. RETTGER

The normal growth saw all the usual courses offered and also graduate work leading to the higher degrees. Investigation by Rettger and his early associates dealt with bacterial nutrition, emphasizing nitrogen metabolism and the fact that most bacteria cannot utilize complex nitrogenous substances without the aid of specific hydrolytic enzymes. The original isolation of *Salmonella pullorum* by Rettger and Harvey[9] and methods for the eradication of the pullorum disease (white diarrhea of chicks) came mostly from this laboratory.

Bacterial variation was so striking an observation that it became at Yale, as in many of the early laboratories, a major object of study, with increasing appreciation here of the importance of environment, carbon dioxide requirements, oxygen want, and nutrition as determining factors. Rettger and his colleagues worked over the question of life-cycles and filterable variants of the acid-fast group and the aerobic spore-formers and found no evidence of such forms.

Interest in the intestinal flora (beginning in 1912) came about as the result of co-operative research with Osborne and Mendel when they were seeking for the significance of fat-soluble vitamins in the albino rat. The correlation determined between lactose and dextrin feeding and the increase in *Lactobacillus acidophilus* in the intestines, both of the rat and man, calls to mind the earlier recommendations of Metchnikoff, the feeding of *Lactobacillus bulgaricus* as a means of maintaining a long, if not a happy life. Rettger's studies indicated a superiority of the *acidophilus* over *bulgaricus* as a persisting organism in the intestine and gave a basis for his thesis that feeding these organisms prevented the growth of putrefactive and coliform bacteria in so-called cases of autointoxication. His findings have not been satisfactorily confirmed.

In spite of prolonged effort from the time of Escherich (1886) to the present day, our knowledge of the role of intestinal bacteria in nutrition is meager. Many of the studies have been more concerned with the physiology of the bacteria than that of the host. Is any other bacteriologic field so exceedingly complex? Synthesis of several essential vitamins by bacteria in the gut of different species, including man, has been demonstrated; studies with sulfa drugs and antibiotics have given both favorable and antagonistic results; and emotionally induced illness is highly significant in gastrointestinal disorders. Many years of painstaking efforts through the co-operation of persons of widely differing training will be required for more complete knowledge.

Rettger was a shy, introspective man with whom ready and close association was difficult. Not an effective teacher of undergraduates, he did arouse the intellectual curiosity and appreciation of his graduate students; seventy-eight persons signed the silver tray presented to him at the time of his retirement. He was a typical absent-minded professor, but enjoyed laughing at his own weaknesses. His presidential address before the Society of American Bacteriologists in 1917 gives a good picture of the inner man as he stresses the necessity of using more quantitative methods with synthetic media of known constitution as a basis for metabolic studies on bacteria. He joins Sedgwick and other early bacteriologists in emphasizing that bacteriology should have a place as an independent branch of biology and not merely as a servant of medicine and agriculture.

In the Yale Medical School bacteriology had its beginnings about 1890 as an elective lecture course given by C. J. Foote. In 1905–6 an optional laboratory course, which soon became a requirement, was offered by C. J. Bartlett. His interest in tuberculosis led to studies on the occurrence of tubercle bacilli in market milk, which in turn hastened the requirement of pasteurization of the city milk supplies. Bacterial variation was also studied in the medical school laboratories with Stephen J. Maker and Harold S. Arnold as collaborators.

About 1915 a reorganization of the Medical School was in progress, and in 1917 Winternitz, another pupil of William Welch, was appointed professor of pathology and bacteriology with George H. Smith responsible for the bacteriology. A closer affiliation between the New Haven hospitals and the Medical School was arranged, so that the professional appointees in the latter assumed responsibilities in the hospitals. The many organizational changes, with the numerous bacterial sproutings in several of the clinical departments, immediately important locally, gradually became important nationally through the excellence of the experimental work produced. But these studies are largely beyond the time of our story.

CHARLES-EDWARD AMORY WINSLOW

Another bacteriologist at Yale was Charles-Edward Amory Winslow, 1877–1957. His remarkably productive life might be considered under any one of the three major areas of his professional career, Boston, New York, or New Haven, but since the longest period was spent as Lauder Professor of Public Health at Yale, 1915–45, I elect to present his story here, although most of the New Haven period extends beyond the terminal date of this chronicle. Winslow received his early inspiration and professional instruction from his much admired teacher, W. T. Sedgwick, of the Massachusetts Institute of Technology, and there, after his graduation in 1898, he carried on his teaching and investigations for twelve years. During this period much of his experimental work was done with his associates E. B. Phelps and S. C. Prescott, and involved quantitative studies on sewage and methods of sewage disposal and purification of public water supplies. His first book, *Elements of Water Bacteriology*, was written with Prescott in 1904; its value is attested by the fact that it has gone through some half a dozen editions. At this time also, he began the study of the "Systematic Relationships of the Coccaceae" with Anne F. Rogers, who later became his wife and constant helpmate. Another investigation related to his later interests in ventilation showed that the air in the sewer mains of Boston had a lower bacterial content and fewer organisms that might be termed pathogenic than did the air from the streets above.[10] But ancient myths are essentially immortal.

With the initial meeting (1899) of the Society of American Bacteriologists in prospect, Sedgwick brought along with him to New Haven his two brightest young men, Prescott (aged twenty-seven years) and Winslow (aged twenty-two years). Although neither of them had won his spurs at the time, all persons who answered the letter of October, 1899, and any others who attended the first meeting became charter members,[11] so Winslow became the youngest and and throughout his life remained one of the strongest members of this society. Since both Winslow and Prescott sat for years at the feet of the first generation bacteriologist, Sedgwick, they become by my definition members of the second generation.

In 1910 Winslow left Boston to become associate professor of biology in the City College of New York and curator of public health in the American Museum of Natural History. The latter position gave him an opportunity he had been seeking, the founding of the American Type Culture Collection, a project that has almost died several times with several painful resuscitations, but it continues to grow as a boon to all working in microbiology.[12] New York gave Winslow more intimate contact with many leaders in the public health movement such as Hermann Biggs, Haven Emerson, and William H. Park. His interest in ventilation, industrial hygiene, protection of river and harbor waters from pollution, and his zeal in spreading the gospel of public health are increasingly apparent in his articles. He was forever writing pointed papers in encyclopedias, in reports of committees, and in the public press, both popular and scientific. At this time also, he began his first regular editorial task in the *Health News*, monthly bulletin of the New York State Board of Health.

In 1915 Winslow was called to Yale to the chair of the newly endowed Lauder professorship of public health, and here he found his métier in a congenial university atmosphere. For thirty years he enlarged the dimensions of the chair along lines of industrial hygiene, sanitary bacteriology, housing and ventilation, as well as public health nursing and medical care of the sick. In 1916, with understandable reluctance because of its inevitable pull away from the laboratory, he accepted the editorship of the newly born *Journal of Bacteriology*, official organ of the Society of American Bacteriologists. We have taken this date as the coming to maturity of bacteriology in this country. For twenty-eight years, this journal continued to grow under his guiding hand. With a suitable successor available in the person of James M. Sherman of Cornell University, Winslow resigned one editorship and took over another even more to his liking, that of the *American Journal of Public Health*. This, too, he enriched in scope and flavor especially with his pungent editorials. Both his words and their substance stick in the mind.

Strictly speaking, Winslow's highest earned degree was a Master of Science in 1899 from the Massachusetts Institute of Technology; the degree of Doctor of Public Health was an honorary award, conferred upon him by New York University in 1918. The lack of higher degrees never seemed to trouble Winslow; he moved with assurance and success into any field that interested him. Even one who knew him from the days of the old Boston Bug Club is aghast upon reading his bibliography of some 574 items. Most of these are brief, such as committee statements, general articles of a more or less popular character, radio talks, book reviews, biographical sketches, and editorials; but many are extended studies, chapters in books, six or seven books by himself alone, especially noteworthy being the *Life of Hermann Biggs* and *The Conquest of Epidemic Disease*. His range of subject matter is also bewildering, from the bacteriology of the toothbrush to sex hygiene, tuberculosis among workers, a study of an outbreak of septic sore throat, important taxonomic studies, to the effect of putrefactive odors upon growth and resistance to disease, health surveys of communities, and the costs of medical care, both in this country and for the World Health Organization.

He was the urbane polished gentleman, but the zealot in issues he considered important. He was a master of our ancient mother tongue with a flare for the sharply cut phrase, whether on his feet in impromptu debate or writing at leisure in his study. The word leisure is improperly used; his brilliant mind was ever in action. Because he always had something to say and said it well, he was in demand as a public speaker: "His was the yeasty thought that rattled the skeleton of public bureaus . . . and roused the enthusiastic support of a generation of his colleagues."

One further contribution of inestimable value to many phases of microbiology which has been emphasized at Yale has been the cultivation of tissues in suitable media outside the body. Although several investigators had accomplished this earlier both in Europe and in this country, the method devised by Ross G. Harrison,[13] while still at the anatomy department of Johns Hopkins, was more useful and was developed further at Yale and later by Carrel at the Rockefeller Institute. This became the starting point of an unbelievable quantity and variety of studies, one phase of which has been the use of such cultures to support the growth of viruses, an excellent example of a new method devised in response to one need, providing a means for studies in many directions. Further examples, such as the microscope, the cyclotron, the ultracentrifuge, could fill a library.

CHAPTER X

The Great Metropolis and New York State

*Minerva has never had her chief temples in any
one country for more than a generation or two.*

REID'S *Great Physician*

The City That Was *and Its Rise in Public Health*

Our overwhelming metropolis New York City as well as the Empire
State has been active in all phases of bacteriology, but especially in
large-scale public health measures. In the first quarter of the nineteenth
century the city was relatively clean with favorable housing, gardens,
orchards, and no tenements, and, although the figures are not highly
trustworthy, a favorable death rate for the period, 25 per 1000. The
infant mortality rate was high by present standards, between 120–40
per 1000 live births. No extensive epidemics are recorded save for yellow
fever. Water was obtained from private wells and in part from a
private company that piped water through wooden conduits laid beneath the streets. Some families bought water from carts resembling a
modern street sprinkler at so much a bucketful. Outdoor privies were
the mode until the Croton water was introduced in 1842 when water
closets became possible.[1]

The black side of the picture came with the rapid overcrowding
brought by the industrial revolution, the tremendous influx of immigrants from famine-stricken Ireland (1845 potato famine), and the
social revolution of 1848 on the continent. With the incredible growth
of slums came the high morbidity and mortality rates. The standards of
living dropped; the cholera epidemics of 1832, 1834, and 1849 took
nearly 10,000 lives; by 1850 the infant mortality rate (probably the

best single index figure) had increased to 180 per 1000 live births. We have already mentioned the distressing conditions presented in the Griscom report on New York in 1845. Even more repulsive facts were uncovered by the crusading zeal of the Citizens Committee of 1865 with Stephen Smith as vigorous organizer and Elisha Harris as editor of the report. One should read the brief summary of this report written later (1911), *The City that Was* by Stephen Smith. The disgusting and epidemiologically dangerous facts, although the bacteriologic basis was not recognized at the time, compelled public attention resulting in the introduction of a bill to create a Metropolitan Board of Health. Unfortunately, this was defeated in the state legislature by the self-interest of the ward politician inspectors. Too much money would have been turned from their control. The political issue having been created, the occurrence of an opportune epidemic of cholera carried a similar bill through in 1866.

Four years later, however, the full-time politicians had regained control, and the board was discontinued. A New York City Board of Health was salvaged however, and it is chiefly the laboratory work under this board that we wish to follow. Charles V. Chapin, of Providence, in his voluminous report, *Municipal Sanitation in the United States*,[2] gives details of the organization and political vicissitudes of similar boards of health, with high praise for the pioneering practices of the New York City laboratories.

As in other areas in this country and in Europe, humanitarian motives and a sense of decency were strong elements in the campaigns. Incidentally, more space per individual and per family and improved food and water supplies with more adequate sewage disposal reduced the rapid exchange of pathogenic organisms, thus contributing to lower mortality rates. Private associations such as that for Improving the Condition of the Poor (1843) and the American Public Health Association (1872) took the initiative, and tax-supported organizations followed. Much of the overcrowding in New York was because it was the chief port of entry for the hordes of immigrants who came to our shores during the middle of the nineteenth century[3] seeking better living conditions. Many of them never got beyond the lower east side of New York. Whatever the conditions of their former homes, the "fever nests," the typhoid, typhus, dysentery, and tuberculosis rates as presented in the citizens report of 1865 showed appalling centers for the spread of infectious diseases.

Bacteriologists sometimes fail to give adequate credit to pathologists. Morgagni (1662–1771), father of pathology and author of the famous work *Sites and Causes of Disease,* and later Virchow and his followers began the overthrow of the doctrine that only one disease, fever, exists by demonstrating specific lesions in various diseases.

Although we quite properly think of William Welch and his associate, T. Mitchell Prudden, chiefly as pathologists, they were active in New York in their early days as proponents of the new approach to pathology, the specific microbic origin of infectious diseases. We have already given an all too brief account of Welch and his contributions in the Hopkins-Baltimore section. His colleague, Prudden, somewhat hesitantly gave up a life in general practice and accepted the minor opening at the College of Physicians and Surgeons to begin a career of influence in pathology and bacteriology. The first laboratory was a space with "a narrow store on one side and a harness shop on the other." Here and later in the new building on Fifty-ninth Street, Prudden worked and grew in wisdom. We, in the richly equipped laboratories of today, can with difficulty imagine the working conditions and the meager support provided in the latter part of the nineteenth century. The annual director's report usually ended with this statement: "on the basis of last year's returns, there is this year a deficit of $777.38 which, according to present arrangements, is very simply made up by a deduction of that amount from the salary of the Director [Dr. Prudden]."[4]

Prudden was a shy, sensitive man, an aristocrat in his personal habits, exemplifying the puritanical virtues and rarely unbending to his students; like Welch, he remained a bachelor. In his early days he did an immense amount of diagnostic and routine investigation. Among his students who later pursued bacteriology successfully, we should mention Hermann Biggs, Philip H. Hiss, William H. Park, George A. Soper, Augustus Wadsworth, and Hans Zinsser.

As did all but two or three of our early bacteriologists, Prudden commonly followed trails already blazed by European scientists. It was necessary to demonstrate and to persuade both himself and others that invisible microbes were the primary exciting agents in tuberculosis, diphtheria, typhoid fever, and other infectious diseases. Most of his published papers were on strictly pathological themes; his *Textbook of Pathology* (with Delafield) went through many editions from 1885 on, eleven under his own lucid mind. Dr. Prudden described himself as "a slave to teaching and to keeping the breath of life in a textbook in pathology for successive generations of students and practitioners of medicine."

Papers on the occurrence of the *Bacillus tuberculosis* in tuberculous lesions (1883), bacteria in ice and their relations to disease (1887), on the etiology of diphtheria (1889), experimental pneumonitis in the rabbit induced by the intratracheal injection of dead tubercle bacilli (1891) indicate not only his own continuing interests, but also the type of bacteriology that was going on both in New York and in other centers of this country. With his ready mind, Prudden also wrote a number of informative articles for the laity in such journals as the *Popular Science Monthly, American Review of Reviews*, and *Harper's Magazine*. One should not overlook his contributions to anthropology, arising from his well-ridden hobby, studies among the cliff dwellers of our Southwest.

The teaching of bacteriology at the College of Physicians and Surgeons was begun, as elsewhere, in a tentative fashion for a few students (1885). More systematically a course for graduates in medicine and other technically qualified workers was offered in Prudden's laboratory by T. M. Cheesman in 1887. The next year, the course for the regular medical students was designated "Course in Pathology and Bacteriology."[5]

HERMANN M. BIGGS

Another only slightly younger man, Hermann M. Biggs (1859–1923),[6] whom Welch described as his most eager student, was destined to play a larger part in the advance of bacteriology in this area. Following the granting of his medical degree (1883), Biggs spent a year as an intern and then two years studying medicine in Germany. Upon his return in 1885, he began as instructor in the new Carnegie Laboratory at Bellevue Medical College. Strangely enough, Biggs had had no instruction in bacteriology during this first period of European study in Germany, so he approached microbiologic problems that came his way without that aid. The lack of an adequate bacteriological text in English led him to translate Hueppe's *Methods of Bacteriological Investigation* published in 1886. An earlier American book (less satisfactory because of the date of its origin and the rapid growth of the science) had been available to our students through a translation of Magnin's *Les bactéries* by our self-taught bacteriology pioneer, George Sternberg.

Before Biggs had been a month in the new laboratory, only a year after Gaffky had isolated the causative agent of typhoid fever, a severe epidemic of this disease in Plymouth, Pennsylvania (with 1104 reported cases and 114 deaths, about the usual 10 per cent mortality rate of that period), gave Biggs the opportunity to try his epidemiologic and bacteriologic wings. With Professor A. A. Breneman he surveyed the epidemic area and the distribution of the cases, and made chemical analyses and gelatin plate studies of the different sources of the Plymouth water supply.[7] The water from the suspected Davis well yielded high bacterial counts and high ammonia, chlorine, and solid matter, thus confirming and amplifying the earlier investigations of H. L. Taylor, health officer of the neighboring city of Wilkesbarre, whose beautifully analytical report is one of the finest in epidemiological literature.[8] After critical examination and elimination of one hypothetical source after another, Taylor had found that high in the hills, in an isolated area, a single case of typhoid fever had occurred during the winter months. Stools passed at night had been thrown out on the ground and during the daytime into a shallow privy; these became frozen, but melting occurred with the sun of late March, polluting a surface stream that fed an upper emergency reservoir of the Plymouth water supply. Later in the month water was drawn from this reservoir and the epidemic began, continuing for weeks. The confirmatory evidence from all investigations was convincing. This was the first well-studied, large, water-borne epidemic of typhoid fever in this country, a shocking initiation for young Biggs with death and disaster to so many from one case of preventable disease. Highly interesting is the reaction of Biggs and Breneman, well-trained men of the period, to the mode of origin of the typhoid fever.

If it be possible for typhoid fever to originate *de novo* in filthy surroundings and in the use of polluted water, no more remote point may be looked for as the starting point of the disease which spread from a single patient in this house to hundreds in the village. Moreover the time for the departure of the patient for Philadelphia and his return with the disease was less than that required for its development. [December 24, 1884, to January 2, 1885, is a brief period but within the minimum limits of incubation of typhoid.] Everything points, therefore, to the conclusion that the disease that spread from this house also originated there.

That same year (1885) Pasteur had announced the success of his antirabies vaccine, and the press both lay and medical was full of praise as well as of sceptical condemnation. Biggs went to Paris and was at Pasteur's laboratory while some American children were being treated.

He was tremendously impressed by Pasteur and came back to this country a convert ready to inject others with his enthusiasm. We should bear in mind that Pasteur's dramatic success with anthrax vaccination at Pouilly-le-Fort had occurred just three years earlier, in 1882, and this was the same year that Koch cultivated the tubercle bacillus. Our philosophies of infectious disease were changing rapidly. Biggs wrote several articles supporting antirabies vaccination.

An epidemic of dysentery in the almshouse on Blackwell's Island investigated by Biggs in 1886–87 gave him another shock that affected his whole life, for it was an instance of gross laxity in a public institution. His report gives his findings as well as his own attitude of mind, that of an unusually well-informed physician of the period. He found that a series of dysentery cases had been occurring through three years with a total of seventy-two deaths. A casual inspection showed an uncleaned, unflushed toilet with the sewer outlet blocked and some two to three feet of semisolid fecal matter, not all of it inside the closet, in use by some eight hundred women. A thorough cleaning and disinfection brought about an immediate drop in the incidence of the disease. Biggs stated in his article describing the epidemic "that the dysentery was an infectious disease and under certain conditions, contagious; apparently, like typhoid fever, it was generally a miasmatic contagious disease propagated by the stools of dysentery patients."[9]

The same year (1887) Biggs also published the results of what was, we believe, the earliest application of bacteriology to the diagnosis of Asiatic cholera in this country. Cholera was present in Italy, and a boy from the ship *Britannia*, arriving from Naples and Marseilles, had died four days later with a diagnosis of *cholera morbus*. Organisms with the morphology and reactions of the cholera vibrio were isolated from the case independently by Biggs, Prudden, Kinyoun, and Weeks, a satisfying basis even for a sceptic. These observers stressed the impossibility of making a diagnosis in obscure cases by clinical means and the importance, therefore, of bacteriologic procedures. The violent cholera epidemics of 1892, especially that in Hamburg, contributed more cases to our ports; at one time the cholera fleet detained at the Quarantine Station consisted of seven vessels with some 76 deaths during the voyages, 44 among the immigrants, and 11 other cases in New York City. Papers by Biggs and E. K. Dunham, director of the Carnegie Laboratory who carried out the bacteriologic studies, tell the story in detail. Again the specific organism was isolated from most of the cases.

It is interesting to observe that neither petri dishes nor agar-agar had come into use at this time in this laboratory. The beneficent result of a shocking epidemic and resulting panic may once more be observed in the creation of a Division of Pathology, Bacteriology, and Disinfection in the New York City Department of Health with Hermann Biggs as chief inspector.

WILLIAM HALLOCK PARK

Meanwhile another young man, William H. Park (1863–1939), had enjoyed the course in pathology and bacteriology under Prudden, given at that time on an optional basis. After his internship and a year of study in Europe, largely clinical, he began to practice medicine, specializing in laryngology. This experience forced upon him the tragedy of the many deaths among children from diphtheria. In discussing the question with Prudden, who had been impressed in his studies with the importance of streptococci in some cases, Park stated that on the basis of work he had seen in Europe, true diphtheria was caused by the *Bacillus diphtheriae* of Klebs and Löffler. Prudden immediately asked Park if he would care, as a volunteer in his spare time, to study the bacteriology of diphtheria. His response was the beginning of two happy years spent in this work with Prudden. Then Park found himself ready to accept an appointment in the new laboratory of the City Health Department under Biggs to develop the diagnosis of diphtheria by microscopic examination of throat cultures on Löffler's blood serum.

In spite of the turmoil of New York politics, Biggs continued efficiently in the city board of health for more than twenty-five years. The important steps in the development of organized public health in New York City are well presented by Weinstein (1947). As early as 1912, diagnostic tests for both syphilis and gonorrhea were provided by the city laboratory under Biggs and from May 1, public institutions were required to report all cases of venereal disease as a confidential record. This was one of the early public attacks on the prevalent venereal diseases. In 1915, although not in robust health, Biggs became commissioner of health of the state of New York, a position that he held with distinction until his death in 1923. Early in his public life, he began to preach the control of tuberculosis by compulsory notification of the disease and by teaching the modes of spread to physicians, to patients, and to the public.

Park began his long and distinguished service in the laboratories of the New York City Board of Health on May 4, 1893, as bacteriological diagnostician and inspector of diphtheria and, when we think of that laboratory and the development of its public services, we think at once of Park and his able associates, especially Anna Williams and Charles Krumwiede, as well as a host of others. The diagnostic work in this laboratory was begun the previous year in the studies under the threat of Asiatic cholera. This is commonly spoken of as the first municipal public health laboratory, although Gorham in his delightful chapter on the history of bacteriology in the *Jubilee Volume* of the American Public Health Association credits Charles V. Chapin and Gardner Swarts with the establishment of the first municipal laboratory in this country. In Providence (1888) this small initial effort was devoted chiefly to the study of water supplies and filters but later was developed the general diagnostic work of a public health laboratory. The New York City laboratory has certainly been our accepted model both for public service and for research.

Following Löffler's successful cultivation of the diphtheria bacillus in 1884 and the more detailed studies of Roux and Yersin (1888) with their demonstration that these organisms produce a specific soluble toxin, the causal relation between the bacteria and the disease diphtheria became established. But questions still remained. Observers in all countries reported pseudomembranes without diphtheria bacilli, bacilli persisting days or weeks after the disappearance of the membrane, persons never sick with the disease carrying the organisms in their throats, and at times organisms resembling *Bacillus diphtheriae* morphologically that produced little or no reaction in susceptible guinea pigs. Only a year after Park began his studies at the city laboratory, he, with A. L. Beebe, reported throat culture findings from 5611 cases of suspected diphtheria, the largest series extant. They established the culture method as an invaluable aid in diagnosis and also the importance of convalescent and well carriers in the spread of the disease. They examined 2566 cultures from throats of convalescent cases of diphtheria to determine the duration of survival of the bacilli. Completed observations in 605 consecutive recovered cases showed a great variation in this persistence; in 304 the organisms were not cultivable three days after complete disappearance of the exudate; in the other 301 cases the organisms remained in the throat for varying periods, 176 cases for seven days, 64 cases for twelve days, 35 cases for fifteen days, 12 cases for twenty-one days, 4 cases for twenty-eight days, and 2 cases for nine weeks. What is the significance of such findings?

The literature contains examples of not a few small epidemics of diphtheria arising apparently from contact with a healthy nurse or other well carrier; for example, the cases reported by Escherich (1893) and a similar outbreak involving seven children reported by Freer (1894). Park and Beebe stated that they had met many similar examples. Accordingly they took throat cultures from healthy children in fourteen families, in which one or more of the other members had diphtheria, or forty-eight children in all. In 50 per cent of these, diphtheria bacilli were found, and 40 per cent later developed lesions of diphtheria. In these families, the conditions for transfer of organisms were excellent; in numerous instances, in families where the case was isolated, diphtheria bacilli were found in less than 10 per cent of the contact children.[10]

I stress this report because of its detailed excellence in the study of well carriers, not the first, but the best of many in the diphtheria literature. The broad conception of the carrier, temporary or chronic, the latent, subclinical, or missed case is probably the most important change in our understanding of sources and modes of infection since the demonstrations in the 1880's of specific pathogenic bacteria. I have been unable to determine to my satisfaction who first presented this idea. Ledingham and Arkwright in their informative book *Carrier Problem in Infectious Diseases*[11] mention Sternberg's isolation of a virulent pneumococcus from his own saliva (1880), but a causal relation with pneumonia was not recognized at that time. They and most writers give chief credit to Koch for emphasizing the vibrio carriers in his cholera studies of 1893, to Park and Beebe for their diphtheria investigations of 1894, and again to Koch and his associates (1902–3) in insisting on the epidemiological importance of carriers in the enteric fever epidemics around Trier, Germany.

Soper's highly dramatic series of ten known outbreaks of typhoid with fifty-one cases arising from one cook-carrier over a period of almost two decades captured both the public and the professional eye, partly because of the nickname "Typhoid Mary" attached to the carrier, and partly because of the violent legal controversy that arose over the right of the state to restrain Mary Mallon permanently after she broke her parole a second time, promising never to serve as a cook. On this occasion she wound up under another name, spreading her fruitful typhosus seed among nurses and patients in one of our best hospitals, the Sloane Maternity of New York, with the result of twenty-five cases. Justifiably, the court sustained the action of the board of health.

We need more spectacular nicknames like "Typhoid Mary" and "Pertussis Pete" to catch the ear and we must have controversy to waken us out of our smug complacency. The degree to which we swap intestinal organisms even in our wealthy, well-sewered country is realized only when someone like Mary Mallon becomes the cook for several families. Someone, I believe it was Milton Rosenau, after he had studied the typhoid-carrier rate in Washington, D. C., suggested that we would all outshine Joseph's coat of many colors if only the bacteria we exchange daily produced different dyes. "It pays to know one's cook." [12]

> *We may live without friends; we may live without books;*
> *But civilized man, cannot live without cooks.*
>
> OWEN MEREDITH's *Lucille*

Park's potent influence in increasing the control of diphtheria continued throughout his life. With the development of serum therapy chiefly by Behring in 1890–94, (first human case treated on Christmas Day, 1891) and Biggs' enthusiastic conviction that a new era was dawning, Park began the tedious immunization of horses for the production of antitoxin. The *New York Herald* ran a popular subscription for funds to provide free antitoxin for treatment of the poor. Published letters like the following opened larger purses: "Please accept $1.00 for your antitoxin fund from a father who lost a dear boy, five years old, and his golden-haired baby girl, two years old, inside of one week, from the dreadful diphtheria." The use of special gift funds and unused balances became a common procedure with Park when he wished to introduce a novel service. After the new practice had proved itself and had won the approval of physicians and the people, he would ask for and receive public financial support for the project.

The concentration of antibodies from horse serum (Gibson, Banzhaf, and others),[13] the broad use of the Schick test for diagnosis, and later the vaccination with T-AT and diphtheria toxoid, by Park and Zingher, followed in due course as these methods were developed. In 1933, when the millionth child of New York City was successfully vaccinated against diphtheria, Dr. Park was honored at a large public gathering.With characteristic humility, as well as accuracy, he stated, "I have done nothing alone."

Another outstanding public health achievement of Dr. Park was clean milk for the great city. With the pediatrician, Luther Emmett Holt (1902–3 *et seq.*), he showed the role of high bacterial content in milk in causing infantile diarrheas and so prodded the public conscience that New York City did finally obtain a relatively clean supply of pasteurized milk. As always, many persons contributed to the desired end; during Lederle's second term as commissioner of health, 1910–14, compulsory pasteurization was finally introduced.

In striving to paint the broad picture of early bacteriology in this country, I must necessarily omit detailed studies such as those that Park and all lesser bacteriologists have contributed to the whole. Many of these are important in our knowledge of individual species of microorganisms and their functions in nature or in disease, but are of little value from the point of view of the broad development of the science or its impact on the history of our country. One feels apologetic concerning these omissions, as this type of filling in is all that most persons, even those of considerable note, succeed in doing. One hopes that a simple salutation "well done, good and faithful servant" may be earned.

In addition to the long list of younger associates in the city laboratories for whom Park was both leader and warm personal friend, he taught generations of medical students in the Bellevue Medical School and in the later years held there the Biggs professorship of preventive medicine. In many editions, with different associates, he wrote one of the most influential texts on *Pathogenic Microorganisms*. It was begun in 1899 with Guerrard and continued under Park and Williams, and Park, Williams, and Krumwiede; the eleventh and last edition (1939) was carried to completion by Park shortly before his death; the preface to that edition is a gem of bacteriologic history and gives credit to the many who gave him special aid. So many laboratory methods have been developed and improved at the City Laboratory and so many persons have contributed that further mention of names seems invidious. The translation of Ehrlich's important *Studies in Immunity* by one of Park's colleagues, Charles Bolduan (1906), was a distinct service to the many bacteriologists in this country who read German only with difficulty.[14]

Park was a warm-hearted, kindly, helpful, modest man of integrity and sound judgment, who through the New York example provided a model for other public health laboratories. A bit from an obituary sketch by Hans Zinsser is so characteristic of both men that it deserves repeating. "When a man like William H. Park dies, something is irretrievably lost which far transcends the contributions which he might still have made to his science. There is built up, in the course of the lives of men of this kind, an accumulated judgment, a penetration and a view of professional standards which together constitute a personality unique and entirely individual."

By the 1890's the doctrine that specific microorganisms are the causative agents in infectious diseases had become widely accepted. The importance of public control of these diseases to preserve our greatest asset, the health of the citizens, was increasingly recognized, although the battle was long and still continues.

Columbia University

PHILIP HANSON HISS, JR., AND HANS ZINSSER

Following Prudden in bacteriologic interest at Columbia College of Physicians and Surgeons, comes Philip Hanson Hiss, Jr. (1868–1913) who, beginning as assistant in 1895, was advanced to full professorship in 1906 when bacteriology was given departmental status. As was true with most bacteriologists at this time, Hiss was busy with methods of differentiating morphologically similar organisms, especially pathogens, from their associated nonpathogens. He developed one of the early methods for separating typhosus bacilli from *Escherichia coli* by using a semisolid gelatine-agar medium plus glucose. Gas formation by *E. coli* and fuzzy threading colonies by the more motile *Bacillus typhosus* were the tests for separation. For the streptococci and pneumococci he developed a medium still in use, the Hiss serum water plus the polysaccharide inulin, which is fermented by most pneumococci, but not by streptococci. He tried leucocytic extracts in the treatment of pneumonia and erysipelas without marked success. A variety of *B. paradysenteriae* bears the names of Hiss and Russell.[15]

Hiss was fortunate in having as his younger associate Hans Zinsser (1878–1940), one of the few to whom I can happily apply the adjective brilliant. Together, they published one of our much appreciated texts in medical bacteriology (first edition, 1910) that was ably continued under Zinsser and later by other competent authors. Born in New York

City of prosperous German-American parents, Zinsser, with both A.B. and M.D. from Columbia, held the chair of bacteriology successively in three medical schools; at Leland Stanford, 1910–13, Columbia, 1913–23, and Harvard, 1923–40. He was a student of infectious diseases on four continents, both in the laboratory and in the field. He was in Stanford only briefly; we must bless his inadequate laboratory facilities there, because that lack provided him with time to write a large part of his important *Infection and Resistance*, rich in the immunology of the German and French literature. Zinsser was always greatly aided by his fluency in three languages.

Although much of his active life extends beyond our period, his early death from lymphatic leukemia and his wide stimulating influence lead me to ignore the confining influence of dates. Of his more than 170 scientific papers, many with colleagues, his most noteworthy dealt with rickettsial diseases, especially typhus fever, whose biography he has told in arresting fashion in *Rats, Lice and History*. "And God was on everyone's side. And when we had all gone to war and the stage was set, typhus woke up again. Not everyone realizes that typhus has at least as just a reason to claim that 'it won the war' as any of the contending nations." Cultivation of the rickettsia, methods of injecting the lice, transfer of the infection, and preparation of vaccines all responded to his zeal, although most of his methods are now outmoded. His work on what he called residue antigens led him early to a generalization emphasizing the antigenic significance of the nonprotein constituents of bacteria, now recognized as so important through the investigations of Avery and his colleagues. The unitarian theory of the nature of antibodies, the relative size of viruses, and the characterization of bacterial allergy were illuminated by Zinsser's studies and those of his associates.

Personally he was gay, dynamic, voluble, a lover of horses and of music, an exponent of good living and keen thinking, much enjoyed by his friends and loved and admired by his intimates. He describes himself as "one of the persons on whom all controversial questions of his time acted like horseflies on a half-broken mule." Zinsser enjoyed a good tale, especially if it was a bit Rabelaisian, and he loved a practical joke. I place him on Mount Olympus, at the top of the second generation of American bacteriologists. He was honored everywhere, by membership in societies both foreign and domestic, by the presidency of several, by honorary degrees, and by exchange professorships, in France, 1935, and in China, 1939. "Student, philosopher, scientist, organizer and executive, poet, friend and companion." Who else has written two such outstanding texts? Who else has written such a gripping history of a world pestilence, lousiness, typhus fever, and in a different vein, such a dramatic, lively autobiography? Who else has contributed so brilliantly to scientific meetings, to scientific writings as well as to the humanities, and to the upbuilding of three departments of bacteriology? And who else has shown a more gallant spirit when slow but certain death bore down upon him?

> Now is death merciful. He calls me hence
> Gently, with friendly soothing of my fears
> Of ugly age and feeble impotence
> And cruel disintegration of slow years.
> Nor does he leap upon me unaware
> Like some wild beast that hungers for its prey,
> But gives me timely warning to prepare,
> Before I go, to kiss your tears away.
> How sweet the summer! And the autumn shown
> Late warmth within our hearts as in the sky,
> Ripening rich harvest that our love had sown.
> How good that 'ere the winter comes, I die!
> Then ageless, in your heart I'll come to rest
> Serene and proud, as when you loved me best.[16]

Another prominent member of the Columbia medical faculty was dignified Christian A. Herter, professor of pharmacology and therapeutics. Departmental barriers were low. From the early days of the century, he and his associates made extensive studies on the bacterial flora of the digestive tract. He showed a high realization of many of the biologic symbioses and antagonisms. A multitude of similar but commonly less complete studies had been published before and have been made since, chiefly in Germany and France. In this country those by Welch and his associates at Hopkins, Rettger at Yale, and as always those by the searching mind and hand of Theobald Smith are noteworthy. Pasteur had raised the question of possible desirable values to the individual from the rich alimentary fauna and flora, and Metchnikoff suggested that we might all live a hundred years by ingesting acid-producing lactobacilli to cut down putrefactive organisms. Herter *et alia* studied the infections of the tract and the chemical products of putrefaction, such as indols, skatols, and sulphur compounds, and the various organic acids and gases from fermentation of carbohydrates. He cultivated the anaerobes more thoroughly than many observers who have frequently neglected these organisms because of technical difficulties. He made no effort to study the fungi, protozoa, or helminths, and this was before the day of vitamins and sulfa drugs. Herter's investigations gave us a favorable start, but the greater understanding of this entire field is still a major problem that must be attacked by a group of persons of widely varied training.[17] Herter will be remembered especially as the founder of the *Journal of Biological Chemistry* and as an important early member of the first Board of Scientific Directors of the Rockefeller Institute.

Brooklyn

New York's sister city, Brooklyn, became an integral part of Greater New York in 1898, but even before that date many of the activities of the two cities, including bacteriology, were closely linked. The Hoagland Laboratory that has aided in the development of the basic sciences of medicine in Brooklyn should have special comment.[18] In 1884, of the 385 recorded deaths from diphtheria in Brooklyn, one was that of an eight-year-old boy, Freddie Tangeman. His devoted grandfather Cornelius N. Hoagland, a retired physician, who had become wealthy as part owner of the Royal Baking Powder Company, was so deeply affected that he resolved to build a laboratory devoted primarily to research and instruction in bacteriology. The building was completed in 1888 and Dr. George M. Sternberg, although remaining in the army, was induced to be the part-time director. The building at different times served several departments of the Brooklyn Medical School and before the union of the two cities housed the laboratories of the Board of Health. Ezra Wilson was chief, and urged on by the interest of the founder in diphtheria, he produced the specific antitoxin in horses as early as 1895. Bacteriologists are more interested, however, in the opportunities this laboratory gave to two men, Benjamin White and Oswald T. Avery, who later added greatly to our knowledge of pneumococci.

The Rockefeller Institute for Medical Research

SIMON FLEXNER, HIDEYO NOGUCHI, PEYTON ROUS, OSWALD T. AVERY

As the faculties of our universities and colleges, with conspicuous exceptions, paid little attention to the advancement of knowledge until after Johns Hopkins University led the way, another type of institution with special emphasis on research came into being. The first of these, the Smithsonian Institution, was bequeathed to the United States in 1829 by an English scientist, James Smithson, for the increase and diffusion of knowledge among men. Owing to legal and political difficulties this institute was not chartered by Congress until 1846, with Joseph Henry, distinguished physicist, as the first and highly efficient secretary. In Paris, the Pasteur Institute was founded in 1888, the original of a large number scattered throughout the world, the early aims of which were the production and scientific control of antirabies vaccine and of other vaccines and of antisera. Broader objectives for investigation and advanced instruction were gradually added. Similarly, the Koch Institute was founded in Berlin in 1891 and the same year the Lister Institute in London. In this country in 1901, through the generous philanthropy of John D. Rockefeller, Sr., and the vision of his adviser, Frederick T. Gates, the Rockefeller Institute for Medical Research was founded for the "good of humanity." After establishing some grants-in-aid, they rented a building, and in 1906 opened the first laboratory building, now known as Founder's Hall.

Simon Flexner (1863–1946), first director of the Institute in its formative period from 1902 and until his retirement in 1935, was born into a first generation Jewish family in Kentucky, poor in this world's goods, but rich in ideals, family solidarity, and the drive to get ahead, especially in the learned professions. The older members of the family consistently helped the younger ones to obtain higher education. With this background, Flexner became a clerk in an apothecary's shop and later carried the additional load as a student in the Louisville Medical School. The entire instruction consisted of four months of lectures, repeated through a second year "lest the wisdom imparted should exceed the student's power of retention" as Flexner later put it. Graduation, all but automatic, followed in 1889, but Flexner had a strong urge for a career in medical science with little desire for the life of a medical practitioner. In 1891, two years after the opening of the Johns Hopkins Hospital and two years before the admission of the first class in medicine, he went to Baltimore to learn pathology under William Welch. He remained there through eight years of rapid growth, first as he put it "as a sort of understudy to Councilman." Later (1892) when Councilman became professor of pathology at Harvard, Flexner was appointed his successor, as professor of pathological anatomy.

Flexner's experience at Hopkins was broad, resulting in a stream of papers; his contributions in infectious diseases included reports of anatomical lesions in tuberculosis, typhoid fever, the pneumonias, and less common diseases. With Welch he studied diphtheria, demonstrating that the microscopic lesions in experimental animals were similar to those in man. In a critical examination of the pathological changes caused by certain so-called toxalbumins, he described hypersensitivity eight years (1894) before the classic studies of Richet and Portier (1902). Animals (rabbits) that had withstood one dose of dog serum would succumb to a second dose given after a lapse of days or weeks, even when this dose was sublethal for a control animal. But dog serum is toxic for rabbits, causing hemolysis, and he was interested in the resulting tissue changes and did not appreciate the broader implications of his observations. These studies did, however, lead to his later investigations of snake venom carried out at Pennsylvania with Noguchi.

He shared with L. F. Barker and several younger men, including F. P. Gay, a Johns Hopkins Hospital expedition to investigate prevalent diseases in the Philippines among our troops stationed there after the capture of the islands in the Spanish-American War. One of the results of this expedition was the discovery by Flexner of a dysentery bacillus which he considered identical with the organism described earlier by Shiga and by Kruse. Subsequently Martini and Lentz (1902) differentiated this and similar organisms such as those described by Hiss and Russell and by Strong from the Shiga bacillus by exacting agglutination procedures and by the use of mannitol as a substrate for fermentation. Todd (1903–4) showed that only the Shiga organisms produce a soluble exotoxin. The Shiga dysentery bacillus is then quite a different organism, and the so-called Flexner bacillus and closely related organisms are more properly designated *Shigella paradysenteriae*.

Shortly after he had accepted the chair of pathology at the University of Pennsylvania, Flexner had another spectacular opportunity. A diagnosis of bubonic plague (1900) had been made by Kinyoun of the United States Public Health Service in some cases of disease among the Chinese residents of San Francisco. Such a storm of denial and protest arose (this episode will be considered in greater detail in the California chapter) that it became necessary to appoint a committee of recognized authorities to determine the truth or falsity of the conflicting statements. Accordingly, Flexner for pathology, F. G. Novy for bacteriology, and L. F. Barker for clinical medicine were named. They found six undoubted cases of the plague, which were confirmed by the various methods of study.

Although Flexner regarded himself chiefly as a pathologist, as did all the early workers in bacteriology coming through similar training, yet his interests were largely in infectious diseases, so that by far the larger number of his contributions and those of his younger associates at the Institute, properly come under scrutiny for this chronicle.

An epidemic of meningococcal meningitis hit New York in 1904 and 1905 with death losses of approximately three of four of those attacked. After establishing that subdural injections of his potent antiserum gave some control over the experimental disease in monkeys, Flexner advised physicians to treat human cases similarly. In 1913, analyses of about 1300 widely distributed cases treated with specific antiserum produced at the Institute showed that the mortality figures were reversed with about 70 per cent recovery and fewer sequelae. If the serum was administered during the first three days of the disease, the recovery rate was increased to 82 per cent. The antiserum remained the preferred method of treatment for about three decades until penicillin and the sulfa drugs became available.

Many investigators in this and other countries contributed to our knowledge of epidemic meningitis, its mode of spread and the importance of the nasopharyngeal carrier state. As to its serum therapy, our British bacteriologic mentors Topley and Wilson agree that, although this was first introduced by Jochman in Germany (1906), it was Flexner and Flexner and Jobling in the United States who were mainly responsible for its development and for the early assessment of its results.

Epidemic poliomyelitis was the next major disease attacked by Flexner with Paul A. Lewis, and later with other associates, Clark, Amoss, and Noguchi in the laboratory, and Peabody, Draper, and Dochez in the hospital. The ease with which the disease could be produced in rhesus monkeys by dropping the virus into the nose and the finding of the virus in nasal washings from a normal person in contact with a case suggested the importance of carriers in this disease. These observations led the Rockefeller group to stress the olfactory nerves as a probable portal of entry. The importance of this route of infection was disproved later by post-mortem studies in man, by demonstration of an early viremia, and by finding the virus in large quantities in the

stools of human cases. The "globoid bodies" in this disease will be discussed in our account of Noguchi who did the major share of that work.

Opie, his life-long associate, said: "Dr. Flexner's greatest contribution to American medical science was the organization and administration of the Rockefeller Institute for Medical Research, but the background of this accomplishment was his own development as pathologist
and investigator." His several hundred papers in many phases of the
medical sciences attest both the quantity and quality of this background.
The breadth of Flexner's philosophy is well presented in the following
quotation from an address to the graduating class at Cornell Medical
School in 1933, two years before his retirement:

There are no closed compartments in nature into which man, animals, and plants can
be separately placed. All are related organically and, as we may say, united physiologi-
cally and pathologically. No essential biological division exists between man and the
lower animals and plants, whether in respect to health or to disease. If, therefore, we
would learn, and through learning grow more powerful and effective to prevent and to
cure disease, to lengthen life and to increase happiness through security in all its varied
forms, then we should endeavor to advance in biological knowledge, which alone can
free us still further from the evils of disease.[19]

Flexner was a severe critic and taskmaster of himself as well as his
associates and a stickler for controls and nicety of experimental procedures. He wrote readily and with pen and ink even relatively unimportant directions or a preliminary draft of a paper. Several times he
stated to me that he thought that harsh methods would get the most out
of a man and were best for his development. He said that Chiari had
done that for him and he wanted to aid his assistants similarly. He was
extremely deferential towards those he regarded as his superiors whatever the field. With his varied background, he could tell of his experiences with a pleasing directness, could be as disarmingly charming on
occasion as sharply critical at other times. In his approach to his associates, he was quite formal but, in his own home, always an appreciative
host. He did not, I think, enjoy these formal necessities of his position;
Mrs. Flexner was especially gracious on such occasions. He was vitally
interested in the growth of his younger colleagues. He gave them repeated opportunities even following failures, especially those due to
ignorance, and always he worked for their advancement. A stream of
men came into the Institute; a few, especially adapted to investigation
and its rather restricted life, were retained while many were sent forth
preferably to positions of leadership with the hope that they would

maintain high ideals of productive scholarship. A few failed, always a bitter disappointment to "S. F."

His honors, public interests, and duties on committees were many; he was the capable, persuasive champion of animal experimentation, so frequently under fire in New York State. His last major work, following retirement, was the biography *William Henry Welch and the Heroic Age of Medicine*, written in association with his son James Thomas Flexner. That difficult task was admirably handled. He realized how much Dr. Welch had done for him personally and was profoundly grateful, and he knew through intimate contact the tremendous influence of Welch in that heroic age of medicine in our country, but he realized also the importance of contrast in any picture. Along with the extraordinary and praiseworthy qualities of Welch, were weaknesses, follies, and foibles. These also were depicted, creating a living picture, not of a demigod, but of a truly great man.

One is overwhelmed by the published "Studies" from the Rockefeller Institute even in this early period of its growth. Most of these are, however, contributions not to microbiology, but to other underlying medical sciences. I shall try to select the more significant ones in our own field.

Of the first members of the Institute staff, Eugene L. Opie was an outstanding figure, and his long, fruitful life extends well beyond our period and to areas other than New York. While still an undergraduate at the Johns Hopkins Medical School, he made major contributions to our knowledge of diseases of the pancreas, demonstrating especially that severe injury to the islands of Langerhans is associated with diabetes. This opened a path that later led to the discovery of insulin by Banting and Best. His studies on hematozoa of birds with MacCallum have already been mentioned. Opie became one of our leading pathologists holding that chair from 1910 on, in Washington University at St. Louis, the University of Pennsylvania, and Cornell Medical School, and he contributed over a hundred papers, full of import. After official retirement, he returned to the Rockefeller Institute where he is continuing his productive life well beyond four-score years.

Before he left for St. Louis, he had begun important studies in tuberculosis, a disease that occupied much of his attention for decades, and is a basis for claiming some of his laurels for bacteriology. These early investigations in tuberculosis seem to have followed from his experience with the pancreatic ferments. From two different types of cells in tuberculous and other inflammatory processes he found two different enzymes, leucoprotease similar to trypsin from the polymorphonuclear leucocytes and from the large mononuclear elements, a lymphoprotease, similar to pepsin.

The reorganization of the medical school of Washington University, World War I, and exacting studies on the pneumonias in the 1918–19 influenza epidemic left Opie little time for research on tuberculosis. With his change of base to the University of Pennsylvania, including with his professorship also the directorship of the Henry Phipps Institute for Tuberculosis, came renewed opportunity for investigations in this major disease. Looking beyond our time limits, I must, because of their importance and frequent neglect even today, emphasize Opie's epidemiological studies (with F. M. McPhedran) linking cases with the type and location of the lesions and tracing the spread of tuberculosis in families with its slow transmission from one generation to the next. Opie's distinction between primary and secondary infection lesions, especially in focal pulmonary tuberculosis of children and adults, was convincing to many. His later studies with J. D. Aronson emphasized that a positive intradermal tuberculin test provides in well persons an indication of specific resistance. One would like to follow these carefully built-up investigations to the end for there is still conflict over the relative significance of endogenous and exogenous infection in tuberculosis.

In the special number of the *Archives of Pathology* honoring Dr. Opie, the initial paper, an appreciation of the master by a master, is a wonderfully stimulating survey of his life-work. And such an addiction to painstaking laborious work he did have, with a multitude of carefully studied autopsies, but always he kept his eye on the distant goal. Although practically everything Opie has touched has turned to gold, he has remained modest and kindly with a warm sympathy towards his associates both new and old.

Among Flexner's other associates, Peyton Rous opened a new path for the study of tumors. He studied in detail the first known (1910) transplantable neoplasm of birds—a sarcoma of chickens shown to be caused by a filterable agent.[20] This field continues to extend, now including a number of mammalian tumors such as the Shope rabbit papilloma. These studies also led Rous and his associate, James B. Murphy, to a clearer understanding of the function of the lymphocyte in resistance not only to growth of heteroplastic tumors, but also of the tubercle bacillus and other bacteria. Murphy's gradual build-up of the importance of the lymphocyte is especially worthy of praise.

We have commented earlier on the highly important work of Ross Harrison at Hopkins and later at Yale in growing frog tissues in frog lymph outside of the body. In 1910 Montrose T. Burrows (of Alexis Carrel's staff at the Institute) working with Ross Harrison at Yale broadened the technique by growing frog tissues in blood plasma of the adult frog and chick embryo tissues in chicken blood plasma. Carrel and Burrows[21] developed this technique further and applied it not only to the cultivation of adult tissues and organs outside of the body, but also to the Rous fowl sarcoma, caused by a filterable virus. The many viruses gave us a new specialty and tissue culture provided a method for in vitro cultivation of these organisms. The success in growing poliomyelitis virus, resulting in the development of a highly successful vaccine, and the important studies of the genetics of the bacteriophage viruses are but two examples of the widespread usefulness of this new method. This is another example of what one sees so frequently, a method developed for one purpose later applied successfully in widely differing areas.

In 1910 the clinical facilities of the Institute were greatly increased by the opening of the Rockefeller Hospital endowed for the study of selected diseases with no support from patients' fees. Rufus Cole, trained at Hopkins as Flexner had been, was chosen director. He made an especially wise choice of one of the diseases to be studied, the pneumonias and the pneumococci, and his choice of younger associates was possibly even wiser.

Among the scores of researches on the pneumococci from the Institute in this period one should stress the serum studies of A. R. Dochez and O. T. Avery and the beginning paper of Dochez and L. J. Gillespie.[22] In this study, they followed a lead given by Neufeld (1902) who demonstrated specifically different types of pneumococci by the agglutination reaction and by the swelling of the pneumococcal capsules. They distinguished three types, I, II, and III, and a heterogeneous group, IV. This was the beginning of the differentiation of many types of pneumococci, each producing a specific soluble substance. The treatment of cases with the antiserum produced in horses (later in rabbits) against the specific soluble substance of the infecting type was the successfully used procedure until the advent of chemotherapy and antibiotic therapy.

In the 1880's and 1890's many variations in bacterial and colonial morphology were described; in fact, sharp controversy arose between men such as Cohn and Koch, who held a monomorphic theory, and other observers, who saw in these variations only phenomena similar to those in higher plants and animals. The causes for these changes have only gradually come to light and are still only partially understood. We have already described the studies of Smith and Reagh, who found the basis of certain rough and smooth variations in some enteric organisms. The broad, far from clear term, microbic dissociation has been used and presented in detail by Philip B. Hadley.

Among the pneumococci, changes in morphology, growth characters, and virulence were well described by Kruse and Pausini as early as 1891. Indeed they tied capsule formation to virulence. Many investigators, especially Avery and his associates at the Rockefeller Institute, have added results so striking that we may be pardoned for looking over the fence beyond our period. Bacterial genetics, mutations, transmissible lysis all come into the confused picture that is gradually becoming less confused. Griffith,[23] of the British Ministry of Health, made the next startling observation, finding that mice injected with a small amount of living rough unencapsulated organisms of Type I, for example, together with a large inoculum of heat-killed Type II smooth encapsulated cells, frequently succumbed to infection, and from the heart's blood of these animals, pure cultures of Type II were obtained. Many doubted this transformation thinking that it must be an error in technique, but it was soon confirmed both abroad and in this country. A still more startling step came later when Avery, MacLeod, and McCarty isolated the transforming substance of pneumococcus Type III, a highly polymerized deoxyribonucleic acid.

Oswald T. Avery (1877–1955), leading man in these dramatic discoveries, was warmly admired and loved by his many colleagues. He was a small man physically, never robust, with a large head and a delightfully modest, shy manner, not altered by the world fame that came to him, yet conscious of the importance of the work and its broad implications. He never married. His distinguished researches into the structure and serology of pneumococci and the fostering of immunochemistry, especially with his colleagues Michael Heidelberger and W. F. Goebel, brought high honors. He held the presidency in all the societies allied to his studies; he was an honored member of the Royal Society and of our own National Academy of Sciences; he was a member of many national committees and the recipient of many medals and honorary degrees. With it all, he remained the wise but humble investigator carrying on his fruitful studies five years after he was officially numbered with the emeriti.[24]

Of other bacteriologic contributions of note, several must be mentioned. In the conflict over the enigma of anaphylactic shock, John Auer and Paul A. Lewis[25] gave the first adequate anatomical explanation of the sudden death in guinea pigs. They proved by exacting histological and physiological studies that in these animals death is due to the tetanic contraction of the smooth muscle in the bronchioles.

Martha Wollstein added appreciably to our knowledge of the etiology of mumps by transmitting the disease in series through cats. She inoculated filtered bacteria-free saliva from acute cases into the parotid glands and testes of the experimental animals, producing characteristic lesions, temperature, and blood changes. The saliva of man and both the saliva and inoculated glands of the cats contained the filterable agent. The virus was found in the blood of patients showing marked constitutional symptoms. The serum from recovered cats contained immune bodies that diminished or neutralized the action of the virus. A more complete demonstration awaited the use of monkeys, the new method of cultivation in embryonated hens' eggs, and transfer back into susceptible persons.[26]

HIDEYO NOGUCHI

Of the microbiologists at the Rockefeller Institute, Hideyo Noguchi (1876–1928)[27] stands out as the most dramatic and controversial of our period. He became a world figure, a skyrocket that soared high and later fell sadly to earth. Born of the poorest of illiterate parents in northern Japan, after some meager training, at the age of twenty-three years, he descended out of the blue on Simon Flexner, professor of pathology at the University of Pennsylvania. Wreathed in smiles and laden with gifts, he was overcome with chagrin to find that a letter to the professor did not provide a definite position for him in this foreign land.

As usual in Noguchi's history, a friend came to the rescue, in this case S. Weir Mitchell, the prominent Philadelphia neurologist and novelist, who years before (1860 *et seq.*) had found that snake venoms were complex proteins. Since most proteins are antigenic, Mitchell agreed to support Noguchi in investigating venoms by the new immunologic methods. And so Noguchi's scientific life began in a busy laboratory with introduction to American ways provided by his colleagues, especially Charles Henry Bunting and John Lawrence Yates, who were working under Flexner. Noguchi beamed when Yates termed him the "yellow peril"; he enjoyed stumbling through limericks; he entered the seventh heaven when he was made, with appropriate ceremonies at a nearby tavern, a charter member of the "Society for the Liberation of Captive Balloons." He liberated his full share. He was sensitive, naive, generous to a fault, save where his honors were concerned, a spendthrift in time, money, and energy, a man of extraordinary drive and industry. All those who were privileged to work with or near him became fond of him; we appreciated his childlike simplicity, directness, and the fire-ball intensity of his purpose, and forgave his foibles and weaknesses. He did so desire to be "Hideyo" (great-man-of-the-world), his adopted name.

Noguchi's work with Flexner on snake venoms was a well-organized study extending over a number of years and culminating in a distinguished monograph published by the Carnegie Institution of Washington (1909). A detailed description of hemolysis produced by venoms and a knowledge of the specific damage to the endothelium of blood vessels, resulting in edema and hemorrhage, were the significant contributions. Calmette, pre-eminent in this field, in his monograph (1907) expressed appreciation of the work of Flexner and Noguchi, but he gave credit to Henry Sewall, then at the University of Michigan, for the earliest (1887) preventive inoculation against snake venoms, following repeated inoculation of sublethal doses of rattlesnake venom into pigeons. On the basis of his venom studies, Noguchi received a grant from the Carnegie Institution to work a year with Madsen in Copenhagen. There he learned much, especially quantitative methods, and with Madsen produced in goats an antivenin against rattlesnake venom.

The discovery of *Treponema pallidum* as the causative agent of syphilis by Schaudinn (1905) and Wassermann's application of Bordet's complement fixation reaction to the diagnosis of this disease (1906) led many, including Noguchi, into detailed serological studies. These in turn increased his interest in spirochaetes, and shortly he was attempting to cultivate these organisms from every source. Soon he reported the cultivation of virulent *T. pallidum* with production of specific skin lesions and positive Wassermann reactions in monkeys and chimpanzees following the injection of his cultivated organisms.

Others have been unable to duplicate these results. Later, Noguchi produced an excellent monograph on spirochaetes beautifully illustrated with many photographs and his own drawings. In the eyes of many, his greatest achievement was the demonstration of *T. pallidum* in brain tissues from cases of general paresis and *tabes dorsalis* thus settling the long controversy over the etiology of these diseases.

Possibly I should close the story at this point, approximately the end of our designated time period, when we could look with pride and praise on Noguchi's contributions. But since his life is now a closed book, the rest of the story demands a brief telling, if only to serve as a warning to those who follow. The filterable virus diseases from smallpox and yellow fever down to hog cholera and influenza have led many investigators astray. Secondary invaders on the one hand and inadequate experimental models, especially for diseases peculiar to man, have been constant hazards. Noguchi followed several of these false paths. His success in growing spirochaetes led him through the rest of his life to investigate a number of diseases caused by difficultly cultivable agents, including rabies, trachoma, poliomyelitis, and yellow fever. We shall consider only two of these, poliomyelitis and yellow fever.

In 1913 Flexner and Noguchi reported the finding of so-called globoid bodies in tubes inoculated with material from the central nervous system of monkeys suffering from poliomyelitis and also directly from human cases of the disease. Injections of normal monkeys with such cultures produced the typical experimental disease. Confirming results were sparse and irregular and no immunologic relationship between the "bodies" and the disease was established. The later observations of Long, Olitsky, and Rhoads at the Rockefeller Institute are illuminating. Although they found "bodies" in 11 per cent of their 315 cultures and observed that "effects characteristic of experimental poliomyelitis could be induced," with some of these even to the tenth transplant generation, yet "a study of subplants from these minute morphological particles did not convince us that we had in hand actual cultures of the globoid bodies or indeed of any living microorganism."

The probable explanation of the globoid bodies has been supplied by Lo Grippo, who found similar micrococcoid bodies either in the presence or in the absence of virus; these bodies passed into suspension from the tissue lipoids, migrated in an electric field like lipoids and took the fat stains Sudan III and osmic acid. He suggested that in the cultures by Noguchi's methods the virus may occasionally be adsorbed on such particles. Since living cells were present in the media both from the kidney tissue and in the ascitic fluid and since the final dilutions seem too high for mere survival of the virus (in one instance 1.3×10^{-18}), it is not unlikely that growth of the virus did occasionally occur.

Noguchi did have one late success, the clearing up of the enigma of Oroya fever and *verruga peruviana*. He succeeded in cultivating from blood from a case in Lima, Peru, an organism previously described by Barton, *Bartonella bacilliformis*. With this organism, by using different volumes and different routes of injection, he was able to produce either type of the disease. By injecting the cultivated organisms into the veins of monkeys, he produced the irregular remittent fever; by injecting them into the skin, a bloody wart was produced. From each type, *B. bacilliformis* was recovered. He was happy to confirm the early self-inoculation of the lone worker, Carrión. He himself deeply disliked teamwork.

Noguchi's tragic end came through his most extensive efforts, his studies in yellow fever. Aside from manifest difficulties in diagnosis, the major errors in his long series of yellow fever experiments (thirty-four papers) were failures to realize the serological differences in strains of *Leptospira icterohaemorrhagiae*, the causative agent of lepto-spiral jaundice, and the use chiefly of guinea pigs, an experimental animal known to be susceptible to the jaundice and known to be resistant to yellow fever. Noguchi, the master of spirochaetes, tripped and fell over these hazards.

Gradually, however, other workers demonstrated that the serological differences between the spirochaetes were not greater than those we find between organisms that form part of a single group, showing them simply to represent different strains. Increasingly, the tide of observation and opinion swung against Noguchi's interpretations. Among others, Sellards (1927) reported that serum of patients convalescent from typical yellow fever gave negative Pfeiffer reactions to *Leptospira icteroides* and that this organism and *L. icterohemorrhagiae* were immunlogically identical. The air was filled with gloom. As the contrary evidence increased, Noguchi became terribly depressed. He realized that it was imperative for him to carry out crucial experiments in Africa, the original home of yellow fever. In spite of illness of body and spirit he made the trip to Accra where everyone co-operated. Again, many monkeys, up to five hundred, hundreds of tubes, and thirty helpers at one time were used; there was plenty of yellow fever, but no leptospiral jaundice, and there were no spirochaetes. Noguchi became seriously ill, the diagnosis—yellow fever. He said, "It is the end and I want it to be." He died on May 21, 1928, a disillusioned man, old at fifty-two.

Cornell Medical School

Cornell Medical School in New York City was founded in 1898, but had only temporary quarters on Bellevue Hospital grounds until 1907 when the new Payne Building on First Avenue was opened. Until that time, bacteriology and the other preclinical sciences had meager facilities, so that they come under our purview for only a few years. Epidemic meningitis was rampant at that time and therefore an important public health problem in New York and elsewhere. The bacteriologists at Cornell, M. J. Elser (1872–1952) and his associate F. M. Huntoon[28] (1872——), made a searching prolonged study of the meningococci and the related Gram-negative cocci as part of the work of a commission appointed by the city board of health. In their study of the disease in man, they demonstrated the organism in the cerebrospinal fluid either by direct smear or by culture in 114 of 130 cases, although repeated attempts were sometimes necessary. They were unsuccessful in reproducing the disease in the small laboratory animals they used. Investigators commonly have found it necessary to use monkeys for this purpose and usually the intraspinal route of injection. Elser was a strange but likeable personality, exceedingly reluctant to publish his observations. He was one of several bacteriologists in this country to develop the freeze-drying of bacteria early in the twentieth century (about 1912), but he did not publish until 1935. Huntoon also was a quiet, restrained person whom we all liked. After more than a decade in the department at Cornell, he became director of the medical laboratories of Mulford and Company, Glenolden, Pennsylvania (1918–25). This was still in the antiserum period, and he made a long study of the many factors influencing dissociation of antigens and antibodies. As part of this he obtained active, filterable, antipneumococcic solutions relatively free from serum proteins by using weakly alkaline reagents somewhat similar to those employed earlier by Gay and Chickering.

Public health and preventive medicine at Cornell were under John C. Torrey (1876–1946), who with Morton C. Kahn also studied epidemic meningitis. Torrey's studies on bacillary dysentery and on the aciduric sporeformers deserve attention.

Arthur F. Coca (1875–1959)[29] was in charge of immunology and made extensive contributions to our knowledge of allergy, especially to the group of clinical syndromes that show a familial distribution and to which he applied the term atopy. Coca was instrumental in founding the American Society of Immunologists and was the competent editor-in-chief of the *Journal of Immunology* for years after its inception in 1916.

Northern New York, especially Cornell Veterinary College, the Agricultural Experiment Stations at Ithaca and Geneva, and the Saranac Sanitorium

VERANUS A. MOORE, EDWARD L. TRUDEAU,
ROBERT S. BREED

Early bacteriology at Cornell University (Ithaca) was centered in the Veterinary College with Veranus A. Moore (1859–1931) as the guiding spirit. From the age of thirteen years, following the death of his father, Veranus worked on the farm to support the family. A nail wound in his foot with resulting infection caused him years of lameness and repeated treatments at Bellevue Hospital, New York. The frequent hospitalizations gave him a deep interest in medicine; between these periods, he taught school to earn his living. He worked his way through Cornell and continued to need crutches until his third year. Always thereafter he walked with a limp. He was such a good student that by vote of the faculty he was permitted to accept a position in the young Bureau of Animal Industry in Washington before the actual completion of the courses for his B.S. degree. Here he had the opportunity of working with D. E. Salmon and Theobald Smith chiefly on hog cholera and swine plague. With Smith he published several papers on these diseases including immunity studies, both active and passive. He made good use of his evenings by attending classes at Columbia Medical School and in 1890 was granted the M.D. degree.

When Smith was called to Harvard in 1895, Moore succeeded him as chief of the division of animal pathology. Only a year later, reorganization at Cornell took him back to Ithaca as professor of comparative pathology, bacteriology, and meat inspection at the Veterinary College. Here he remained active in many positions until his retirement in 1929 at the age of seventy years; from 1908, he was dean and director of the Veterinary College. In the changing scene at Cornell, Moore gave courses in general bacteriology to students from all the colleges and conducted courses in pathology and bacteriology for veterinary students and, after the formation of the medical school in 1898, for students in the Ithaca branch of that school.

Both as teacher and dean, Moore was influential in improving the standards in veterinary medicine. The control of bovine tuberculosis and pasteurization of milk were his major research interests. His book *Bovine Tuberculosis and Its Control* and, in broader fields, his *Pathology and Differential Diagnosis of Infectious Diseases of Animals* were significant contributions to veterinary medicine. Moore was a quiet, unassuming, friendly person, admired by his students and colleagues. For years he wrote a Christmas letter to each alumnus. He served on several consulting boards; Theodore Roosevelt appointed him a member of the International Conference on Tuberculosis; President Hoover appointed him a member of the Conference on Child Life; he was president of the Society of American Bacteriologists in 1910 and was active during World War I in organizing the veterinary corps of the United States Army.[30]

Aside from the opportunities under Moore, bacteriology received surprisingly little recognition at Ithaca during these early years either in the college of agriculture or in the experiment station. A. R. Ward served part time while he was a student in veterinary medicine, and in 1901 Otto Hunziker, trained in Switzerland, succeeded him for a single year. After a lapse of four years, the teaching of agricultural bacteriology was resumed in 1906 by W. A. Stocking. In 1923 he was succeeded by James M. Sherman (1890–1956), trained at Wisconsin and with L. A. Rogers in the United States Department of Agriculture; bacteriology at Cornell now entered its active modern period.[31]

Sherman's exceptional influence in the American Dairy Science Association and in the Society of American Bacteriologists and its projects impels me, because his career is completed, to include a brief biographical note here, even though his life-work was largely after World War I. He was president of the Society of American Bacteriologists in 1937, but the brief tenure of such officials gives them little lasting influence. More important, he was the shrewd, successful secretary-treasurer, essentially business manager, of that society during eleven crucial years, 1923–34, and the competent editor of their journal, following Winslow, from 1944 to 1951. He was author of over one hundred scientific publications, including the tastebud tickling work with the propionic bacteria in Swiss cheese, many papers, and a monograph on the streptococci, emphasizing physiologic methods of study. His diverse contributions on bacterial physiology, including his distinction between *Streptococcus fecalis* and *S. lactis* should have more adequate recognition. Sherman was modest, loyal, exuberant, an excellent speaker, devoted to his professional duties and to his many students and always cheerfully, promptly, helpful to his many friends. He was much appreciated and is deeply missed.

The New York Agricultural Station at Geneva, organized in 1882, has been active in studying the problems of the area. As elsewhere, microbiological investigations were not begun until the 1890's and later when the advances in our knowledge gave new methods of approach. H. A. Harding went to the Geneva station from Russell's laboratory at the University of Wisconsin in 1899; from that time bacteriologic studies especially of dairy products were encouraged. His paper with M. J. Prucha gave attention to the bacteria of Cheddar cheese and methods of curing and storage. This study was built on the earlier classification of dairy bacteria by Conn, Esten, and Stocking at the Storrs station and the still earlier studies of Duclaux in France (1887). The studies of milk enzymes by Harding and L. L. Van Slyke through the use of chloroform to repress germ life are still referred to in surveys of this field. As in many stations, bacterial soft rot of certain vegetables was early studied here, Harding and V. A. Moore contributing.

In 1913 Robert S. Breed (1877–1956) came to the station as chief of research. Although most of his active life comes after our period, it began within our time and is now ended, so we can properly glimpse his major achievements. Quantitative and qualitative estimates of bacteria in milk and their public health importance engaged the attention of many bacteriologists and because varying methods gave differing results, the American Public Health Association appointed a committee for standardization of procedures. Breed was, for a time, chairman of this group. He developed a method differing from the usual plating procedure, a direct microscopic counting along lines familiar in estimating the cells in the blood. This has certain advantages in saving time and equipment, but has not been widely used.[32] The development of a committee of the Society of American Bacteriologists to assist D. H. Bergey in his monumental work in determinative bacteriology drew

Breed into these taxonomic struggles. He served actively on this committee for years and on the Bergey Manual Trust. After the death of Dr. Bergey, Breed assumed the major responsibility for this invaluable job until his own death. Breed's omnivorous reading, meticulous attention to detail in taxonomic studies, and wide interest in dairy problems brought him membership in a number of international congresses. He was for years secretary of the International Committee on Bacterial Nomenclature.

Harold Joel Conn, son of H. W. Conn who was one of the three men most prominent in founding the Society of American Bacteriologists, came to the Geneva station from his graduate student years and work in the experiment station at Cornell, Ithaca, in 1911. His detailed studies of the fungi and bacteria in soil and especially his valuable work in aiding the development of American biological stains and stain technology receive our commendation. Both Breed and H. J. Conn served as presidents of the Society of American Bacteriologists, the former in 1927 and the latter in 1948.

State public health laboratories have been prominent in contributing to preventive medicine in the United States. The date and type of organization have varied but most of them, in the period of our scrutiny, were concerned chiefly with diagnostic aids, control of water supplies and sewage disposal and, in some instances, the production of antisera. The work in all of them was important, but highly similar, so that only occasionally shall we give them further comment. As has been said the laboratories under the Massachusetts Board of Health were leaders in most aspects of the work.

The New York State Laboratories developed slowly, initially by arrangement with the Bender Hygiene Laboratory, a private laboratory in Albany, where in 1891 a few diagnostic services were offered. In 1901 a more complete organization was set up with many bureaus including one of pathology and bacteriology under George Blumer and an antitoxin laboratory under Herbert D. Pease. Soon large quantities of diphtheria and tetanus antitoxin were distributed. In 1910 the diagnostic work was moved to the building erected for antitoxin production.

Under Pease' successor, Williams S. Magill, land for further growth was purchased, and in 1914 under Hermann M. Biggs, as far-seeing commissioner, and Augustus B. Wadsworth (1872–1954), as director of the Division of Laboratories and Research, the modern period began with a new building completed in 1919.

Wadsworth had been a student of Prudden at Columbia University Medical School and later had taught bacteriology there until the death of Hiss. Tall, handsome, competent, an excellent tennis player with a long reach to return the balls that should have gone by, Wadsworth built up a well-articulated state organization with many branch laboratories. His development of standard methods of high accuracy for all the co-operating laboratories was a major contribution that led him into similar work for the Health Section of the League of Nations. He was a member of all the appropriate scientific societies and president of the American Association of Immunologists in 1933. After his retirement, Wadsworth received the Hermann M. Biggs Award, 1953, for outstanding service in public health in New York State.

Deep in the beautiful lake and wild woodland area of the Adirondack Mountains, before the bursting of bacteriology, in the seventies, eighties, and nineties, the bed-rest treatment of tuberculosis was slowly developing. It began through the love of a sportsman for the forests, his delight in hunting and fishing, and his decision to spend the last days of his apparently fatal illness where he had been so happy. It is an epic tale of the young physician Edward Livingston Trudeau (1848–1915) and his loyal, loving wife, of his recurring illness and physical misery, of the death of their children, of the destruction of laboratory and home by fire, but with it all, of courageous, optimistic persistence with some progress in meeting man's greatest bacterial enemy, and of the joy in sharing work and life with friends.

Who was this Trudeau and what were his contributions to early American bacteriology? Born of well-to-do parents who were divorced early in Edward's life, he and his grandparents lived fifteen years in France, returning to this country at the end of the Civil War. Trudeau's somewhat reckless life was soon tragically interrupted by the rapidly progressive pulmonary tuberculosis of his older brother. During the final four months, Trudeau was nurse and almost constant companion to his brother, living in the same room, frequently sleeping in the same bed. The physician came once a week with some cough medicine, but as evidence of the medical attitudes of the period (and indeed much later), he made no suggestion of contagion or of any danger to the younger brother. Trudeau was deeply affected mentally by his brother's death; the intimate contacts were the probable source of Trudeau's own subsequent life of illness.

At the age of twenty-three, Trudeau was graduated in medicine from the College of Physicians and Surgeons, which had provided the typical didactic lectures of the times and almost no bedside instruction. In his eagerness to marry his fiancée, he could not bear the thought of an eighteen-month internship at Bellevue or New York Hospitals; without any clinical experience, he became for six months resident physician at a new small hospital. Then, he was married and went off with his trotting mares to the White Mountains, and thence to a further honeymoon in Europe. A cold abscess during his medical course and scrofula eighteen months later, after his return from Europe, were both passed over unrecognized as to the underlying tuberculous pathology. He then had several attacks of fever and was told he had malaria; everybody had it. But when his fever reached 101°F. one afternoon, he ventured to see his friend Dr. Janeway.

After the physical examination: "Yes, the upper two-thirds of the left lung is involved in an active tuberculous process." Again the attitude towards tuberculosis is shown by the medical advice he received. Go south, live out-of-doors, and ride horseback. He was urged to exercise daily. Upon his return to New York he was still ill and was deeply despondent. After waiting for the birth of their second child, a son, he retreated in May, 1873, to Paul Smith's in the Adirondacks. That area, especially Saranac Lake, where he moved with his family in 1876, was to be his home for the rest of his life. At Saranac Lake, though frequently downed, Trudeau fought the common enemy both in his own body and in hundreds of his patients from all walks of life. He became the beloved physician to many, and to all who knew him the embodiment of optimism even in defeat. Horses, dogs, hunting (he was an excellent rifleman), fishing, and sailing were his sources of relaxation whenever he had time and was well enough. "Up to 1880 I did little but hunt and fish, but after that my interests began gradually to be divided equally between medicine and hunting. . . . In the nineties, I hunted only when I could get away from work." He had a Gallic temperament, inclined to extravagance, a good sense of humor, was modest, praising others rather than himself for any small successes.

Aided by his friend, Dr. Alfred Loomis, and others, in 1884 he built two small cottages, the forerunners of the famous institution. He became a good beggar for his sanitarium needs, but he rejoiced to tell that the first land bought for the sanitarium was a sixteen-acre piece of Preacher Smith's pasture, purchased by the hunting-fishing guides of the region. As the sanitarium grew and more patients were sent to

Saranac, it became apparent to Trudeau that both in his own case and in that of his patients, more improvement was made in the winter than in the summer. Indeed the saying became common that one winter was the equal of two summers towards recovery. To what could this be ascribed? In the winter the cold and the snow made bed rest easy and almost a necessity, but in the summer a more active life was alluring; less bed rest gave the tuberculous process more opportunity. Trudeau in his history of the tuberculosis work at Saranac Lake states that "Brehmer," in Silesia (1859), "was the originator of the sanitarium method, the essence of which was rest, fresh air, and a daily regulation by the physician of the patient's life and habits."

In bacteriology, Trudeau followed eagerly the early procedures of Koch, first the staining of sputum, and then attempted cultivation of the organism. In spite of primitive equipment he was finally successful in obtaining pure cultures. Again, as did Koch, he began excitedly to work on various vaccines or tuberculins, a line of experiment he continued hopefully for many years. In several small series of rabbits (1892–94) treated with living avian tubercle bacilli, subsequent injection of virulent human type bacilli into the anterior chamber of the eye gave some success over the controls. His final statement (1894) runs: "Uncertain, imperfect and generally only relative as this artificial immunity against tuberculosis appears, it is nevertheless sufficiently marked to be demonstrable." In all Trudeau's vaccination experiments, he obtained this "relative success" only with living organisms, never with killed organisms or extracts.

These experiments of Trudeau were carried out on a small scale; they are typical of several studies in that period and later, attempts to find a successful vaccine against tuberculosis. These papers are rarely cited, but one is reminded of the modern "relative success" with B.C.G. and with the vole bacillus. Another meritorious article by Trudeau in 1887 records experiments querying the influence of environment on experimental tuberculosis. In a small series, five rabbits were injected with tubercle bacilli and permitted to run wild with ample food on an isolated island. At the end of four months, the animals were sacrificed and only one of the five showed tuberculous lesions. The controls all showed extensive tuberculosis. At this period, the distinction between the bovine and human types of tubercle bacilli was not recognized, and it is probable that Trudeau's pure culture was the human type isolated from a case of human pulmonary tuberculosis and therefore less virulent for rabbits. From these and other experiments, environmental factors always loomed large in Trudeau's view of the tuberculous process.

The development of the cottage sanitarium at Saranac, the subsequent rapid growth of similar institutions throughout the country with emphasis on the bed-rest treatment, the Saranac Laboratory with its succession of competent investigators and scholarly publications, the American Trudeau Association as the medical division of the National Tuberculosis Association, these were the monuments to a sick optimistic dreamer. Honors were his from all sides, with some achievement in the treatment of tuberculosis and warm appreciative friends to carry on. "We have the sanitarium now but the hope of the future is in the laboratory" was his constant theme. I wonder what Trudeau would have accomplished if he had not repeatedly suffered from tuberculosis. Would he not (in all probability) have been another successful New York City physician, without major achievements?[33]

CHAPTER XI

Pennsylvania, New Jersey, and Delaware

I love fools' experiments. I am always making them.

CHARLES DARWIN

A naturalist's life would be a happy one
if he had only to observe and never to write.

CHARLES DARWIN

Pennsylvania

JOSEPH LEIDY,

JOSEPH MC FARLAND, ALEXANDER C. ABBOTT,

DAVID H. BERGEY, AND A. PARKER HITCHENS

Our ideas of early Pennsylvania and Philadelphia derive largely from William Penn and the Quakers and their endeavors to deal with the original owners of the land in a spirit of fairness not found in the other colonies. Here also we find the colony with greater appreciation of those who differed in religious faiths, the seat of our harassed Continental Congresses, the home of the great internationalist and early experimental scientist, Benjamin Franklin, the man who founded our first scientific society with a continuing history, and who aided in founding both the first medical school in the area to become the United States of America and the first general hospital. Yet here on the other hand we find strong obstructionist points of view both during the period of the yellow fever outbreaks and later when Hodge and Meigs ridiculed the idea of contagion in puerperal sepsis, called Oliver Wendell Holmes "a sophomore orator" and as late as 1854 maintained that this disease was due to miasmic, telluric, and cosmic origins. The conflict proved a spur both to Holmes and the public.

The first noteworthy microbiologist of Pennsylvania was Joseph Leidy (1823–1891),[1] although he was more important as the founder of paleontology in America, as an anatomist, and as the last of the great naturalists. Among pioneer paleontologists, he antedated both Cope and Marsh, and among zoologists, he was the last important one to study the entire animal world from protozoa to man. He is the only American accorded a brief biography among a series of thirty-five microbiologists given that honor in the journal, *Parasitology* (British), under the editorship of G. H. F. Nuttall, himself born and trained in America.

At the age of ten, Leidy was sent to the Classical Academy, a private school conducted by a Methodist minister. Such was the rivalry between this and another private school, that Joseph's stepmother hired a Negro lad, Cyrus Burris, as a bodyguard, to accompany her boy to school. A lasting friendship grew up between the two as they went back and forth and on botanizing expeditions together. Leidy was not a methodical student; his love of natural history led him to spend much of his spare time, and some that his teachers thought belonged to them, wandering along the Wissahickon Creek and in the Bartram Gardens, botanizing, collecting minerals and many a living thing to be subsequently dissected and drawn with exquisite skill and unusual attention to detail. Leidy said of himself, "I was always what other boys called 'a queer boy,' never caring much to join in their sports but as anxious to see how plants and animals were made as other boys were curious about the internal construction of their toys."

Since his father, a hatter, was well to do, Leidy never had to struggle with the poverty as have so many, both in the sciences and the arts. The practical father urged that his son's talent in freehand drawing could well be directed to sign-painting as a means of honest livelihood, but Joseph's stepmother appreciated the boy's capacities and yearnings and persuaded the father to continue his schooling towards the professional career of medicine.

Accordingly, young Leidy at sixteen began a series of preceptorships characteristic of the period, attended three sessions at the Medical School of the University of Pennsylvania, and received his degree in 1844. His thesis was on the comparative anatomy of the eye of vertebrated animals. In the course of his busy life, Leidy held various academic positions in the Philadelphia neighborhood; the most important of these was the chair of anatomy in the University of Pennsylvania Medical School, which he enriched for thirty-eight fruitful years. It is interesting that his first experience as a young student in the dissecting room was so repugnant to him that he left at once and for six weeks could not persuade himself to return.

Of his more than 600 scientific contributions, no less than 120 relate to helminths. These papers, many of them brief, his extensive monograph, *Freshwater Rhizopods of North America* (1879), and *Flora and Fauna within Living Animals*, the first important study in this country of the parasites of the alimentary tract, make it appropriate for microbiology to claim some of the prestige of this remarkable man. He was the only early American naturalist who took an interest in parasitology. He described and named more than 100 new species of intestinal parasites in various hosts. *Cryptobia helicis* (Leidy, 1846), very similar to a trypanosome, found in various species of snails, the common *Amoeba proteus* (Leidy, 1879), and *Endamoeba blattae* (Leidy, 1879), the type species of this genus, readily found in the cockroach, are a few of the commonly studied parasites that bear his name. His endless enthusiasm for his work with protozoa is brought home to us by a tale of a dinner party at the home of Dr. S. Weir Mitchell, where he was always welcome. Another guest was complaining of boredom, whereupon Leidy responded, "How *can* life be tiresome so long as there is still a rhizopod undescribed!"

Leidy gave his recipe for successful achievement and for happiness in one's work.

The study of natural history in the leisure of my life, since I was fourteen years of age, has been to me a constant source of happiness; and my experience of it is such that independently of its higher merits I warmly recommend it as a pastime, which I believe no other can excel. At the same time, in observing the modes of life of those around me, it has been a matter of increasing regret that so few, so very few, people give attention to intellectual pursuits of any kind. In the incessant and necessary struggle for bread, we repeatedly hear the expression that "man shall not live by bread alone," and yet it remains unappreciated by the mass of even so-called enlightened humanity. In common with all other animals, the engrossing care of man is food for the stomach, while intellectual food too often remains unknown, disregarded or rejected.

His most notable medical contribution was his observation of cysts of *Trichinella spiralis* in pork muscle (1846). Cysts of this parasite had previously been observed in man, but with no notion of their relation to the acute disease or any idea of the transmission from the pig. Leidy's finding suggested the mode of spread subsequently proved by the studies of Leuckart, Virchow, and more completely, by Zenker.

In a paper delivered before the Philadelphia Academy of Natural Sciences in 1849, Leidy described several "moving filamentous bodies belonging to the genus Vibrio, probably of the character of algous vegetation. . . . In the stomach and small intestine of the toad (*Bufo americanus*) there exist simple delicate filamentous bodies which are of three different kinds. . . . One is exceedingly minute, forms a spiral, is endowed with a power of rapid movement and appears to be the *Spirillum undula* of Ehrenberg." Thus bacteriologists have a claim on Leidy.

Leidy's life was full and happy save that he had no children; his only child, the daughter of a near friend, was adopted. Many honors both in this country and abroad, where he traveled and studied repeatedly, were showered upon him, but they left him the same simple, lovable, modest scientist. His lack of any pretense is shown by the circumstance of his regular visits to a busy fish market for material for study. About any unusual specimen, he would at once write the name and brief descriptive note on a scrap of paper; the fishman would copy the remarks in large letters for the edification of visitors, for example: "Horse Crevalle—*Caraux hippus*, Cape Cod to the West Indies. Belongs to the Pilot fish family and related to the Mackerels." Natural history was his first love and constant source of happiness. He knew Darwin and supported him firmly. He was primarily a morphologist, highly exact in his descriptions and in his drawings; rarely did he venture into speculation. His vigor and industry made it possible for him to fill a major chair in human anatomy and at the same time produce such a classic as the *Ancient Fauna of Nebraska* (1854). The extent of his learning is overwhelming, and his contributions to science range from reports on the mite in the ear of an ox, an ant infected with a fungus, and the fossil horse of America to an *Elementary Treatise on Human Anatomy* and an American edition of *Quain's Anatomy* with his own additional notes and drawings. We who follow Leidy from afar, in whichever of his fields our work touches his, give him our deep admiration.

A somewhat older Philadelphia contemporary of Leidy, William Wood Gerhard[2] (1809–72) has given the best American example of the separation of two microbic diseases by correlating clinical and post-mortem findings half a century and more before the specific agents of these diseases were described. Osler writes,

In 1829, Louis' great work appeared in which the name "typhoid" was given to the fever. At this period typhoid fever alone prevailed in Paris and many European cities, and it was universally believed to be identical with the continued fever of Great Britain where in reality, typhoid and typhus coexisted. The intestinal lesion was regarded as an accidental occurrence in the course of ordinary typhus.

Of Louis' American students, Osler states further that "W. W. Gerhard was the most distinguished in Paris between 1830 and 1840."

During Gerhard's two to three years in Europe, he was chiefly in Paris where he saw much typhoid fever both in the clinic and at autopsy and became familiar with the characteristic intestinal lesions. He also visited Edinburgh, where he observed typhus fever. On his return to this country, he had a splendid chance to study cases of typhus fever which was ravaging Philadelphia that year, 1832. Of the 214 cases, many came to autopsy, and he wrote in his classical paper "the glands of Peyer were found not merely free from the peculiar lesion occurring in dothienenteritis or typhoid fever, but these follicles and the rest of the intestines were more healthy in the petechial fever than in the majority of other diseases." A careful comparison with his Paris experience as well as with the cases of typhoid fever in Philadelphia made it clear to him that these were two distinct diseases, and students of medical history award him the palm. In addition to this study, his paper on the 1832 epidemic of cholera in Paris is frequently cited and more especially is his monograph, "Cerebral Affections of Children," which is an early account of tuberculous meningitis in children. W. S. Middleton characterizes Gerhard as "placid in temper, kind and generous in his feelings, genial and gentle in his manners, his influence on students and physicians of this period was long felt."

Although many road-breaking discoveries were being made in Europe during the 1880's, including proof of the microbic origin of devastating diseases such as typhoid fever, Asiatic cholera, diphtheria, and tuberculosis, only slight and sceptical attention was paid to these findings even in our leading medical schools. Public attention was not aroused until the early 1890's when Koch made his announcement of the curative properties of tuberculin, subsequently proved incorrect, and Behring and Kitasato proclaimed the therapeutic value of diphtheria and tetanus antitoxins. If such antisera were effective, why not antisera against other bacterial diseases? Our enthusiasm pushed far beyond the boundaries of our knowledge, and for the time we failed to realize the marked individual differences in the metabolism of organisms that looked so simple and so similar. Pioneers we had, but save for one or two such as Leidy, they followed paths laid down by European investigators.

After Leidy and Gerhard came a succession of young men working their way into the new field of bacteriology. In the pathology department of the University of Pennsylvania Medical School they included Edward O. Shakespeare, Henry Formad, Allen J. Smith, later professor of pathology, and Joseph McFarland.

Edward O. Shakespeare (1846–1900), after a short period in general practice in Delaware, returned to Philadelphia, held an appointment as ophthalmologist, but was more interested in the underlying sciences and in 1882 became pathologist and in 1889 bacteriologist in old Blockley, the Philadelphia General Hospital. He is said to have possessed the only good microscope in Philadelphia. With Dr. H. L. Taylor of Wilkesbarre, he contributed to the resolving of the disastrous epidemic of typhoid fever in Plymouth, Pennsylvania, in 1885, by demonstrating characteristic lesions in several autopsies. At the instance of the United States government he studied cholera in Spain, Germany, and India, reporting in an impressive government publication in 1890. During the Spanish-American War he was attached to the office of Surgeon General Sternberg, and with Walter Reed and Victor Vaughan was commissioned to examine the shocking outbreaks of typhoid fever in our army camps. Their detailed survey, with its conclusions, seemingly incredible but true, did much to awaken the country to the inadequacy of our medical preparedness and to the high incidence of this preventable disease throughout the country.

Of this early group, Joseph McFarland (1868–1945) was the most active in bacteriology. He studied extensively in Europe after his medical schooling at the University of Pennsylvania. On his return he occupied many positions. Among these were assistant to the professor of pathology at the Pennsylvania Medical School, 1891 (at that time Juan Guiteras, later of yellow-fever fame); lecturer in bacteriology, 1895; the chair in pathology and bacteriology in the Medico-Chirurgical College for several years; director of the biological laboratories of H. K. Mulford Company, 1894–1900; professor of pathology at the Woman's Medical College in Philadelphia, 1910–14; and director of the Phipps Institute, 1907–10. The Medico-Chirurgical College merged with the University of Pennsylvania in 1916, and thereafter McFarland devoted himself until his retirement to his rather loosely defined professorial duties. The overlapping periods and positions held should give us no concern, as full-time professorships were rare in those days even in the underlying sciences.

In his entertaining recollections, "Beginnings of Bacteriology in

Philadelphia,"[3] McFarland states that during his four years as a student in the Medical Department of the University of Pennsylvania (1885–89), "I never heard a lecture upon a bacteriological subject, nor made a culture of any kind nor was shown a culture of any kind." A staining of the tubercle bacillus in sputum was the sole experience, performed with considerable uncertainty, since the instructor, Henry Formad, was sceptical and the available microscopes very poor. Since, according to McFarland, Formad's highest power objective was a $\frac{1}{5}$-inch dry lens, one can understand that this might lead to scepticism rather than to a visual image of the tubercle bacillus. McFarland was not a productive investigator, but he wrote several well-organized textbooks in a lucid style. His *Pathogenic Bacteria and Protozoa* went through nine editions from 1896. That text and Sternberg's *Textbook of Bacteria* (1892) were well thumbed and much appreciated by all the early students in the field.

In 1892 the University of Pennsylvania Laboratory of Hygiene opened the doors of its grand new building with John Shaw Billings, who had been so vital in planning the Johns Hopkins Hospital and Medical School and in the upbuilding of the Library of the Surgeon General, as director, and Alexander C. Abbott, a protégé of Welch, as his first assistant. When Billings at a later time was asked how he ever succeeded in getting such a huge volume of work done he replied, "I'll let you into the secret—there's nothing really difficult if you only begin. Some people contemplate a task, until it looms so big, it seems impossible, but I *just begin* and it gets done somehow." One is reminded of Osler's favorite motto from *Macbeth:* "The flightly purpose never is o'ertook unless the deed go with it." Mazyck P. Ravenel was one of the medical graduates who matriculated in the first class at the laboratory of hygiene, and the following year we find on the books the name of David H. Bergey. During this period, it was said that the only rapprochement between the Laboratory of Hygiene and the Medical Department lay in the fact that Billings, director of the former, was professor of hygiene in the latter.

When in 1896 Billings accepted the call to New York City to invigorate and build the public library, Abbott took over both of his Philadelphia positions. In 1899 under Simon Flexner's regime as professor of pathology, bacteriology was granted a seat at the high table, and Abbott's title became professor of hygiene and bacteriology. Medical students now went to the laboratory of hygiene for instruction in bacteriology and David Bergey was advanced to the position of assistant professor of bacteriology.

Alexander Crevar Abbott[4] (1860–1935) had broad training both in this country (under Welch) and in Germany. As did many of our early American bacteriologists, he devoted his attention largely to the water-borne diseases and the organisms causing them. The Schuylkill River that provided most of the Philadelphia water was heavily polluted by sewage wastes from towns up the river, so the typhoid rate was shockingly high, over 100 per 100,000 in 1875, down to 40 in 1895, and up to 70 for several of the years in the early 1900's, with an average of 55 per 100,000 during the years 1898 through 1906. Slowly filtration plants were built and the typhoid rate was gradually reduced.[5] In his water studies, Abbott described in 1896 *Vibrio schuylkiliensis*, one of a number of spiral organisms that were confused with *V. cholerae*. It is probably identical with *V. metchnikovii* described by Gamaleia in 1888. With Jordan of the University of Chicago and Conn of Wesleyan, Abbott was one of the three men most active in founding the Society of American Bacteriologists. After the early years, Abbott became more involved in administrative duties both at the laboratory of hygiene and in the Philadelphia Board of Health.

Personally, Abbott was a short, well-formed, handsome man; his dark brown hair always carefully trimmed, heavy eyebrows accentuating his dark eyes, clothes well tailored, a man perfectly groomed on every occasion. He was always punctual for his lectures, appearing in a freshly laundered white coat. A white towel placed at the end of the lecture table was tucked into his right trouser pocket before he began to speak. His lectures were not inspiring, rather stereotyped, and delivered from notes in a perfunctory manner. He was a gracious *bon vivant*, enjoyed his gay social life, was not a hard worker; in his later years, he became especially interested in painting as a hobby and was more addicted to his palette and brush than to the scalpel and the platinum transplant needle.

Abbott's longtime colleague and, after his retirement in 1926, his successor in the chair of bacteriology and hygiene was David H. Bergey[6] (1860–1937), who was about as different a personality as one can imagine. A shy, reserved man, an indefatigable, patient worker, meticulous and methodical in all of his reading and his investigations, he carried a large share of the departmental duties. He published several papers on anaphylaxis and phagocytosis, studies on the influence of food preservatives, and a substantial *Principles of Hygiene* (1901) that went through seven editions. His major contribution, a *Manual of Determinative Bacteriology* (1923) was characteristic of the man, involving an enormous amount of reading and weighing of the taxonomic evidence. Prior to this time in America, our basic aid in this field was the *Manual of Determinative Bacteriology* (1901) written by Frederick D. Chester[7] of the Delaware Agricultural Experiment Station and the Delaware State Board of Health. This and a similar German compilation by Ehrenberg (first edition 1885) served as a beginning for Bergey's careful studies. The first board of editors consisted of D. H. Bergey, Robert S. Breed, and E. G. D. Murray. Bergey's industry and vision carried this invaluable manual through four editions. All royalties accruing from the sale of the volumes he devoted to the development of systematic bacteriology under the control of a board of editor-trustees.

After Bergey's death, Robert S. Breed carried on as chairman and A. Parker Hitchens became the third member of the board. This ponderous work, full of the detailed descriptions provided by hundreds of bacteriologists, continues now in its seventh edition with Buchanan as chairman, since the death of Breed in 1956. One hopes that eventually this work may come under an appropriate committee of the International Congresses of Microbiology.

The Henry Phipps Institute was founded in 1903 by Mr. Phipps with the medical leadership of Lawrence F. Flick. The study, treatment, and prevention of tuberculosis were its aims; from the beginning, the staff stressed the contagiousness of tuberculosis before it was commonly recognized by the medical profession. Of the early staff associates we should mention Leonard Pearson and his initiation of the tuberculin test in cattle and Mazyck P. Ravenel who confirmed the findings of Theobald Smith that showed essential differences in cultures and in virulence of tubercle bacilli from human and from bovine sources. The Institute became an integral part of the University of Pennsylvania in 1910, and a new building was opened in 1911. The more important investigations of the later period are therefore tied in with the appointments in the pathology department of the medical school, notably Paul A. Lewis and still later, Eugene L. Opie, both men of outstanding capacity.

Microbiologists and industrialists in America have co-operated with remarkable success. In the Philadelphia region such an instance requires our attention because of the ideas and foresight of one man, A. Parker Hitchens, and his work with the Society of American Bacteriologists.

In 1894 Joseph McFarland[8] made a gentleman's agreement with a businessman, H. K. Mulford, to direct a laboratory of biology with the production of diphtheria and tetanus antitoxins as the immediate aim. No contract was deemed necessary; it was agreed that the duties would not interfere with McFarland's teaching, and he states that the arrangement proved entirely satisfactory. They began work in an old stable in West Philadelphia with much helpful advice from the always generous W. H. Park of the New York City laboratories. The stable proved to be more successful as a contributor of contaminating organisms than as a usable laboratory, so that about 1898, excellent modern buildings were made ready in Glenolden, and the Mulford laboratories were moved to the new quarters.

J. J. Kinyoun, later to become famous for his courageous support of the truth in the bubonic plague outbreak in San Francisco, and young A. Parker Hitchens, fresh from the Medico-Chirurgical College of Philadelphia, where McFarland was teaching, joined the venture and adequate results, though not highly important for our chronicle, were soon achieved. From 1900, when McFarland resigned to become consultant to Parke, Davis and Company, Hitchens gradually took over responsibility at Glenolden, becoming director of the Mulford Antitoxin Laboratories in 1906. While in this position, Hitchens became increasingly active in the young Society of American Bacteriologists. From 1913 to 1923, a period including World War I, the disastrous 1918–19 pandemic of influenza, and the rapid growth in all the natural sciences including microbiology, he was the secretary-treasurer and the capable genial spark plug of this society. He it was who more clearly than others saw the need of a journal as a unifying force for the continued progress of the science. His energetic proddings[9] carried other leaders along, and at the 1915 meeting at Urbana the wise counsel of the white-bearded Nestor, Professor Burrill, persuaded the doubters. The *Journal of Bacteriology* was instituted in 1916 under the editorship of C.-E. A. Winslow, a task that he carried with signal distinction for twenty-eight years.

In 1916 also, the Society of Immunologists began publication of the official organ, the *Journal of Immunology*, under the editorship of A. F. Coca; *Soil Science* with Jacob Lipman as editor was started the same year. The continuing success of these journals is evidence that these sciences have come to maturity in the United States. I am therefore considering this date (of course no one date is entirely satisfactory) as the approximate although somewhat elastic end of the period of my chronicle. After this, bacteriology and microbiology became more intricate and more involved, with biochemistry becoming increasingly important both as a tool for all related sciences and as a separate discipline, so that several volumes and more than one brain and pen should tell the tales.

Parker Hitchens conceived of the *Journal of Bacteriology* as a lineal descendant in this country of the *Centralblatt für Bakteriologie;* accordingly, a few years later the Society of American Bacteriologists began, under his editorship, the *Abstracts of Bacteriology.* This journal persisted with the usual stormy difficulties of such publications through 1925, when it was merged with *Biological Abstracts* as Section C., *Abstracts of Microbiology, Immunology and Parasitology* continued for several years under the enthusiastic editorship of Hitchens. We still await an international multilingual abstract service, possibly through the United Nations, that will provide essentially complete coverage. Marked improvement has become apparent in the last few years as a result of our fears of Russia.

In his colorful career Hitchens served successfully in many positions, including the Mulford Laboratories, the United States Public Health Service, the Army Medical School, adviser in public health to the Governor General of the Philippine Islands, and professor of public health and preventive medicine in the University of Pennsylvania Medical School. Probably his most important scientific publication was the monograph with Siler and Hall on dengue fever.[10] This confirmed and amplified the earlier (1907) road-breaking study of Ashburn and Craig who proved that dengue fever is a virus disease transmitted by mosquitoes, commonly by *Culex fatigans.* Hitchens was an attractive, genial, versatile far-seeing person, full of enthusiasm for his dreams; through his persuasive vigor, these dreams frequently became realities. We need more such prodders, especially those with so many admirable qualities.

Mazyck P. Ravenel, after receiving his medical degree from the Medical College of South Carolina in 1884 and spending several years in private practice, matriculated in 1892 in the first class of the University of Pennsylvania Laboratory of Hygiene. He held many positions in the Philadelphia area for short periods, spent the summer of 1895 studying in Europe, and became bacteriologist of the Pennsylvania State Livestock Sanitary Board in 1897. Here he made his most important scientific contribution, comparing during a two-year period the relative virulence of some fifteen cultivated strains of tubercle bacilli from human and from bovine sources.[11] He confirmed the earlier observations of Theobald Smith, asserting the cultural differences between organisms from the two sources and the greater virulence of the bovine type for the available experimental animals, especially guinea pigs and rabbits. He gave credit also to similar studies by R. R. Dinwiddie of the Arkansas Experimental Station and to his chief, Leonard Pearson. On the basis of experiment and observation, he maintained the pathogenicity of the bovine tubercle bacilli for man, especially in the early years of life.

Always sharp in argument, Ravenel delighted in taking issue with Koch at the British Congress on Tuberculosis in London in 1901 and the International Congress in Washington in 1908. Fortunate in having such a potent adversary as Koch in the bitter conflict, Ravenel enjoyed the contest and continued to emphasize the issues until the battle was won. In 1907 Ravenel became professor of bacteriology at the University of Wisconsin and in 1914 moved to a similar position at the University of Missouri. For years he was active in the American Public Health Association and was energetic editor of their important journal from 1924 to 1941.

During the period of our chronicles, bacteriology achieved only minor importance in the various smaller institutions of Pennsylvania. At Jefferson Medical College, Samuel Gross (1805–84), the distinguished surgeon, was asked to lecture for a week on bacteriology. He stated, "The trustees require this course, but my opinion is 'taint worth a damn.'"

New Jersey

JACOB G. LIPMAN, SELMAN A. WAKSMAN

The conspicuous successes in microbiology at the New Jersey Experiment Station and Rutgers University during recent decades (antibiotics, tyrothricin, streptomycin, the Nobel Prize) are likely to dazzle our eyes, so that we fail to observe that these were built up patiently on earlier humble foundations. The New Jersey station was one of several begun before federal aid was available, but as elsewhere the early studies were directed towards the analysis of fertilizers, fodders, etc. Voorhees and Street began work in soil bacteriology about 1900, publishing an important paper on denitrification. A department of soil chemistry and bacteriology was organized and during the next years Jacob Lipman and his associates devoted themselves to a wide variety of problems on the relation of bacteria to soil fertility, principally the various nitrogen-fixing bacteria both the free-living and the symbiotic organisms. From about 1911 Lipman, by then director of the station, and Selman A. Waksman,[12] his new assistant from 1915 on, became deeply interested in the physiology of actinomycetes in the soil. With R. E. Curtis a number of new species were isolated and described. In 1916 the journal, *Soil Science*, began publication under the editorship of Lipman, an important service that he continued for twenty-four years; thus that branch of microbiology came of age in the same year that the *Journal of Bacteriology* and the *Journal of Immunology* gave greater opportunities in their fields.

Other phases of bacteriology received at the New Jersey Station much the same attention as in the neighboring states. The use of the tuberculin test to determine the incidence of tuberculosis in cattle was studied by J. Nelson as early as 1893, bacterial diseases of tomato and potato plants by Halsted and Cook from 1891 on, and about 1899, the several commercial bacterial inoculants for legumes and cereal crops by members of the station without favorable results.

The New Jersey State Department of Health established a central laboratory of hygiene at Princeton University in 1896 for "applying bacteriological methods for the diagnosis of tuberculosis and diphtheria, the two most fatal diseases in New Jersey." Gradually, as in other state laboratories, additional proved procedures were added.

Prior to 1907 there was no course at Rutgers College solely devoted to bacteriology, but from that date on, courses both in general and in soil bacteriology were offered; by 1915 soil bacteriology had proliferated into six courses. At Princeton, also, bacteriology got a late start under Ulric Dahlgren in general bacteriology after 1918. We think more especially of the later investigations at Princeton of E. Newton Harvey on phosphorescent bacteria as part of his extensive work in bioluminescence.

The achievements at the Department of Animal Pathology of the Rockefeller Institute under the leadership of Theobald Smith have been mentioned elsewhere. Since active work did not commence there until 1917, their studies come only slightly into our field of vision.

Delaware

FREDERICK D. CHESTER

Important early contributions to systematic bacteriology in this country came from Frederick D. Chester[13] (1861–1943) of the Delaware Agricultural Experiment Station and Delaware College. As was common in our early days, he occupied a whole settee, geology, botany, as well as bacteriology and mycology. He made one of the early studies on nitrogen assimilation by soil bacteria (1904). In spite of the heavy load, his carefully prepared *Manual of Determinative Bacteriology* (1901) was our chief support in taxonomy until it was superseded by Bergey's *Manual* in 1923.

CHAPTER XII

Important Contributions
to Microbiology by Federal Agencies

In illness one should take care of two things,
to do good and not to do harm.   HIPPOCRATES

A merry heart doeth good like a medicine. . . .
                                        PROVERBS 17:22

Any attempts to view the bacteriologic activities of our federal agencies of today is blinding and bewildering. But they had small, one might appropriately say, microscopic beginnings. For the most part, we can consider the major achievements in our field as they were developed by the Marine Hospital and Public Health Service, by the several agencies of the United States Department of Agriculture and, by special commissions, as in the case of the yellow fever investigations, of the medical corps of the Army. With the rapid development of our country, especially the rise of the new West,[1] the huge crops from the deep topsoil of our marvelous Mississippi Valley, the tremendous timber and mineral resources, and the transcontinental railroads heavily subsidized by federal grants came the inevitable increase in the strength of the central government and a sense of nationalism. We observe the rise of federally supported scientific agencies under several executive departments and during and since World Wars I and II, the alarming increase in many federal bureaus, especially those with regulatory functions, those of the armed services, and those of the Atomic Energy Commission. We shall look only at the bureaus that up to 1918–19

have contributed importantly to microbiology. Most research, whatever the field, adds details only, threads that soon get woven into the
general fabric of our knowledge.

United States Marine Hospital Service and Hygienic Laboratory

J. J. KINYOUN,

MILTON J. ROSENAU, JOHN F. ANDERSON,

GEORGE W. MC COY, AND ALICE EVANS

Way back in the days before our federal government had grown to
such massive proportions with its almost limitless control over our
well- or ill-being, while we were still struggling to become a workable
federation, on July 16, 1798, President John Adams approved a bill
providing for a system of compulsory sickness insurance for American
seamen to be supported out of their wages and administered by the
United States Marine Hospital Service. In this we were following the
example of England in attempting to protect persons without a local
community claim.

The first scientific report by the United States Marine Hospital
Service, before there was any Hygienic Laboratory, indeed before
microorganisms had been accepted as important agents in disease, was
an extensive monograph published in 1881 by W. C. W. Glazier,[2]
Trichinae and Trichinosis, a disease caused by a small round worm
Trichinella spiralis visible to the naked eye. Glazier gave an excellent
history, an inclusive bibliography with references to all reported cases
in man both in this country and in Europe. The first in this country
were in three cadavers reported by Bowditch (1842). The first diagnosed case from this country was described by Virchow, in a woman
who returned to Germany, having acquired the infection apparently in
Iowa (1856). Reference is made to Leidy's discovery of trichinae in
the hog (1846), but credit is given correctly to Zenker, Virchow, and
Leuckart for determining the important routes of transmission (1860
et seq.). Leuckart (1866) stated "the rat is its principal host and the
chief cause of infection." Larvae encysted in human muscle had been
described earlier by Tiedeman in Germany (1821) and by Peacock in
London (1828), although there is controversy because the microscope
was so little used in the drawings and descriptions. Paget, while a

student at Bartholomew's Hospital, London, made dissections of a cyst with more accurate sketches.

The Marine Hospital Service early became involved in quarantine measures against epidemics, although the legal authority still remained with the states. Since we knew neither the causes nor modes of spread of these diseases, conflicting notions and emotions produced many sharp states rights conflicts. In the last quarter of the nineteenth century, as different bacteria were shown to be the causative agents in specific infectious diseases, methods of diagnosis of both cases and carriers gradually became possible, so that the quarantine responsibilities of the Marine Hospital Service led it to attempt to confine epidemics at the port of entry. Asiatic cholera was the epidemic disease most feared at this time, and New York was the major port of immigration. In August, 1887, therefore, a single room on the ground floor of the marine hospital at Stapleton, Staten Island, was opened for cholera studies with J. J. Kinyoun (1860–1919) in charge. This was called a laboratory of hygiene and it was here that the Public Health Service first made its official acquaintance with bacteria.[3]

Kinyoun had had some training in bacteriology both with Koch and at the Pasteur Institute in Paris and was ready to apply his knowledge. With Biggs and Dunham[4] he demonstrated the cholera vibrio in stools of immigrants, enforced specific rather than general quarantine with good results. Four years later the Hygienic Laboratory was moved to larger quarters in Washington, Kinyoun still serving as Director until 1899, when he was sent to take charge of the quarantine station in San Francisco Bay. Plague had appeared in Honolulu in that year, and the health officers were alert to the possibility of vessels entering the port with plague on board. The next year the plague did break out in San Francisco. Dr. Kinyoun showed his robust courage in standing up under the attack that broke over the heads of both city and federal health officers. "Perpetrators of the greatest crime that has ever been committed against the city," was one of the milder charges hurled upon them.

As the first director of the Hygienic Laboratory,[5] despite meager facilities, Kinyoun set standards for public service and also stressed the need of developing research. He remained with the service until 1903, when he became director of the H. K. Mulford Laboratories at Glenolden, Pennsylvania. In 1907 he made another change, when he accepted the chair of pathology and bacteriology at George Washington University Medical School. Stimson described him as "solid, dependable and industrious in bacteriology." In 1909 he served as president of the Society of American Bacteriologists.

Milton J. Rosenau[6] (1869–1946) was the second director of the United States Hygienic Laboratory from 1899 to 1909. He was graduated in medicine from the University of Pennsylvania in 1889 at the amazingly early age of twenty years and was immediately commissioned in the United States Public Health Service in which he served nineteen years. During this active growth period of the country, although the major efforts of the service were still control and routine practices, increased emphasis on investigation was noteworthy. In 1901, ten children in St. Louis died from tetanus, apparently as a result of contamination of diphtheria antitoxin. As often happens, a tragic accident was necessary to obtain action long recommended. The next year the Public Health Service was reorganized providing expansion and full responsibility for all "biologicals," including the preparation and standardization of antisera and vaccines. Disinfectants and disinfection were also part of the day's work and in Rosenau's hands became the subject of a useful book. Many members of the laboratory, including the chief, contributed to a comprehensive study of milk and its relation to public health (1909); this study is still a valuable source for details and the hygienic aspects of this all important food.

In 1906 appeared the first of the most important researches of Rosenau's Washington period, a short paper with John F. Anderson, his colleague and successor as director of the laboratories, on *A study of the cause of sudden death following the injection of horse serum*. Producers of antisera had observed these accidental deaths among guinea pigs used for standardization of diphtheria and tetanus antitoxins, and occasional severe reactions, even death, had occurred among treated patients. To determine, if possible, the basis of such reactions, Anderson queried a possible common cause in all these dramatic incidents. In their papers, the authors refer to the work in this field by von Pirquet and Schick (1905) and that of Otto the same year and 1907, but they were not aware of the earlier suggestive papers (1902) by Richet and Portier. They pressed on with these studies during the next three or four years with excellent results essentially synchronous with those from Europe, but arrived at independently. The fact that the hypersensitive or allergic reaction was not due to the antitoxin as such, but was a specific reaction to the horse protein, that bacterial and other proteins would also sensitize, that an incubation period of several days between the sensitizing and shocking dose was necessary, that the off-spring of sensitized mothers were also hypersensitive, and that guinea pigs may be sensitized by feeding were all brought out by their studies, which were highly important in the history of these complex phenomena.

Since anaphylactic shock in guinea pigs is frequently referred to as the "Theobald Smith Phenomenon" because of the title of Otto's illuminating studies (1905 and 1907), I am giving Smith's only published reference to the reaction in an abstract of discussion following one of the Rosenau and Anderson papers before the American Medical Association in 1906. Smith stated that he had been interested in the phenomenon since 1902, but had made no special effort to analyze it. In his sample experiment given in a table, he allowed an interval of only 2–3 minutes between the first and second injections and used 3–5 cc. volumes in each injection. A small percentage of Smith's animals died (neither symptoms nor autopsy findings described in the abstract); actually a larger percentage of his controls that had not received the primary injection died than in the group that had received such injections. Possibly the serum was toxic in such doses. At any rate, informed persons would agree that, in these experiments, Smith was not dealing with anaphylactic shock or allergy, making apparent the confusion existing at that time.

In 1909 Rosenau accepted the chair of preventive medicine and hygiene in Harvard Medical School, a position he held until he reached the age of retirement in 1935. A highly important contribution was his *Preventive Medicine and Hygiene*, the first edition in 1913, continued through six editions under his hand; now it is in the eighth edition with many authors under the editorship of K. F. Maxcy. No one had produced so readable, arresting, authoritative a volume full of personal experience, invaluable to all persons studying, teaching, and working in the fields. A sanitary survey of a city or town, which he emphasized as an excellent method of learning, for each medical student, has been used profitably by several institutions. During much of this period (1913–22), Rosenau was also active in organizing and in teaching in the Harvard–Massachusetts Institute of Technology School for Health Officers. During the decade this school rendered excellent service.

In experimental contributions, Rosenau's most important work in his Harvard period was, I believe, a continuation of his studies on allergy. With Harold Amoss, he demonstrated that the condensed moisture from the expired breath of five of eight persons tested would specifically sensitize guinea pigs to the subsequent injection of normal human blood serum. They obtained definite symptoms of anaphylactic shock in twenty-six of ninety-nine animals.

The obstinacy with which we cling to unproved but seemingly plausible hypotheses is exemplified by the long history of so-called ptomaine poisoning. That ptomaines are nonspecific secondary cleavage products of protein putrefaction, most of them inert or no more poisonous than the corresponding ammonia salts, has been shown by the many students of this question. Authoritative statements such as these have been common: "Ptomaine poisoning is a refuge from etiologic uncertainty" (Jordan). "Ptomaine poisoning is a good term to forget" (Chapin). "Ptomaine poisoning is a term clearly incorrect" (Savage). "It is not so much decomposed food as infected food that may be dangerous" (Rosenau). The question of food habits of different peoples is highly disturbing to emotions. In this country, we eat raw oysters and clams, including the whole intestinal tract of the delectable bivalves, and in China, they enjoy somewhat decomposed ancient eggs. Which seems to you the more esthetic? Under suitable conditions, neither is dangerous. Rosenau in his studies (with others) on the "Milk Question" (1912) and in his survey of typhoid fever in Washington was brought sharply into the problems of enteric diseases and the related difficulties of preservation of foods. Similar studies were continued in his Boston era, especially by his students John Weinzirl and L. R. Bartlet. In connection with the repeated charges of ptomaine poisoning following ingestion of commercially canned foods, Rosenau acquired a poison squad, volunteers from his medical class. These men over a considerable period of time ate anything and everything, canned asparagus and other vegetables, salmon, chicken, sardines, etc., sent to the laboratory from the packs that had been charged with containing poisonous ptomaines. The men throve, saved money on their food bills, and Rosenau told me that not even a case of diarrhea occurred among the volunteers during the experiment. Thus were unjustified assertions again overthrown.

Rosenau's studies with Brues on the possibility that the biting stable fly, *Stomoxys calcitrans*, might transmit poliomyelitis stimulated many investigations with these and other insects as possible vectors. So far none has proved important.

Retirement from Harvard was only a spur to Rosenau. He at once accepted a call to the University of North Carolina where for eleven years, until his death in 1946, he was active in the upbuilding of the new division of public health in that institution and in that area. In a biographical sketch, Winslow remarked, "It is probable that no single individual has ever taught so many public health workers so much as Milton J. Rosenau."

Rosenau, although never robust, enjoyed an unusually long career. Fifty-seven years of successful professional life were his with the background of a closely knit affectionate home-life, so characteristic of Jewish families, and noteworthy in these days of casual divorce. Rosenau, personally as well as professionally, was appreciated for his quiet dignity, his hospitality, and his gracious almost silent pleasure in helping associates. He received many well-deserved honors, including the presidency of several national societies such as the Immunologists, the Epidemiologists, the Society of Tropical Medicine, and the Society of American Bacteriologists. His presidential address before the last-named society revealed much of his charm and his philosophy of life. He borrowed the title and theme from Horace Walpole (letter to Horace Mann, 1754) and also from Walter Cannon who had used the theme for a chapter in one of his books. "The Princes of Serendip," as their highnesses traveled, "were always making discoveries by accidents and sagacity, of things they were not in quest of; for instance, one of them discovered that a mule blind of the right eye had travelled the same road lately, because the grass was eaten only on the left side, where it was worse than on the right—now do you understand Serendipity." With this magic cloak over his shoulders, Rosenau roamed the centuries, giving stimulating examples from the lives of men from many fields, including microbiologists such as Ronald Ross, Theobald Smith, Alice Evans (a Princess of Serendip), and from his own work on anaphylaxis with Anderson, emphasizing that with sagacity plus much work these men had made advances not apparent in the announced primary purpose of their investigations. And there was joy in the work. A bit of serendipity resulting from scientific studies may be even more valuable than the actual discoveries.

One of these secondary effects is the infiltration of the scientific method into the mode and thought and attitude of herd psychology. It has taught a frank facing of realities calmly and impersonally. It has shattered shackles and traditions and superstitions, that have long chained our attitudes and methods of thought. . . . It is no longer impious

Upper left   JOSEPH LEIDY, 1823 1891
                    Photograph taken during his middle robust years.

Upper right   CARLOS JUAN FINLAY, 1833–1915
                    From a portrait painted in his later years.

Lower left   DAVID HENDRICKS BERGEY, 1860–1937
                    Photograph taken about 1915, at the age of fifty-five.

Lower right   ARTHUR PARKER HITCHENS, 1877–1949
                    Photograph taken about 1914, at the age of thirty-seven.

Upper left   CHARLES WARDELL STILES, 1867–1941
         Photograph taken about 1905, at the age of thirty-eight.

Upper right   ERWIN FRINK SMITH, 1854–1927
         Photograph taken about 1906, at the age of fifty-two.

Lower left   LORE ALFORD ROGERS, 1875——
         Photograph taken about 1922, at the age of forty-nine.

Lower right   CHARLES THOM, 1872–1956
         Photograph taken about 1950, at the age of seventy-eight.

to doubt. All our problems, even those of an emotional nature, may now be discussed with calm detachment.

And this Rosenau said in 1934. How far from the truth his optimism led him! In closing, he said, "Longevity is a poor index of progress. It is of no use to live longer unless we can live better. In other words, progress is measured in spiritual rather than material terms. Our next step then is mental and moral hygiene."

In the Anderson period of the Hygienic Laboratory (1909–15) increased appropriations gave opportunity for further emphasis on investigation. The successful production of measles in monkeys by Anderson and Goldberger[7] (1911) was an outstanding advance in our knowledge of this almost universal virus infection of man. Hektoen had successfully infected human volunteers, but as always in the history of a disease, its experimental production in lower animals was a beginning of rapid advance. The Hygienic Laboratory investigators found the virus in the blood in sufficient quantity during the first twenty-four hours of the rash to reproduce the disease. And they also demonstrated, with some difficulty, the presence of the virus in the nasopharyngeal secretions early in the disease and the absence of infectivity of the desquamating scales. This research confirmed epidemiological observations.

Another major achievement was the experimental production also by Anderson and Goldberger of one of the world's great plagues, epidemic typhus fever (1909, 1910, 1912). They were able to infect monkeys directly by injecting blood from sick patients, also by louse bites, and by injections of crushed lice from similar sources. This success will be described in our discussion of Ricketts' experiments with Rocky Mountain spotted fever. Goldberger was unquestionably one of our country's most successful research scientists, his greatest achievement not in microbiology but in nutrition in relation to pellagra. As head of a large team (1914, *et seq.*), he proved that inadequate protein diet, hog and hominy, was the cause of this disease so prevalent in many southern states. Dr. Goldberger's early death was a great social loss.

George W. McCoy[8] (1876–1952) began his long and noteworthy career with the United States Public Health Service in the first year of this century, climbing the various ranks and serving as third director of the Hygienic Laboratory from 1915 to 1937. A large-scale reorganization occurred in 1930 with the elimination of the well-known name of Hygienic Laboratory and the establishment of the National Institute of Health, later several Institutes. It was a period of rapid growth.

We shall describe McCoy's discovery of *Bacterium tularense* in the chapter on California. Besides the finding of this new organism, his work on the wide distribution of sylvatic plague and on the relative nontransmissibility of leprosy in temperate climates are especially noteworthy. He had a rare combination of qualities; accomplished in administration, painstaking in the inspection of laboratories for approval of their biologicals, alert to the unusual in routine studies (*B. tularense*), and imaginative in research. In line of duty, he contracted typhoid fever, tularemia, and dengue fever. McCoy was modest and kindly, lovable, easy of approach, definitely not puffed up. After his official retirement, like Rosenau, he accepted a teaching position, exerting a favorable force in Louisiana as professor of public health and preventive medicine at the state university where he grew old gracefully, passing on his valuable experience to a younger generation.

Just as the Public Health Service first became officially aware of bacteriology through an epidemic of cholera at the port of New York, its concern with bacteriology was further increased by the 1900 epidemic of plague in San Francisco. Because of clashing statements and interests, the city and California boards of health were glad to turn over their troubles to the federal Public Health Service. Similar attitudes have appeared elsewhere, and one after another the maritime states have given over their quarantine duties and sold such properties to the United States. In 1906[9] Congress appropriated half a million dollars for such purchases; New York, the last to hold out, sold its property in 1921. One great advantage of the federal control is the privilege, obtained by reciprocal agreements, of stationing our officers as guests in the important ports of the world. This prevents many hardships for immigrants and meets epidemic difficulties nearer their source.

A disease in which Americans have made significant contributions is brucellosis. Both the name and the appreciation of the importance of the disease in man come after the period of this survey, and the earlier observations were made not in the United States, or as so commonly was the case, in Europe, but in this instance, on the island of Malta. David Bruce (1855–1931), an English bacteriologist and military physician, isolated from an obscure disease in man a small coccoid organism that he later found in the urine and milk of goats. In 1897 another apparently unrelated observation was made by a Danish bacteriologist, Bang (1848–1932) who cultivated a small bacterium from one of the important and widespread diseases of livestock. Later (1914) a similar organism was isolated from a disease in hogs by Traum of the United States Bureau of Animal Industry. From 1912, Alice Evans (1881——),[10] first at Wisconsin, later in the United States Department of Agriculture, and then at the Hygienic Laboratory, gradually brought order out of the confusion by laborious application of well-known agglutination techniques and cross-absorption methods. She demonstrated that all of these organisms were closely related, with common as well as specific antigens; thus the genus *Brucella* was created.

Of the manifold functions of the Public Health Service one more, frequently bacteriologic in nature, must be mentioned with cordial approval, that of examination into the possible value of unconfirmed "cures." Dr. McCoy when director of the laboratory was especially patient and fairminded in meeting the claimants, many of them sincere.

Cures for tuberculosis have easily headed the list of these preparations. . . . In most of these cases, the claims had been made that experimental animals could be protected against or cured of tuberculosis infections, and the whole argument was allowed to rest on the outcome of animal tests. Since these tests always turned out negatively, the claimant left without the license, and it is believed without ill will.[11]

I must give one example of another type, the unfortunate experience with Friedmann of Berlin in his sensational visit to this country especially in New York City and Providence.

Dr. Friedmann had made many claims for his turtle bacillus vaccine (1912–14), and many patients with tuberculosis, always hopeful, had been brought together even from long distances by the exaggeration of newspaper statements. As a result of a careful study by the committee of the Public Health Service, John F. Anderson, at that time director of the laboratory, and Arthur M. Stimson, assisted by James P. Leake, forced the refusal of a license. They found Friedmann secretive, antagonistic, and vascillating; he would not divulge his method of preparing the vaccine. They did observe its use on some eighty-eight human patients and on many guinea pigs, rabbits, and monkeys. The vaccine was not harmless as Friedmann had stated; it produced abscesses in some cases, and in some seemed to be a factor in the exacerbation of the disease.

Each one of us tends to be gullible in fields in which he is not well informed: from batteries for automobiles, and even more important, to vaccines for tuberculosis, we need examination by competent, unbiased investigators of products offered to the public.

With the reorganization of the public health services in George McCoy's period, if we may be permitted to peep over the fence once more, one now finds three hundred rolling acres at the center, Bethesda, Maryland, with many excellent laboratories and a large competent staff, as well as regional laboratories such as the Rocky Mountain Laboratory at Hamilton, Montana, and the Communicable Disease Center at Atlanta, Georgia. And one finds many hospitals including the enormous one at the Bethesda center, a specialized National Leprosarium at Carville, Louisiana, and the large replacement on Staten Island, where the original Hygienic Laboratory was born. Somewhat overwhelming are the enormous expenditures involved, until it is remembered that all of these represent a small fraction of the sums spent for military purposes and these institutions are for constructive rather than destructive and defensive objectives.

United States Department of Agriculture
### *All flesh is grass.*						ISAIAH 40:6

Local societies of natural history and for the improvement of agriculture were numerous in the colonial days. Indeed the gentleman farmers among whom one should include the two presidents, Washington and Jefferson, contributed both influence and actual experience. The farmer of Mt. Vernon, as he was often affectionately called, became an honorary member of one of the earliest societies, the Philadelphia Society for the Promotion of Agriculture, during its first year 1785; that same year a society was founded in South Carolina, and others followed. The United States Department of Agriculture grew directly out of the Patent Office established April 10, 1790. During the 1830's the reorganized Patent Office, then in the State Department, began to distribute seeds and collect agricultural statistics.[12] From these small beginnings with the stimulus and pressure from the local societies, some of which became national in scope (United States Agricultural Society, 1852), new functions were added with ever changing organization and increasing appropriations. Under Lincoln in 1862, what is now the United States Department of Agriculture became a separate agency headed by a commissioner of its own, and in 1889 this department was raised to cabinet rank[13] with Norman J. Colman as the first of the secretaries of agriculture. The Homestead Act of 1862 extended our farming areas broadly, and the Morrill Land Grant College Act, also of that year, gave incentive and strength to scientific farming with its varied problems. Increasingly, branches of the department were formed with changing titles and organization.

BUREAU OF ANIMAL INDUSTRY

DANIEL E. SALMON

Epizootics among domestic animals as serious menaces to our economy and fears that such little understood diseases as hog cholera, pleuropneumonia, and Texas fever of cattle might spread to man brought federal appropriations as early as 1869 for the study especially of the last named disease. An outbreak of pleuropneumonia in New Jersey and New York in 1879 and the consequent decree of the British Privy Council requiring that all American cattle arriving at British ports be slaughtered promptly on the dock hit the pocketbooks and brought prompt action. By prompt diagnosis and slaughter of infected herds, the disease was eradicated in this country by 1892. By a ban on all shipment into this country of animals from countries where the disease persists, it has not reappeared in the United States, a truly remarkable achievement.[14] Daniel E. Salmon was appointed department veterinarian, and a few years later (1884) the Bureau of Animal Industry was established with Salmon as chief. All manner of derision was cast at the "horse doctor" bill, but the diseases were not myths as was asserted in Congress, and the solution of the mysterious Texas fever, one of our microbiological achievements of world significance, came from their laboratories in a few years time.

Bovine Tuberculosis

THEOBALD SMITH AND JOHN R. MOHLER

The control of bovine tuberculosis in our enormous land has been a conspicuous achievement in world history. This success has been due to innumerable persons, to practically all legislative units from town meeting to the United States Congress, to the intelligence of informed farmers, to our courts of law, and to the expressed wishes of the humble ultimate consumer. It was an audacious undertaking and was correlated with the campaign against tuberculosis in man. We might discuss this campaign and its almost incredible success in our Massachusetts chapter, because it was Theobald Smith who made clear the differences between the bovine and human types and showed that the bovine organism could infect man. Massachusetts was the first state (1894) to adopt a plan to tuberculin test all cattle, the reactors to be slaughtered and the owners reimbursed according to an appraised value.[15] But heavy opposition developed; the accuracy of the test was questioned; the high costs and the destruction of so many cattle with minimal lesions brought hostile resistance. To meet the situation, a committee of experts was appointed by the legislature to consider and report. The majority was convinced and urged the continuance of the plan, but the highly vocal minority won the day because of the lack of public knowledge of the disease and of its contagious character.

We might equally well consider the problem in the Pennsylvania section, because late in December, 1891, Leonard Pearson, head of the State Livestock Sanitary Board, returned from Koch's laboratory with some of the new reagent, and on March 3, 1892, near Philadelphia, he administered the tuberculin test to 80 cattle of which 30 reacted positively. Between 1892 and 1895, Pearson personally tested many of the best herds in America. This was done at the expense of the owners without reimbursement for the loss of the positive reactors. A campaign of education was developed, and in 1896 the Pennsylvania board adopted a modification of the Bang-Guttmann plan in use in Denmark and in Germany. The testing was voluntary on the part of the farmer rather than compulsory as in the Massachusetts attempt; the tests were carried out by veterinarians in the employ of the board, and the owner was reimbursed to an appraised limit for the positive reactors that were slaughtered. An alternative procedure permitted the establishment of two separate herds, the reactors in one and the nonreactors in the other. Calves from reacting cows were removed at birth and brought up in the nonreacting herd. Thus a slow method for acquiring tuberculosis-free herds was developed. The Pennsylvania farmers were not enthusiastic over this Bang method, partly because of the difficulties and expense of maintaining two herds and the restrictions on the marketing of the milk and partly because the incidence of reactors was much higher in Denmark and in Germany than in Pennsylvania, so that it seemed possible in Pennsylvania, but impossible in the European countries, to provide moneys for reimbursement for slaughtered cattle. By 1900 despite opposition and perfectly legitimate questions, considerable tuberculin testing had been done in different states under a variety of controls. Progress towards tuberculosis-free herds was especially rapid among the pure breeds. Ravenel, of the Pennsylvania Livestock Board, confirmed Theobald Smith's findings and was active in combating Koch's early contention that the bovine organism was essentially harmless for man.

In the District of Columbia, the tuberculin testing of all the dairy cattle was begun in 1906 under the direction of J. R. Mohler of the Bureau of Animal Industry. This brought the men of that bureau more directly into the movement; their influence was strong, and federal moneys were so important that I am placing the story of this astounding achievement in the control of a devastating disease under the aegis of the federal agencies. J. A. Meyers wrote of bovine tuberculosis:

> In the nineties, the United States required that all animals imported from Europe and Canada for breeding purposes be tested with tuberculin and the reactors eliminated before they were sent into this country. Quarantine was established at our ports of entry and all imported cattle in due time were again tested, to make sure that no reactors reached the farms of this country.
>
> In 1909, provision was made whereby all cattle in the District of Columbia must be tested with tuberculin and the reactors removed. No animal which reacted to the tuberculin test was permitted to enter the District. This was the beginning of area testing by the United States Bureau of Animal Industry. On the first test approximately 19 per cent of the animals in the District reacted, by 1916 only 1.1 per cent, and by 1925, there were no reactors. . . . The first herd to be accredited as free from tuberculosis was that of Ford and Graham of Garrett Park, Maryland, on April 27, 1908.

From this small beginning, with many professional, educational, governmental, and economic forces involved, the accreditation spread more rapidly than had been expected. The economic pressure exerted by important cities, such as Milwaukee and Chicago, both of which refused to permit the sale of milk from any but negative reacting cattle, should not be underestimated. The Milwaukee statute was to become effective April 1, 1909.

The provisions of the amended ordinance [that portion of the section quoted above which required tuberculin testing] were attacked in the court by an aggregation of dairymen organized for that purpose. The constitutionality of the provision was attacked and the accuracy of the tuberculin test itself was challenged. The case was tried in the Circuit Court of Milwaukee County, was remanded for hearing before Joseph G. Donnelly, Referee Court Commissioner. His findings of fact were reported to the Circuit Court on September 7, 1909 and upheld the position of the Commissioner of Health. The Circuit Court upheld the findings of its referee. The plaintiff, named John Quincy Adams, then appealed to the Supreme Court of Wisconsin, which on January

10, 1911, upheld the opinion of the Circuit Court. The plaintiff then appealed to the United States Supreme Court and that body, on May 12, 1913, affirmed the decision of the Wisconsin Supreme Court.[16]

Other large cities such as Minneapolis and Chicago had similar conflicts, but these were slowly overcome. Actually the opposition was helpful in maintaining interest.

In 1917 the Tuberculosis Eradication Division of the Bureau of Animal Industry was established. Under the direction of the able veterinarians, John A. Kieran, John R. Mohler, and A. E. Wight, a cooperative plan with the states was set up similar to that found successful in the District of Columbia. With a high degree of co-operation on the part of members of the veterinary profession, increasing appropriations from the federal government, counties, and states, and growing demands for tuberculin testing on the part of the farmers, accreditation of herds and areas swept on. Taking the so-called modified accredited standard, less than .5 of 1.0 per cent reactors, these areas grew rapidly until the whole country received the accolade by January, 1941.[17] Some idea of the magnitude of the task can be obtained by observing the number of cattle tested each year, beginning with 20,101 in 1917, reaching a peak of 3,131,252 in 1932, then dwindling because of reduction in number of reactors, with a total of 46,137,586 during the twenty-two years to 1939. The total public cost for this achievement from 1917 to 1939 was about $224,000,000 or approximately that of the large plane-carrier *Forrestal* with its necessary complement of planes and guns. In 1921 it was estimated that the annual loss from tuberculosis among cattle in the United States was $30,000,000,[18] so that the elimination of these losses over eight to nine years would be sufficient to compensate for the entire public expense. And this takes no account of the reduction in scrofula and other types of human tuberculosis incited by the bovine bacillus.

Hookworm Disease

CHARLES WARDELL STILES

Another man who worked in several federal laboratories contributing importantly to microbiology was Charles Wardell Stiles (1867–1941). With much of his scientific training in Europe, a Ph.D. degree from the University of Leipsig and having been a student at the Pasteur Institute and Collège de France, he was appointed shortly after his return in 1891 as zoologist in the Bureau of Animal Industry, where he was associated with D. E. Salmon and Theobald Smith.

Helminths are worldwide with a higher incidence as parasites among the lower vertebrates than in man. In man their occurrence is greater in tropical and subtropical areas where the lack of prolonged low temperatures and the habits of the people, in rural areas especially, are favorable for their spread. Stiles' researches in this broad field were outstanding. His exhaustive detailed index catalogues of medical and veterinary zoology (1902–12) with Albert Hassal and many collaborators are quoted throughout the world, as are his monographs on many phases of helminths and other animal parasites. These were begun in his early days at the Bureau of Animal Industry with studies on the tapeworms of poultry, then the tapeworms of hares and rabbits (1896), followed by a report of broader researches on the verminous diseases of cattle, sheep, and goats.[19]

In 1880 Germany prohibited the importation of sausage from the United States because of its alleged causing of trichinosis in Germany, and for the same reason in 1883 all our pork was excluded. This led to desirable attacks on trichinosis in hogs in this country. The Imperial German government finally agreed to permit shipments of hogs from the United States, provided these were passed after microscopic examination. Local government restrictions in parts of Germany, however, continued to interfere seriously with our export of hogs.

In 1898–99 Stiles was sent as agricultural attaché to our embassy in Berlin. Here he did a remarkably convincing job. In a voluminous report based on follow-up of cases of trichinosis in Germany, Stiles showed that not a single reported case of the disease was traceable to American certified pork and that the charges against our uncertified pork could not be substantiated. He also showed that the expensive microscopic inspection gave a false sense of security. Over 32 per cent of the cases in Germany from 1881 to 1898 were traced to pork that had been passed by microscopic inspection. This method save for checking purposes has now been largely discontinued.

Because of the spectacular nature and the public disputes over Stiles' work with hookworm disease, many of his other publications have been overlooked save by those working in the immediate fields. In May, 1902, he published a description of a new world species of hookworm, *Uncinaria americana* (later *Necator americana*), parasitic in man. The public health significance of this study, including also the earlier investigations of Bailey K. Ashford,[20] physician in the United States Army, to whom Stiles gives major credit for the recognition of this disease in Puerto Rico, took Stiles over into the Hygienic Laboratory, where he remained active until his retirement thirty years later. In 1903 he issued a long report upon prevalence and geographical distribution of hookworm disease in the United States, emphasizing that in those southern rural areas he had studied, this ground itch was one of the most important and most common diseases and that the proverbial laziness, anemias, and dirt-eating were due in large measure to this infestation.

Mark Sullivan in "Our Times" in the *New York Sun* headlined that the "germ of laziness" had been found. Did that ever get under the skin of our southern friends and when one thinks of the mode of entrance of hookworm larvae, that was *actually* occurring in more ways than one. Walter H. Page of Theodore Roosevelt's Country Life Commission enlisted the aid of Frederick T. Gates, the far-seeing, white-haired, florid-faced giant, advisor in philanthropy to John D. Rockefeller. Gates became interested in the important fact that the disease is largely preventable, and Mr. Rockefeller agreed to underwrite a five-year program.

The Rockefeller Hookworm Commission set to work with Wycliffe Rose as administrative secretary and Stiles as scientific secretary. Both men were aware of the necessity of obtaining local co-operation and achieved it with skillful diplomacy. Stiles gave lectures and demonstrations everywhere; he stressed that the problem was one of only 20 per cent treatment but 80 per cent prevention. Harsh criticism was thrown at Stiles and the Commission, but they continued the campaign, and towards the end of the period, Stiles admitted that the unwarranted attacks had actually helped by widely advertising the work. We must expect and we need conflict, but it should be kept to the issues rather than permitted to descend to personal attacks. The work of the Commission and collaborating agencies was so successful that the Rockefeller Foundation has carried on similar practices in other parts of the world.

Stiles was a vigorous, outspoken, versatile scientist who occasionally aroused antagonisms, but we need such competent accurate-visioned gadflies. A listing of his astounding bibliography with monographs in many fields, both synthetic and analytic in type, would be out of place here. He received merited honorary degrees and many other honors both in Europe and in this country, including the gold medal of our own National Academy of Science for eminence in the application of science to the public welfare.

DAIRY BACTERIOLOGY

LORE A. ROGERS, JAMES M. SHERMAN, AND WILLIAM MANSFIELD CLARK

Problems of the dairy industry have pressed hard on the United States Department of Agriculture. The Dairy Division was instituted in 1895, and its bacteriologists under several reorganizations have made continuous studies of production and control of milk, butter, cheese, and related products. Lore A. Rogers, after experience under H. L. Russell at the University of Wisconsin and then at the New York Experiment Station at Geneva, joined the Department of Agriculture in 1902 and later became chief of the dairy research laboratories. He built up an excellent organization, selected able men, gave them freedom of initiative so that he and his colleagues have contributed extensively to the scientific knowledge of dairy practices underlying the centuries old rules of thumb.

One finds in these studies stress on the use of quantitative chemical methods in investigating bacterial physiology instead of the cookbook procedures then so commonly used. As is true in much of the early work, many of their findings are now common knowledge. Early papers of Rogers and associates[21] showed that most of the deterioration in storage butter at low temperatures resulted from chemical changes rather than bacterial action and could be avoided by using sweet cream rather than "ripened" cream, a practice that promptly came into common use, and more or less revolutionized the butter industry in America.

Rogers was one of the American bacteriologists to develop quite early (1914) the preservation of bacterial cultures by drying them from the frozen state by gas removal. He demonstrated its application to the conservation of stock cultures as well as in the production of large quantities of microorganisms for industrial purposes. Improvements in equipment have been made, but the methods used in laboratories today are essentially those described by Rogers. This study led him to the rescue and support of the invaluable American Type Culture Collection during one of its frequent near-deaths.

The several groups of bacteria found in dairy products, some essential, others incidental, and still others pathogenic, were in turn subjected to exacting analyses, frequently requiring the development of new methods. Although much of this work came after our period, the laborious investigations of almost innumerable strains of coliform organisms from dairy products, from feces of different species, and from grain and other nonfecal sources were carried out before the end of World War I. The value of Theobald Smith's earlier contention that the gas ratio of carbon dioxide to hydrogen indicated a fundamental difference in metabolism was sustained by the more exact chemical studies of Clark and Lubs, showing that the *Escherichia*, commonly intestinal in origin, gave a one to one ratio and the *Aerobacter*, widely distributed in nature, a two to one ratio.

In 1914 Eldridge and Rogers published the first of what became a long series of papers from this laboratory on the bacteriology of cheese of the Emmenthal type using almost innumerable cultures from many sources. The propionic acid bacteria of the major European observers, Freudenreich and Jensen, were found only in small numbers, but J. M. Sherman isolated and recommended the use of *Propionibacterium shermanii* for the essential flavor of Swiss cheese, and still later W. C. Frazier, Rogers and colleagues emphasized the significance of the thermophilic bacteria and members of the acidophilus group. "But that" as Mr. Kipling would say, "is another story." To one who delights in the flavors of aged Swiss cheese, the rules of thumb seem still to prevail far too widely in spite of all our laboratory studies.

Rogers has received strong allegiance from his colleagues and well-earned public honors such as the presidency of the Society of American Bacteriology in 1922, several honorary degrees, and Rogers Hall on the campus of the University of Maine, where he took his undergraduate work, named for him. He was a modest person who worked long hours at the bench even when he had a large group of associates and assistants. He loved gadgets and was skillful with his hands. A great honor was the considerable volume *Fundamentals of Dairy Science* by associates of Lore A. Rogers. This was not just a *Festschrift*, but a serious, advanced textbook in the field, fostered by the American Chemical Society. It has been through two editions, 1928 and 1935, and a third is under way. Upon retirement Rogers returned to his home town in Maine, bought a run-down creamery where he built up a business of over a million dollars a year. Although the business is now handled largely by his son, Rogers still makes some poured plate studies of the milk that comes into the plant.[22]

One of William Mansfield Clark's[23] early (1912) contributions to bacteriology, while chemist in the dairy division of the United States

Department of Agriculture, was a splendidly planned and executed study of the gases of Emmenthal cheese, demonstrating that they were chiefly carbon dioxide with a minute amount of nitrogen. Later (1915) his study of the reaction of bacteriologic culture media demonstrated the fallacies of the Fuller titrable acidity method then commonly used. Following Arrhenius, he recommended the titration of the hydrogen ion concentration either by electrometric means or by dye indicators. This led to the many investigations of Clark and Lubs that provided bacteriologists the world over with dyes, sensitive to acid-base changes and oxidation-reduction potentials.

Another of Clark's close collaborators and friends over many years was Barnett Cohen (1891–1952), the biochemist-historian-bacteriologist to whom we are dedicating these chronicles. He devoted himself so effectively to furthering bacteriology and so generously to all, that although most of his active career (now unfortunately completed) came after our period, I shall attempt a fragmentary picture here. Among his early publications, we find studies with Winslow on the effect of chemical changes on bacterial growth, in this instance, the viability of coliform bacilli in polluted and unpolluted waters. In the summer of 1917 he began his professional association with Clark in the dairy division of the United States Dairy Association. They found that a broad range of pH had little influence on the growth of certain bacteria during the logarithmic growth phase. Later he worked intensively with Clark at the Hygienic Laboratory on oxidation-reduction indicators and himself synthesized bromcresol green that proved of value in the series. The striking reducing activities of bacteria and the various physico-chemical conditions influencing growth especially under anaerobic conditions continued as Cohen's important interest throughout his life.

As first Archivist of the Society of American Bacteriologists, he fostered symposia on local history of bacteriology, providing authentic backgrounds, personal tales, and grass-roots material for future broader histories. As editor of *Bacteriological Reviews* for its first fifteen years, he set high standards and successfully induced authors to survey wide fields, thus aiding the investigators themselves and keeping us all from falling into the rut of our own limited efforts. His enjoyment of music including the subtle melodies of several foreign languages, his translation of some early Leeuwenhoek letters, his continued interest in nutrition, and the generosity with which he shared his wise philosophies gave him a wide circle of friends.

Aspergilli and Penicillia

CHARLES THOM

In 1904 when Professor Atkinson of Cornell University was asked to name a dairy mycologist for a project in cheese-ripening, he wrote: "I know no man in America that is qualified in dairy mycology. I know nothing about it myself but if I had time, I could learn it, but I am too busy. Thom has training enough and brains enough to learn it and he needs the job." That was the basis of Charles Thom's appointment as mycologist in the United States Department of Agriculture with assignment at Storrs Experiment Station in Connecticut to work with H. W. Conn. Thom (1872–1956) was born on a farm in Illinois, studied at Lake Forest College, spent a summer at the Woods Hole Laboratories, where most eastern biologists gravitate sooner or later, obtained his doctor's degree at the University of Missouri, and was an assistant at Cornell at the time this opening came. He was assigned the problem of the production of cheeses ripened by molds, both the soft varieties such as Camembert, acted upon by surface fungi, and the Roquefort or Stilton types, commonly cured at low temperatures in caves, acted upon by molds within the mass of the cheese.

After a period of observation and study in Europe, Thom isolated and described *Penicillium camemberti* and *P. roqueforti* from imported cheeses and found an enormously confusing literature concerning these and related organisms. Colleagues urged him to clean up the mess in penicillium and aspergillus and that, through much of his life, with the aid of able assistants, is exactly what he proceeded to do. His detailed yet broad-gauge monographs on these groups overwhelm a mere bacteriologist. He has commonly leaned towards practical problems and has consistently kept one foot in the furrow. As his monographic studies emphasize, he has been insistent on carefully detailed studies of the organism, of its ecological environment, as well as the purpose of the work both immediate and distant.

For ten years, while employed by the United States Department of Agriculture, he worked at the Storrs Experiment Station making the production of mold-ripened cheeses more practicable in this country. Then, broader opportunities under changing titles and responsibilities drew him, still under the United States Department of Agriculture to the Washington laboratories. James N. Currie, chemist, followed Thom from Storrs, and Margaret B. Church, mycologist, soon joined the group; they wrote a long series of studies on aspergilli and penicillia obtained from widely varied sources.

In 1915–16 Thom and Currie published papers on oxalic and citric acid production by different strains of *Aspergillus niger*. From these came the later work of Currie leading to the commercially important industry, the mycological production of citric acid. Thom's identification of Fleming's penicillin-producing organism as *Penicillium notatum* is said to have aided in the finding of more productive strains of the organism. His large personal collection of fungi that had been necessary for his comparative detailed studies became the nucleus of the collection of the United States Department of Agriculture, now located at the Northern Regional Laboratory in Peoria, Illinois.

As chief of the division of soil microbiology, Thom became involved in the broad field of plant pathology. He developed a practical important means of controlling a devastating disease, the so-called Texas root rot of cotton and many other crops, caused by *Phymatotrichum omnivorum*. Essentially the method as described in his presidential address before the Society of American Bacteriologists is not specific; but the addition of organic matter by prompt plowing under and the stimulation of the active soil microorganisms to great but temporary activity, "contains" the growth of the fungus.

Thom was a versatile, active, robust, aggressive person, sharing his energy with several national societies; he was zealous in defending his judgments, enjoying the battle of wits in cases brought to court through the pure food and drug act, and appreciative of the association with and opportunities for his younger colleagues. Direct and somewhat blunt in speech, conservative in politics, he received many honors for his attainments including membership in our National Academy of Science.[24]

SOIL BACTERIOLOGY

G. T. MOORE

They not only work for nothing and board themselves
but they pay for the privilege.   DAVENPORT

A national survey of the factors in soil fertility was a task of the United States Department of Agriculture over many years. These activities were carried on during several reorganizations (Division of

Agricultural Soils, 1894, and Bureau status some years later) in co-operation with state experiment stations. The growing of leguminous crops for soil improvement was practiced on an empirical basis, more than 2000 years ago by the Romans and still earlier by the Chinese. The scientific studies of the German chemists, Hellriegel and Wilfarth (1886), showed that the root nodules on these plants were directly associated with the process, and the Dutch bacteriologist, M. W. Beijerinck (1888), isolated pure cultures of bacteria (rhizobia) from the nodules and proved that these organisms are the cause both of the nodules and of the nitrogen fixation from the air. Free-living nonsymbiotic bacteria (azotobacter and others) were also isolated and studied especially by Beijerinck and by Winogradsky. In this country the chemist, Atwater, at Wesleyan demonstrated by quantitative studies the acquisition of atmospheric nitrogen especially by leguminous plants (1885–86) and suggested the possibility that microorganisms were involved.

These exciting discoveries aroused investigators and farmers throughout the world. A flood of studies resulted with attempts to commercialize the practice by different methods without the necessary foundation. Then came the slowly advancing knowledge of the many and variable factors that affect nodule formation. The United States Department of Agriculture did its part in this advance especially through the work of G. T. Moore[25] and his associates. They began distribution of pure cultures to practical farmers for inoculation purposes as early as 1904 and 1905. To insure nitrogen fixation, the use of bacteria to inoculate the seed has become a well-established practice, especially when a leguminous plant is seeded for the first time. The underlying facts were demonstrated and commonly accepted by 1910. Remaining were the important detailed studies of the intricate mechanism; these have been carried on in the laboratories of the United States Department of Agriculture, experiment stations, and universities everywhere.

> *And he gave it for his opinion, that whoever*
> *could make two ears of corn or two blades of grass*
> *to grow upon a spot of ground where only one grew*
> *before, would deserve better of mankind and*
> *do more essential service to his country*
> *than the whole race of politicians put together.*
> JONATHAN SWIFT—*Gulliver's Travels*, "Voyage to Lilliput"

BACTERIA IN RELATION TO PLANT DISEASES

ERWIN F. SMITH

The Smiths are a wonderful family whether we spell it Schmidt, Smith, or Johnson. I appreciate the name not only because of the many splendid men and women of that name I have known, but because it encourages me to think of the excellent genes widely scattered throughout our human race. Given a reasonable amount of health and the opportunity and the necessity for struggle, the Smiths come to the top. In the escape of the British frigate *Amethyst* I find an especially inspiring example of successful struggle. Most of the officers were killed or eliminated early, and the Smiths, the ordinary young men from the streets of London or Birmingham, took over with courage, skill, and some good luck, and in spite of the persecutions and cannon fire of the Chinese communists brought the battered ship down the Yangste River and eventually to its home port.

Interesting that in the early decades of bacteriology in this country, the topmost scientist in the study of diseases of man and other animals was Theobald Smith (Schmidt) and in plant bacteriology, Erwin F. Smith.[26] They were not related, had no background of family professional achievement, carried no silver spoons in their mouths, but they struggled, won their spurs, and became leaders. We have already shown our appreciation of Theobald Smith; may we now present briefly the story of the Smith who in this country and to a high degree in the world at large showed that bacteria were important in causing plant diseases.

I have only a nodding acquaintance with any plant pathology, and I have never sat at their tables save as a guest well below the salt, but I have good friends in the field whose suggestions I shall use liberally. To provide a background, I shall quote and paraphrase statements of George K. K. Link on the relation of bacteria to plant disease. As his statements were written some ten years after our period they present even more sharply than would an earlier history the dearth of early road-breaking work in this as in other fields of microbiology in this country.

Although a series of observations and experiments by botanists, culminating in the classical work of de Bary [of the University of Strasbourg] on the smut and rust fungi [1853] had conclusively demonstrated the association of fungi with diseases and the nature of parasites and infection, and de Bary's brilliant researches on the fungus of the late blight of potato [1861–63] [cause of the potato famine in Ireland] had established the causative role of *Phytophthora infestans* in a specific disease, these researches ap-

parently did not affect the main current of experimentation and of speculation as profoundly as the work of Pasteur and Koch. With the work of these men, especially that
of Koch in establishing the science of bacteriology, leadership in the study of infection
and disease definitely passed to the animal field. . . . Woronine in 1866 had discovered
bacteria in the root tubercles of the legumes, and Davaine in 1868 had inoculated plant
tissues with bacteria and obtained soft rot. . . . It is generally stated that the work of
Burrill of the University of Illinois, on the nature and cause of fire blight, was the first
which conclusively established [1867–83] that a specific bacterium, *Micrococcus amylovorus*, causes a specific plant disease. This however, was not completed until 1885
when Arthur of the Geneva Experiment Station, New York, grew the organism in pure
culture, and produced infection with it.

. . . .

In the main, however, the botanical profession was so blinded by the successes of
de Bary and other mycologists in establishing causal relations between specific plant
diseases and species of fungi, that it failed to consider seriously the possible role of
bacteria in plant diseases. Indeed, the consensus of opinion was that bacteria could not
cause specific diseases of plants. The legume nodules were not considered pathological,
and their bacteria were designated as symbionts. It was contended that if bacteria were
at all involved, they were secondary to fungi, because bacteria could not enter the
stomata of plants.

. . . .

The credit for overcoming this notion, most prevalent in Germany, belongs notably
to Sorauer who in 1886 began to defend the concept that bacteria cause specific plant
diseases, but even more to Erwin Smith who carried on a spirited polemic with Fischer
of Berlin during 1896–1901 and convinced the botanical world that certain bacteria
cause specific plant diseases.

With this background of the intellectual climate in plant pathology,
may we consider the life of this American leader in that field, Erwin
Frank Smith (1854–1927). He was born in the village of Gilbert Mills
in upper New York, but early in his childhood his parents migrated to a
farm in Hubbartson in southern Michigan where he spent his days
under restricted farm conditions with the usual chores and irregular
schooling.

Life led him over rough and hilly roads, but he made the grade. Five
years of working on a farm, three years of teaching in a district school,
two years of working first as a guard and then a keeper in the Michigan
State House of Correction in Ionia, and two years of working for the
State Board of Health under Dr. Henry F. Baker provide an understanding of his slow progress in formal education. He received a bachelor's degree in biology from the University of Michigan in 1886 at the
mature age of thirty-two years.

His friend and sometime colleague, Professor L. R. Jones of the

University of Wisconsin, in writing the biographical memoir for the National Academy, stresses Smith's early association with Charles F. Wheeler, a scholarly druggist, who introduced him to two new languages, French and that of field botany. Years of alert ramblings together over field and bog resulted in Smith's first publication, a noteworthy handbook, *The Flora of Michigan*, by Wheeler and Smith in 1881.

After receiving his bachelor's degree (1886), Smith was immediately appointed to the recently established Laboratory of Plant Pathology in the Bureau of Plant Industry of the United States Department of Agriculture; there he remained, save for interludes of investigation in various centers of plant disease, throughout his active life. It is beyond the scope of these chronicles to list the many important contributions initiated and carried to fruition by Smith.

In the autobiographical synopsis of his research work written in 1922, Smith dismisses the first period of his work (1886–93) with the remark that "it included much proof-reading, reviewing, translating and editorial and miscellaneous hack work." Actually in this period he had worked extensively on peach yellows, which was his doctor's thesis at Michigan, on several other obscure diseases of peaches, on a wilt of orange trees, and on alternaria diseases of muskmelons.

In the next years he studied intensively certain destructive diseases of melons, cotton, cowpeas, potatoes, tomatoes, cabbage, and bananas. Fusaria widely distributed in the soil had been considered saprophytes, but in a paper (1899), "The Fungous Infestation of Agricultural Soils in the United States," and by subsequent isolation and inoculation studies, Smith with D. E. Swingle showed that these fungi were important pathogens; according to L. R. Jones, it was a prophetic paper. Through the work of W. A. Orton, resistant cottons, melons, and cowpeas have been obtained and are now growing in fusarium-infested soils in the South.

In 1893 Smith became fascinated with the wilt of cucumbers, squashes, and other cucurbits, caused by a bacterium, *Bacillus tracheiphilus*, and spread, as he showed, by a beetle *Diabrotica vittata*. These studies led Smith into a sharp controversy, at times rather bitter, with the European plant pathologists, Robert Hartig and Alfred Fischer, who maintained that bacteria were unimportant in plant disease. Fischer published disparaging comments about Smith and the American investigators who were demonstrating bacteria as causative agents in several plant diseases, asserting that their results were due to dirty technique. The progress of the studies both in Europe and America finally vindicated Smith and his associates. In the synopsis of his scientific attainments, Smith stated: "Fischer never forgave me but I could not do otherwise; nor do I regret the polemic since it cleared the air and advanced the science." The conflict was highly stimulating to Smith, and he so enjoyed the wrangling that it was undoubtedly significant in leading him to work intensively for the rest of his life on bacterial infections of plants.

Urged on by the controversy, Smith experimented with a tubercle disease of olives (previously well studied in Italy by Savastano and by Cavara) using pure cultures obtained from tubercles cut from plants in Italy and in California; *Bacterium savastani*, E. F. S., was shown to be the causative agent. Then came the researches, so indelibly associated with Smith's name, on the crown galls, a group of tumors shown by Smith and Townsend to be caused by *Bacillus tumefaciens* (1907). A series of excellent studies with these organisms launched Smith into another debate on the probable similarity and relation of these tumors to malignant tumors of man and other animals. Again he showed keen enjoyment in the contest. Both sides seem to us now to have been unnecessarily vehement at times, and Smith tended to minimize the differences in plant and animal anatomy and physiology, but he showed certain similarities convincingly. About this time (1910), too, Peyton Rous gave Smith additional ammunition for his tumor thesis in his demonstration that certain chicken sarcomata are caused by organisms, in this case, filterable viruses.

Paraphrasing one of Smith's summaries: crown-gall tumors exhibit growth independent of function, are incompletely vascularized with early central necroses. They can be grafted on other plants, can be excised, will recur if not completely removed, the nuclei divide both by mitosis and by amitosis, and the proliferating tumor cells are embryonic in nature. In 1903 the American Medical Association awarded Smith the certificate of honor "for his work on cancer in plants," and in 1925 he was elected President of the American Association for Cancer Research.

Smith's vital interest in bacteria as possible agents in plant diseases led him to review the whole field beginning in 1896 with a series of papers in the *American Naturalist*. These were later (1905-14) amplified into a monograph, three somewhat rambling quarto volumes, the first devoted largely to bacteriologic techniques, on *Bacteria in Relation to Plant Diseases* published by the Carnegie Institution of Washington. In 1920 he boiled this material down into a much needed textbook, *Bacterial Diseases of Plants*.

In Smith's own synopsis of his work, he lists twenty plant diseases from which he and his associates had isolated a bacterium and placed the organism in causal relation with the disease in question. In Bergey's *Manual of Determinative Bacteriology* (Third Edition, 1930) fifteen such organisms are ascribed to Smith with several associates, one in the genus *Erwinia*, and fourteen in the genus *Phytomonas*. Others are named as imperfectly described. In the appreciative biographical sketch of Smith by L. R. Jones, long-time distinguished professor of plant pathology at Wisconsin, the six organisms listed below are specifically named and may therefore be taken as highly important:

> *Bacillus tracheiphilus*, 1893–95; causative organism in bacterial wilt of cucurbits (cucumber, squash, cantaloupe).
> *Bacillus solanacearum*, 1896; brown rot of tomato, potato, and other solanaceae.
> *Pseudomonas campestre*, 1897; black rot of cabbage and other crucifers.
> *Bacillus phaseoli*, 1897; bean blight.
> *Pseudomonas stewarti*, 1898; bacterial wilt of maize.
> *Bacillus tumefaciens*, 1907–26; crown galls.

"No investigations of corresponding thoroughness had been made in this field in Europe."

Erwin Smith was a versatile, aggressive, prolific contributor to his field; he was a good showman, accomplished in the languages of western Europe, and an artist both in spirit and with pen and pencil. He published some 167 original papers and 73 scientific reviews. Most of his associates in the laboratory were young women trained by Smith, and only slowly were they given increasing responsibilities. He was always desirous of checking observations himself.

Among less specific papers, the most noteworthy are a translation, with Florence Hedges, of Duclaux' *Pasteur: the History of a Mind*, and a privately published volume of some two hundred sonnets and other verse on many themes, especially the delights of nature, dedicated to the memory of his first wife, Charlotte May Buffett. In addition to the sonnets are translations in verse from French and Italian poems that he cherished. In ranging through Smith's writings from his rather lengthy reviews to his controversies and then to his appreciation of music and the other fine arts, one is impressed with the breadth and variety of his interests and his rich appreciation of life's opportunities. He has received justified acclaim from all sides including several honorary degrees and membership in our National Academy of Sciences. Those who worked with him emphasize his dogged perseverance and his intense pleasure in the literature of many languages. Unfortunately his two marriages were childless. Those working in plant pathology cherish their memories of Smith and give him great credit.

Contributions from the Armed Forces

The world-important discoveries of the United States Second Yellow Fever Commission have been presented (see Chapter IV), and also the momentous findings of the committee that investigated the disastrous typhoid fever epidemics in our military camps of the Spanish-American War. The wider responsibilities we acquired from that war forced upon us problems of tropical diseases. Amoebiasis had been with us since earlier times, but it assumed greater importance when our troops were stationed in the tropics and returned to this country.

Charles F. Craig of the Army Medical Corps contributed notably to our knowledge of this disease. He successfully distinguished *Entamoeba coli* and *E. histolytica* on morphological grounds and on the modes of reproduction and then proved the pathogenicity of the histolytica by reproducing the disease in kittens through feeding them with this organism, but not with *E. coli*. This careful study is sometimes overlooked because of the more complete demonstration by Walker and Sellards in the Philippines in 1913. These investigators successfully infected 18 of 20 human volunteers with *E. histolytica* and demonstrated as Craig and others had also done that *E. coli* is nonpathogenic. These studies, together with the earlier thorough pathological reports of Councilman and Lafleur (1891), and those of Walker on parasitic amoebae both of man and other animals (1908) furthered world knowledge in amoebiasis. Craig was a modest, thorough scholar, always helpful to colleagues; aside from his contributions in amoebiasis and malaria, he was influential with Stitt, Strong, and others in building our prestige in the broad fields of tropical medicine.[27]

In 1906 an important primary observation was made by Samuel T.

Darling in the Ancon Hospital, Canal Zone, Panama. In sections of liver and spleen from natives suffering from a generalized fatal disease, he found in pseudotubercles of these organs microorganisms that he thought resembled the Leishman-Donovan bodies in a similar disease, kala-azar, of the Orient. Assuming, therefore, that the organism was similarly a protozoan, he named it *Histoplasma capsulatum*. Since then the organism has been cultivated and has been shown to be a fungus; a specific skin test similar to the tuberculin reaction is available. The disease has been found more widespread in this country than was thought at first, especially in the region around the Great Lakes; it should be considered when tuberculosis is suspected.

3

THE CENTRAL VALLEY

CHAPTER XIII

Bacteriology as It Developed in Three Types of Institutions in our Midwest

A foolish consistency is the hobgoblin of little minds,
adored by little statesmen and philosophers and divines.

EMERSON

Our forebears had overpassed the Appalachians or pushed around them along the Hudson River and the Mohawk and Ohio valleys well before the time of the bacteriologic excitement. With few exceptions, as at the University of Michigan with Victor C. Vaughan and Frederick G. Novy as the inoculating forces, the young science grew later in the area we now term the Middle West than it did along the eastern seaboard. Lesser contact with European scientists and smaller resources were doubtless factors. The interest in the young science and the rapidity of its growth varied in the different areas. In each institution and in each state, the men who introduced bacteriology to the curriculum of our teaching institutions or to the public health and dairy laboratories merit commendation and should be considered in any detailed history. But although their enthusiasms ran high, their influence was chiefly local, and most of them played only minor roles in bacteriology on any national or world basis. Medical practice was in a deplorably chaotic state. Here as elsewhere, the new point of view and methods gradually made more accurate diagnoses possible, and also, although more slowly, gave means of prevention by breaking paths of transmission or by immunologic practices.

By the last of the 1880's or early 1890's, most of the larger institutions and many smaller ones were offering a few didactic lectures in bacteriology, usually by someone trained not in bacteriology but in a related science. I have elected to tell the story of its growth in the Midwest, chiefly under three differing conditions; one, Michigan, in the atmosphere of a young university medical school; two, Chicago, in a rapidly growing metropolis with many confusing agencies, and three, Wisconsin, in a budding institution where bacteriology was born in the departments of botany and zoology and grew in strength in the College of Letters and Science and in the College of Agriculture years before the rise of a medical school. In most other Midwestern states, bacteriology grew somewhat more slowly.

Michigan—Bacteriology in a State University Medical School

VICTOR C. VAUGHAN AND FREDERICK G. NOVY

Three faces wears the doctor, when first sought
An angel's, and a god's, the cure half wrought,
But, when that cure complete, he seeks his fee
The devil then looks less terrible than he.

EURICIUS CORDUS, OF ERFURT, GERMANY
FIRST HALF OF THE SIXTEENTH CENTURY

Under the long, enlightened presidency of James B. Angell (1871–1909), the University of Michigan was the first of our great state universities to become prominent. The Medical School also advanced early beyond others of this group, with two vigorous adventurous bacteriologists, Vaughan and Novy, as the ferments. For a young institution to have two such spirits probing into this new science with a background of the better-founded subject chemistry was unusual if not unique. Together they formed a favorable growth medium. It is difficult to speak of one of these men without the other as they worked together for years, and the characteristics of the one effectively complemented those of the other.

Although Vaughan was Novy's senior by thirteen years, they had much in common. They came up the hard way and achieved high distinction both professionally and personally. Both of them began as chemists, and Novy especially maintained this point of view. Following a somewhat different youth, Novy in Chicago and Vaughan on a Missouri farm, they landed by different paths at the University of Michigan when it was a small institution. With slight intermissions they remained there for the rest of their long lives, acquiring about all the degrees the institution offered, including that in medicine. Both men became interested in the exciting possibilities offered by bacteriology in the eighties and went together, as did other first generation bacteriologists, to drink of the water at the fountainheads, with Koch in Berlin and at the Pasteur Institute in Paris.

Vaughan was temperamentally the extrovert, could meet and charm both the sceptical legislator and the callow student; he was the jovial, robust leader of the larger groups. In contrast, Novy, the exacting more isolated scientist, remained a laboratory man with a smaller number of devoted disciples. Vaughan obviously enjoyed the social life of Dean of the Medical School, while Novy, as the years rolled on, withdrew more and more into the laboratory. Each, in his own way, was a dramatic leader and can properly be placed with the productive pioneers in the bacteriology of this country.

Many are the biographical sketches of Victor Clarence Vaughan[1] (1851–1929), including the engaging autobiography *A Doctor's Memories*, written towards the end of his long life, and the Memorial Issue of the *Journal of Laboratory and Clinical Medicine* that he edited successfully for years. That journal has typified the breadth of his medical interests and has emphasized, as he did so successfully, the necessity of bridging the gap between the laboratory and clinical methods of study. He was forced into early maturity by the horrors of our Civil War and was active through two subsequent wars, momentous in the world, but less bitter in this country. In his life, he observed astounding changes in our ideas, our economy, and our lives, and himself aided in the important part medical bacteriology contributed to these changes. The country was bursting both its breeches and its hat bands.

During the War between the States, he learned to move suddenly with his family on the Missouri farm when immediate danger threatened. When the rush of horses brought guerrilla marauders, favoring either or neither side, to the isolated farm, the butt of a musket against the front door would summon young Victor, the man of the house at the age of thirteen, to face the inevitable pistol and query, "Where is your father." (His father, frequently in hiding, had suffered fracture of both legs from a falling tree; one of these had never healed, leaving a suppurating wound.) Vaughan tells in his autobiography, "Then I lied with ease and readiness. We all lied; even the Negroes lied. Irene would say as the searching party went through her cabin: 'Fore God, I hain't seen Mars John for weeks'; when the truth was that she had prepared his dinner not two hours before and he was then in the woods down on Sweet Springs." Also Vaughan tells tales of the prevalent diseases in his own and other families. Three diseases had caused the majority of deaths, the bloody flux in childhood, tuberculosis in adult life (Vaughan himself had this disease but made a good recovery), and cancer in old age.

Vaughan's preparatory academic experience was obtained at a number of small, short-lived, private institutions striving to make do with what they had; he was graduated from one of these, Mount Pleasant College, in 1872. When Vaughan presented himself for admission to the graduate school of the University of Michigan, the kindly President Angell told him that they could not recognize the Mount Pleasant degree, but if he obtained the approval of the professors in his chosen subjects, chemistry, geology, and botany, he might try it for a semester. Obviously the trial was successful as Vaughan stayed on earning a master's degree in 1875, a Ph.D. the next year, and two years later the degree in medicine; he earned the three degrees in four years.

In 1875, three years before he had completed his work for the medical degree, Vaughan was appointed assistant in chemistry; he continued rapidly up numerous steps with different titles, and in 1891, became dean of the growing medical school. Following the granting of his medical degree in 1878, Vaughan engaged also in the practice of medicine for twenty years and was a member of the State Board of Health for thirty years; he was a prolific writer and an efficient administrator. He made good use of the long hours which he devoted to his professional work. He was rarely home from his laboratory before six in the evening, and for many years saw patients each evening beginning at seven o'clock.

Among Vaughan's extraordinarily varied contributions (over three hundred papers and books), the upbuilding of the University of Michigan's Medical School from lean beginnings to an admirable modern institution through thirty years (1891–1921) as dean was his major achievement. With this came his own development in medicine and bacteriology, public hygiene, and epidemiology. In his autobiography, he describes the early years of the institution; the first twenty-five were without any hospital whatever. When he went to Ann Arbor in the seventies, there was only a receiving home called by courtesy the University Hospital. Consultations, free both to physician and patient, brought increasingly greater numbers of outpatients and a growing appreciation of the service. Under his wise leadership, with steadily improving appointments on the faculty, came an astounding growth.

With the prospect of opening the State Laboratory of Hygiene the next year, both Vaughan and Novy went to Berlin in 1888 to take Koch's course, at that time almost a prerequisite for recognition in bacteriology in this country. Koch was still giving the lectures, but the laboratory was in the competent hands of Fränkel. Vaughan's early chemical studies on arsenic and antimony led him into expert testimony in court and indirectly into the field of food-poisoning, first biochemical, later bacteriologic, and the study of ptomaines which were exciting attention at that time. His work with Novy on *Ptomaines, Leucomaines and Cellular Toxins* (1888), his studies with Wheeler on "The Split Products of the Tubercle Bacillus (1907)," and later with two of his sons, V. C., Jr., and J. Walter, on a broad study of *Protein Split Products* (1913) exemplify the period and the effort on the part of many to identify the toxic products obtainable from nonpathogenic as well as pathogenic bacteria. Nonspecific toxic split products, so-called anaphylatoxins, and other still unknown toxic substances produced when serum and a variety of substances in colloidal suspension are brought together, intrigued Vaughan and other investigators. That many of the phenomena of bacterial injury and possibly those of anaphylaxis were due to split products produced by the action of antibodies on the bacteria was an attractive hypothesis. Subsequently the demonstration that no protein cleavage occurred in these antigen-antibody reactions and that indifferent materials such as agar or kaolin acting on serum could produce similar effects and that the anaphylactic reaction was a cellular rather than a humoral process made the simple explanation untenable. The injection of a variety of substances into the body may result in acute symptoms of shock which resemble the anaphylactic syndrome. Rather generally the liberation of histamine from tissues, platelets, etc., is the underlying mechanism.

Vaughan volunteered his services in the Spanish-American War. On the personal side his own severe attack of yellow fever with weeks of illness and loss of weight from 210 to 150 pounds tells the story. On the professional side his work with the Typhoid Commission (Reed, Shakespeare, and Vaughan)[2] was most important, indeed one of the best and most detailed studies in that field ever made. By the time of publication of this report both Reed and Shakespeare had died, and the work of preparation fell largely on Vaughan. Personal contact and flies, not the water supplies, were found chiefly responsible for the tragic losses. As a consequence of his work on this commission, he became involved in the study of typhoid fever in many cities, especially those in the Great Lakes region. At the time of the 1893 World's Fair at Chicago some thirty public and innumerable private sewers poured their contents into Lake Michigan, the source of the city's water supply. Conditions were so bad that the commission appointed to study and report recommended the laying of a pipeline from a spring near Waukesha, Wisconsin, to the fairgrounds, and this was done. Vaughan became only slightly involved in the lawsuit that was subsequently brought by St. Louis against Chicago for reversing the flow of the Chicago River with its heavy load of sewage (this will be discussed in the portion on Chicago). Vaughan's activities continued through World War I and later in Washington where he worked with the National Research Council of which he was a member; he with a son, Henry F. Vaughan, and George T. Palmer wrote as his farewell contribution, an extensive work (two volumes), *Epidemiology and Public Health.*

Vaughan was such an outgoing, appreciative, friendly person that he was loved by many and respected by all. His well-deserved honors were numerous, including membership in the National Academy of Sciences, presidency of the American Medical Association, and the publication of an extensive *Festschrift*, a number of the *Journal of Laboratory and Clinical Medicine* with valuable contributions by many of his students. A major contribution by Dr. and Mrs. Vaughan was a welcoming home and five stalwart sons, all successful physicians.

Frederick George Novy's (1864–1957)[3] early contributions were, as in Vaughan's case, allied to chemistry and pharmacology, especially studies of several important alkaloids. After his trip in 1888 to Europe with the course in bacteriology under Koch and Fränkel and some weeks at the Pasteur Institute working with Roux, Novy dug into bacteriologic investigations, making a complete survey of the methods of cultivating anaerobic microorganisms. The well-known Novy jar and, more importantly, the isolation and description of a pathogenic anaerobic sporeformer, named by Migula and by Bergey after Novy, were among the results. In Europe, a synonym, *Clostridium oedematiens*, is frequently used.

In the years following the establishment of the State Hygiene Laboratory (1887), both Vaughan and Novy gave talks all over the state

Upper left   JOSEPH JAMES KINYOUN, 1860–1919

Upper right   MILTON JOSEPH ROSENAU, 1869–1946

Lower left   JOHN F. ANDERSON, 1873——

Lower right   GEORGE WALTER MCCOY, 1876–1952
From portraits painted by Walmsley Lenhard.
Courtesy National Institutes of Health.

Upper left   VICTOR CLARENCE VAUGHAN, 1851–1929
             Photograph taken about 1910, at the age of fifty-nine.

Upper right   FREDERICK GEORGE NOVY, 1864–1957
             Photograph taken about 1899, at the age of thirty-five.

Lower left   HARRY LUMAN RUSSELL, 1866–1954
             Photograph taken about 1920, at the age of fifty-four.

Lower right   LEWIS RALPH JONES, 1864–1945
             Photograph taken about 1912, at the age of forty-eight.

preaching to a sceptical public the facts underlying the germ theory of disease, the evidence for contagion, and the importance of public health control. Novy succeeded in introducing public examination of potable waters in the early years of the twentieth century and in establishing an antirabies Pasteur Institute at Ann Arbor in 1903, only three years after the one in Chicago.

In 1900 (stated in greater detail, Chapter XVI) he was appointed bacteriologist to the federal committee to determine the presence or absence of bubonic plague in San Francisco. Novy carried out the bacteriologic studies with completeness, leaving no doubt that plague did exist, and with the pathological studies of Flexner showed that in the six fatal cases that came under their microscopes death was due to the plague bacillus.

An interesting sidelight on the slow progression of knowledge can be observed in a serious symposium as late as 1904 on the subject "Is Tuberculosis Due to the Tubercle Bacillus?" This debate was sponsored by the Wayne County Medical Society, and Novy and Vaughan took the affirmative side, while the negative side was upheld by McLean, a former professor of surgery, and Gibbes, a former professor of pathology, at the University of Michigan.

An important series (from 1905), largely with Ward J. MacNeal, included years of investigation on many species of hemoflagellates, especially trypanosomes. Certain malarial parasites and spirochaetes also came in for study during this period. *Borrelia novyi*, recovered from a case of relapsing fever in Bellevue Hospital, New York, resembles *B. recurrentis* morphologically, but differs from that organism in serum reactions; however, the antigenic structure of these spirochaetes apparently changes repeatedly during a single infection. Thorough studies beginning with *Trypanosoma lewisi* using the rat in place of a test tube were continued with successful cultivation on a blood-agar medium. These cultural studies Novy extended to pathogenic species, also cultivable, but with greater difficulty. Of course, everyone knew that these organisms were not bacteria, but that troubled no one; there were no recognizable departmental barriers. The study of protein split products begun with Vaughan was continued for years, chiefly with Paul de Kruif, in their many investigations of anaphylatoxins. Delicate studies in microbic respiration using the tubercle bacillus and other bacteria as the living agents became a major interest during his later laboratory years. Malcolm Soule, his successor in the chair of bacteriology at Michigan, was his collaborator in much of this work.

Novy began his active participation in the affairs of the University of Michigan as an assistant in organic chemistry, passed through the various ranks in hygiene and bacteriology, and spent the last two years, 1933–35, as dean of the Medical School. Both Vaughan and Novy were charter members of the Society of American Bacteriologists; among the many honors extended to Novy was the presidency of that society in 1904. Novy was more completely the laboratory man and the exacting scientist than his colleague Vaughan, and the later history of his graduate students attests the thorough quality of his training.

Novy, tall, gaunt, with a big frame, was somewhat ungainly. His lectures were dramatic, although somewhat wandering, excellent in diction, and he made comments on history, mythology, and the fine arts. He was an excellent showman. His students delighted in his mannerisms, his grimaces, the white vests, the tall wing collars encircling his long neck, the small head on the big body, florid complexion and fierce gray-blue eyes; "none in the world could be more like gimlets" says Paul de Kruif,[4] one of his early graduate students. In the laboratory he could work fourteen hours daily at the bench when the mood was on, wearing down his strongest assistants save possibly Ward MacNeal; then would some a spell of brooding inaction in preparation for the next attack. He had a caustic tongue, pithy and pointed, and yet was appreciative of human foibles and kindly withal. His laboratory class procedures were unpredictable, not well organized; his assistants never knew what he would require. Novy insisted that they should anticipate his demands. He never threw anything away; notes on articles he read, orders for tubes or flasks, inconsequential letters, outworn and outmoded instruments, including vertical autoclaves, were in the collection of stuff and rubbish that remained after his retirement.

He was contemptuous of incompetence. His greatest satisfaction was to leave all of his work "solid," as he termed it, without flaws and presented so clearly that anyone could repeat it with the same results. With the possible exception of the anaphylatoxin studies which still elude us, his scientific desire has been well sustained. We can quite properly think of Novy as the first of Vaughan's assistants, later his colleague. Among Novy's earlier students should be included: Charles McClintock, who built up the Parke Davis laboratories; Charles E.

Marshall, later active at Lansing, Michigan, and after that as professor of bacteriology and dean at the Massachusetts College of Agriculture at Amherst; Ward J. MacNeal, physically a giant, and effective both at Illinois and at the New York Postgraduate Medical School; Paul de Kruif, also a robust fighter, who after a period at the Rockefeller Institute devoted his flaming pen to the spread of the knowledge of *Microbe Hunters* and *Hunger Fighters* to the general public; and Wilfred Manwaring, competent investigator in several institutions both in Europe and in the United States, and finally head of bacteriology and experimental pathology at Leland Stanford University. Novy's students, his three physician sons, and two daughters, who married physicians, carry on.

A Glimpse into the Past

About a year before Novy's death at the age of ninety-two years, I made a trip to Ann Arbor especially to have a last chat with him and to cull what I could from his notebooks. I found him still a great, gaunt giant of a man, but now slightly shrunken, lying in bed in the sun-drenched southern bay on the first floor of his longtime home. The gentle housekeeper-nurse gave him his glasses but, even with them, his vision was defective, and I rather doubted that he recognized me. But we exchanged cordial greetings, and I at once recalled to him the time when we had been closest together as delegates from the Society of American Bacteriologists to the Pasteur Centenary in Paris in 1923. That brought back happy memories, especially the trip of the group to Chantilly with the many guests, including Mrs. Novy and Mrs. Clark. He had delighted in the day at Strasbourg with a special train to that city and university where Pasteur had gone as a young assistant in chemistry in 1849 and where he had made his startling tartaric-acid-crystal discoveries. He also enjoyed recalling other trips to Europe, especially the one in the summer of 1888 when he took his first course in bacteriology in Koch's laboratory. I was impressed again as I had been in my earlier contacts, with his clear-cut phrases, excellent command of language, his still hearty speech, and his flashing spirit. In reply to my inquiry, why he forsook chemistry for bacteriology, he replied that he thought of them as merely different approaches to the same underlying problems. We came away with renewed appreciation of his many contributions to his chosen field and of his high standards in science. Some of his students learned from him that "it did not matter if you worked five years to find out you had discovered nothing worth printing at the end of it, so long as you were always in there trying. Failure was all right so long as you didn't try to fool people with your failures."

MICHIGAN AGRICULTURAL COLLEGE

The Michigan Agricultural College[5] at East Lansing was the first of its kind in this country; it grew strong with the passage of the several federal land grant college acts (1862, *et seq.*) and state appropriations. Bacteriology had little recognition, however, until after the appointment of Charles E. Marshall[6] (1866–1927), who joined the experiment station staff in 1896 on receiving his bachelor's degree. While at Lansing, Marshall continued as a graduate student under Novy and also studied in Europe, including a period at the Pasteur Institute, the common practice among our early leaders. His experimental studies followed lines of the period and the region, the action of bacteria in the souring of milk, the effect of aeration of milk on elimination of odors, on fermentation, and on bovine tuberculosis. His textbook of *Microbiology* (1911 and 1917) with twenty-three authors gave unusually wide coverage such as Pasteur would have approved. Excellent chapters were included, not only in the fields commonly covered, but on yeasts and their uses in industry (Bioletti), molds (Thom), protozoa (Todd, revised in second edition by Tyzzer), microbiology of soil (Lipman), diseases of plants (Sacket), disease of insects (Wyant), and the microbiology of special industries (Buchanan, Edwards, MacNeal). With our increasing specialization, this fine, broadly inclusive text inevitably succumbed.

In 1912 Marshall left for the Massachusetts Agricultural College at Amherst where he had an active career as head of the department of microbiology and dean of the college. Spoilage of canned foods, bacterial rotting of root crops, bitter flavors in milk, and the viability of tubercle bacilli in cheese were fields of his investigations. In his presidential address to the Society of American Bacteriologists in 1914, Marshall emphasized the serial associations of organisms in nature as in the nitrogen cycle, wine-vinegar series, and the complex cycles of many helminths. He urged that "it is pertinent, in our researches, to consider an organism in its natural microbial associations as significant as in a laboratory pure culture," a thesis we have been prone to neglect.

As early as 1916, L. H. Cooledge began publication from the Michigan Agricultural College on Bang's disease, raising the question of its possible relation to disease in man. In later years this work developed into the highly important investigations on brucellosis by I. F. Huddleson and his associates.

Bacteriological Problems
of the Central Metropolis, Chicago, Illinois

LUDVIG HEKTOEN, EDWIN O. JORDAN,

THOMAS J. BURRILL, HENRY GRADLE,

BAYARD HOLMES, AND FREDERICK ZEIT

The King in his carriage may ride,
And the Beggar may crowd at his side;
But in the general race,
They are travelling all the same pace.

EDWARD FITZGERALD—CHRONOMOROS

Bacteriology grew slowly in the metropolis of the northern Mississippi Valley. Inertia, anticontagionism, and other prejudices, as well as practical necessities were strong. The well-documented story of bacteriology in Chicago, prior to the organization of bacteriologic teaching about 1890, has been presented appreciatively by Ludvig Hektoen,[7] and for this period I am leaning heavily on his statements.

After about 1891 Hektoen himself became the leader in pathology and one of the major figures in bacteriology both in this section and in the country at large.

The earliest signs of any interest in bacteriology in Chicago appear to be occasional articles and notes on disease germs, septicemia, antiseptic surgery and related topics which were published in the local medical press, beginning about 1869. There are no indications, however, that anyone in Chicago was following closely and at first hand the early developments and applications of bacteriology in France, Germany and England. The names of Pasteur, Lister and Koch are barely mentioned in the Chicago medical journals of the decade from 1869 to 1879. . . . It was at best a period of ignorance and doubt concerning the germ theory of disease and infection.

But in 1879 (three years after Koch's proof of the etiology of anthrax), Christian Fenger, who had come to Chicago from Denmark in 1877, reported on a case of acute endocarditis from which he made a microscopic demonstration of myriads of micrococci from the heart valves. Hektoen reports this as being the first demonstration of the bacterial nature of acute endocarditis on this side of the Atlantic. Occasional translations of a few significant articles from European journals began to appear in the local medical journals, such as Pasteur's paper on fowl cholera, his dramatic success in vaccination against anthrax, and in 1884, Koch's report on cholera in Egypt. About 1878–79 Lister's antiseptic surgery began to secure a foothold. Just prior to this change, the conditions at Cook County Hospital are vividly described by Roswell Park. "I saw men die after what seemed to me even minor operations. Scarcely a patient entered the hospital with a compound fracture whose doom was not sealed."

Koch's discovery of the tubercle bacillus (1882) was, in Chicago, as in Philadelphia, and New York, the awakening shock; the ease with which the bacilli could be stained in sputum from pulmonary cases, after the method was once learned, brought conversion to many sceptics. William T. Belafield, recently returned from Vienna (1882), demonstrated tubercle bacilli in each of twenty-two specimens submitted to him. In 1891 Belafield was appointed professor of bacteriology in Rush Medical College, although it was not until 1894 that a laboratory course in the subject was established there under the direction of "the silent" George H. Weaver.

In 1883 another young Chicago physician, Henry Gradle (1855–1911), recently returned from study with Koch, published a little book on *Bacteria and the Germ Theory of Disease*. This was based on eight lectures he gave at Chicago Medical College, now Northwestern University School of Medicine. From statements in his book, it is obvious that he himself did some work with bacteria; he made gelatin plates and demonstrated tubercle bacilli in sputum from thirty-five consecutive cases with pulmonary tuberculosis. Gradle, as early as 1886, pointed out the hazards of dumping Chicago sewage into Lake Michigan and then using the lake as the source of the city water supply, especially because there were over 5000 cases of typhoid fever annually in the city and the discharges would contain typhoid bacilli.

Still another early bacteriologist in Chicago, Bayard Holmes (1852–1924), largely self-taught with the aid of Sternberg's translation of Magnin's book, set up a laboratory in his bathroom while he was an intern in Cook County Hospital. With Christian Fenger, Holmes investigated the possibilities of air infection in the operating room and came up with conclusions contrary to the precepts of the day. By exposing gelatin plates for a period and subsequently counting the colonies, they concluded that the danger from air infection was trifling compared with the danger from contact infection. He urged greater care in the isolation of typhoid fever patients; "at that time patients in Cook County Hospital with tuberculosis, pneumonia, typhoid fever and other grave diseases were treated side by side without any special precautions. . . . There was much talk about sewer gas as the cause of diphtheria and typhoid fever, but only contemptuous references to the tubercle bacillus and other bacteria as causes of specific diseases [1887]." In 1890 Holmes became the first teacher of bacteriology in any medical school in Chicago with a laboratory in Chicago Medical College. Here as most everywhere else, the early interest was in the role of bacteria in the causation of human disease. The Chicago Pasteur Institute for the prevention and treatment of rabies, the first in the West, was founded by Antonio Lagorio in 1890.

But in the Illinois Industrial University, later the University of Illinois, a conception of bacteria broader than that of disease-inciting agents in man was being emphasized by Thomas J. Burrill[8] (1839–1916), professor of botany and horticulture. In 1882 he published a monograph on bacteria "silent working denizens of the earth, air, and the water," giving an excellent account of the activities of bacteria as they were then known, including a description of the tubercle bacillus. Earlier, in 1880, he had published one of the outstanding bacteriologic contributions made in this country, describing *Micrococcus amylovorus* as the cause of blight in plants, especially in pear and apple trees. I quote from a brief obituary written at the time of Burrill's death by Erwin F. Smith, our recognized authority in bacterial diseases of plants: "[Professor Burrill] did not publish fully in the modern sense of the word, but he saw clearly in many sections of diseased tissue that fungi were not there and that swarms of bacteria were always present and were therefore the probable cause of this mysterious disease. By inoculating masses of these bacteria (free from fungi under the microscope) he reproduced the pear disease many times." His discovery has been repeatedly confirmed thus opening a new door for plant pathologists.

Smith says of Burrill that he suffered the frequent fate of especially competent investigators in this country—namely, extinction by promotion. He became vice-president of the university and later dean of the graduate scholars. He was rich in honors, serving as president of the American Microscopic Society (1885–86) and president of the Society of American Bacteriologists at the time of his death in 1916. He was a kind, lovable man, and during the years we of a younger generation knew him, he was full of wisdom, a white-haired Nestor with an impressive flowing beard. At the Urbana meeting of the Society of American Bacteriologists in 1915, it was his wise council that persuaded the doubters to vote for the establishment of the *Journal of Bacteriology* that has been so important through the decades.

The chief men in the development of organized teaching and research in bacteriology in Chicago were Ludvig Hektoen[9] (1863–1951) and Edwin O. Jordan (1866–1936); the two worked together efficiently as they grew and achieved in several positions, chiefly those at the University of Chicago. Hektoen, slightly older, came up along stonier paths. He was born in Westby, a small town in Wisconsin, of hardy Norwegian stock, recent immigrants, and grew up speaking the Norse tongue more than the English. The stern discipline of a pioneer family, plenty of farm chores, few childhood games, and fewer books were his lot.

From the ages of fourteen to twenty years, Hektoen attended Luther College in Decorah, Iowa, and was graduated in 1883 with a B.A. degree. The classical type of curriculum was entirely prescribed—Latin, Greek, Norse, English, and German, with some mathematics, but none of the natural sciences. Most of the students were destined for the ministry; Hektoen's desire to escape theology led him into medicine, aided by the premedical course at the University of Wisconsin, taken during 1883–84. A year in charge of the drugstore at the Northern Hospital for the Insane at Oshkosh gave him some necessary money and a skill that stood him in good stead as he ploughed his way on through medical school. He attended the College of Physicians and Surgeons in Chicago for two years, 1885–87, receiving his medical degree at the end of that time. In none of his school years do we find any especially stimulating teacher nor indications of Hektoen's marked future success, although he was a conscientious student commonly at or near the head of his class. We at the University of Wisconsin like to think that the year he spent here with Birge, Daniels, and Trelease was more important than the time-proportion would suggest. After his medical school training, he won an internship at the Cook County Hospital by competitive examination, following a winter of hard study, mostly memorizing, Hektoen states. The two years there, he came under the stimulating influence of Christian Fenger, who had been trained chiefly in Denmark. In succeeding years several positions in pathology in a number of the medical schools and hospitals gave him increasing breadth of opportunity and contact.

The confusing story of the many reorganizations of the medical schools of Chicago concerns us only as bacteriology became increasingly prominent. From this point of view, paramount is the founding of the University of Chicago in 1892 with liberal endowment from John D. Rockefeller under the compelling leadership of President William Rainey Harper. Into this university, Hektoen was drawn in 1901 by appointment as professor and head of the department of pathology and bacteriology. This was a university department with obligations to the medical school that included also rather indefinite arrangements with the older Rush Medical School as well as opportunities for nonmedical and graduate students. The following year Hektoen was named director of the newly formed John Rockefeller McCormick Memorial Institute for Infectious Diseases that provided excellent research opportunities for many years. Unfortunately this institution passed out of existence as a separate research entity during the depression years. Money from this source continues, however, to aid in supporting investigations in the University of Chicago and in the publication of the *Journal of Infectious Diseases*.

Of the more than three hundred publications by Hektoen with his various associates, most of the first third are brief case studies in pathology and need not concern us. In this period, however, the invasive character of the young science, bacteriology, caught him and for the rest of his life the problems of infection and resistance occupied much of his attention.

His most important single contribution was the first production of measles in well-isolated human volunteers by the subcutaneous injection of blood from measles patients, demonstrating that the virus may be in the blood at least during the first thirty hours of the rash. This paper is characteristic of Hektoen's writings, clear and concise with a well-documented history, a model to follow. Here, he gives direct quotations from some of the early controversial papers such as that of Home (1758). Home's efforts were not so much a study of the nature and seat of the virus as an effort to produce the disease in a gentle and favorable degree. Later in 1911, several groups of investigators, including Anderson and Goldberger, Nicolle and Conseil, and Hektoen and Eggers, were successful in transmitting measles to several species of macacus monkeys.

Problems in immunity, especially antigens, antibodies and their specific reactions, including their chemical nature, sites of formation of antibodies, their modes of action in the body and their use as tools in the laboratory, were the subjects of scores of papers by Hektoen with

his younger associates. In all of this immunity work, Hektoen emphasized the necessity of obtaining the curve of antibody production rather
than, as had frequently been the case, the drawing of conclusions from
a single titration at the assumed optimum time. Important studies on
opsonins and phagocytosis and the effects of leucotoxic agents, such
as X-rays, mustard gas, and toluene, correlated with splenectomy and
ablation of other organs led him to state that "the mechanisms for the
fabrication of antibodies are quite secure from certain disturbances,
and they are in no way contradictory of the current view that these
mechanisms are located in the blood-forming organs." The value of
these contributions was recognized when he was asked to give (1910)
the Harvey Lecture on the formation and fate of antibodies. Although
many of the points are even today in a state of flux, this broad yet detailed lecture from a wise leader still repays reading.

The many papers using the precipitin reaction and purified proteins
as produced by Osborne and Wells added to our appreciation of the
specificity of these reactions along species lines, as for example blood
serum proteins, and along lines of organ specificity, for example, the
proteins in the crystalline lens of the eye. By the use of multiple and
of single antigens, Hektoen demonstrated what we now term the anam-
nestic reaction and that in the rabbit at least, "different precipitins
exist as separate entities." Streptococcal studies were an important
part of the work at the McCormick Institute from the beginning. Although much of this, because of inadequate methods, has not stood the
test of later investigations, the work of George and Gladys Dick and
the production of an antitoxin against the erythrogenic toxin of the
beta-hemolytic streptococci stem from these earlier efforts.

With all Hektoen's manifold experimental work (and he got his own
hands dirty) and his administrative duties both in Chicago and nationally, Hektoen became one of our most esteemed medical science editors. The *Journal of Infectious Diseases* from its inception in 1904, through
many years (sixty-seven volumes) and later the *Archives of Pathology*,
also for many years, developed under his editorship. Yet I cannot think
of these journals simply in terms of scores of published papers and
hundreds of pages; I think, rather, with appreciation of his editorial
criticisms written on the margins of manuscripts in his own fine script.
Many men recall these generous, well-minted, critical suggestions and
wish only that they could have received them earlier and followed them
more completely.

His honors were as numerous as his accepted obligations, and only the truly great can carry so many of these so consistently. He was active in the National Academy of Sciences, twice chairman of the Medical Division of the National Research Council, and the recipient of honorary degrees; noteworthy from our bacteriologic point of view, he was president of the Society of American Bacteriologists in 1929, president of the American Association of Pathologists and Bacteriologists in 1903, and was given their highest honor, the Award of the Gold Headed Cane in 1944.

Hektoen was about average height with a fine massive head, a mop of hair, dark in the early days, gradually turning to a brilliant white in his later years, and always he had appreciative, smiling eyes. Some thought him austere; certainly he was restrained, but always kindly, even generous, to his associates, and he did enjoy a good joke. He was very different from William Welch, yet he served for the Middle West and also for the country many of the same functions. He was a more productive investigator especially in immunity and in bacteriology. Morris Fishbein in his admirable biography in the memorial volume of the *Archives of Pathology* dedicated to Hektoen on the occasion of his seventy-fifth birthday states: "I have never seen him manifest pride except after sinking an unusually long putt. I have never seen him inconsistent except in the difference between his golf drive when practicing and the motions that he uses when he actually hits the ball. These are sins that may well be pardoned."

Of many other studies from the Memorial Institute, those on typhoid fever are part of the lurid history of that disease in and around Chicago. Although untreated sewage dumped into Lake Michigan and the use of the lake water for drinking purposes was admittedly the underlying cause in those days of the high morbidity and mortality rates from typhoid, an investigation at the Institute the first year of its service gave evidence that the housefly (*Musca domestica*) could, under gross unsanitary conditions, be a vector. The concept of transmission of disease by insects antedates bacteriology. Since methods have become available, laboratory experiments with flies and the specific organisms have clearly shown the possibility of such spread. The investigations of enteric disease in our army camps during the Spanish-American War gave the strongest circumstantial evidence we had had up to that time that the fly was one of the culprits.

During the late summer of 1902, there was an unusually severe epidemic of typhoid fever in Chicago, which raised the deaths to 402 from this disease alone as against 212 during the same three months of the previous year. The report from the Board of Health showed that because of exceptionally heavy rains and winds the water supply of the city had become highly polluted (shown by the presence of *Bacillus coli*) during these months. It was agreed that the water was the major factor in spreading the infection. The careful studies of Alice Hamilton[10] and her colleagues at Hull House indicate that other factors, namely house-sewage in the back yards of the most heavily involved area and houseflies as vectors were probably additional factors. Epidemiological studies are largely circumstantial, and elements of dosage, virulence, and susceptibility are always significant. The completeness of their house-to-house survey, the descriptions of the conditions in this old part of the city where the sewers were laid before the great fire, and the primitive conditions prevailing in an overpopulated area remind one of the citizens survey of New York City in 1865.

Their conclusions were:

1. The epidemic of typhoid fever in Chicago during July, August, September, and October of 1902 was most severe in the Nineteenth Ward, which, with one-thirty-sixth of the city's population, had over one-seventh of all the deaths from this disease. 2. The concentration of the epidemic in this locality can not be explained by contamination of the drinking water or of food, or on the ground of ignorance and poverty of the inhabitants, for the Nineteenth Ward does not differ in these respects from several other parts of the city. 3. An investigation of the sanitary conditions of this region shows that many of the street sewers are too small, and that only 48 per cent of the houses have sanitary plumbing. Of the remaining 52 per cent, 7 per cent have defective plumbing, 22 per cent have water closets with intermittent water supply, 11 per cent have privies connected with the sewer but without water supply, and 12 per cent have privies with no sewer connection. 4. The streets in which the sanitary arrangements are worst had the largest number of cases of typhoid fever during this epidemic, irrespective of the poverty of the inhabitants. 5. Flies caught in two undrained privies, on the fences of two yards, on the walls of two houses, and in the room of a typhoid patient were used to inoculate 18 tubes, and from 5 of these tubes the typhoid bacillus was isolated. 6. When the discharges from typhoid patients are left exposed in privies or yards, flies may be an important agent in the dissemination of the typhoid infection.

This is, I believe, the only study up to this time in which the typhoid bacilli have actually been isolated from flies in nature during an epidemic.

The studies of Ruediger, of D. J. Davis, and of E. C. Rosenow at the Institute on interrelations in the streptococcus group and more especially later those of the last named on transmutation within the streptococcus-pneumococcus group attracted much attention. The importance of focal infections in obscure illnesses received extensive clinical approval. The basis of much of the confusion in our knowledge of the streptococci and the pneumococci that reigned during this period is now apparent.

At the University of Illinois Medical School David J. Davis[11] was the capable professor of bacteriology through many years. Beginning early (1906) while at the Memorial Institute for Infectious Diseases under Hektoen's influence, Davis carried out a long series of investigations on organisms commonly placed in the *Hemophilus* genus because of their requirement of blood for growth; Pfeiffer's bacillus, originally, though incorrectly, thought to be the cause of influenza, and the pertussis bacillus are the two more important members. On the basis of his quantitative studies of these organisms, using blood and related compounds both from invertebrate and vertebrate sources, Davis suggested as early as 1907 that the necessary component, so minute in amount, was probably a catalytic agent, an accessory growth factor. Subsequently, it was shown that whole blood contained two accessory growth substances (x and r), necessary for the cultivation of Pfeiffer's bacillus. Davis' later work with strains of *Sporotrichum* from various sources demonstrated considerable variation in morphology, pigment production, and pathogenicity. These studies and those of later authors indicate that European and American strains are all probably variants of the same species that may properly be named *Sporotrichum schenckii*.

Edwin Oakes Jordan[12] (1866-1936), the other noteworthy leader in bacteriology in the Chicago area, was a "down Easter" born in Thomaston on the coast of Maine, into a family of well-to-do master mariners and shipowners. With his father, captain of the *Pride of the Port*, and his mother, the young Jordan spent most of his first three years at sea. His father retired from seafaring shortly thereafter; the family continued to live in Thomaston until desire for better schooling for the children led them to Auburndale, Massachusetts. From the neighboring Newton High School, Jordan entered the Massachusetts Institute of Technology in 1884 and was graduated in 1888. In this period, he came into the excitement of the bursting of bacteriology on our world with Sedgwick as one of the energetic American evangels.

Quite opportunely in the year of Jordan's graduation from the Massachusetts Institute of Technology, Professor Sedgwick, whom he greatly admired, was appointed consulting biologist of the newly organized Massachusetts State Board of Health. Jordan was glad of the chance to work with this active group as chief assistant biologist at the Lawrence Experiment Station. In his two years there, he worked intensively on the many species of bacteria found in water and sewage with the hope of finding some indicator of sewage pollution. (*Bacillus coli* had not at that time been sufficiently studied to warrant such an interpretation.) They were using for isolation, the common, messy procedure of the period, gelatin media poured on chilled glass plates. Jordan and Ellen Richards, the latter carrying out the chemical determinations, studied nitrification quantitatively in a large number of samples of soil, sewage, and water. They published a beautifully concise paper, reporting that they obtained nitrification in every instance with these naturally occurring materials, but in no single instance when they used cultures of organisms isolated on gelatin from these sources. Finally at the suggestion of their immediate chief, Allen Hazen, they obtained growth and action of nitrifying organisms, using the simple dilution method in solutions of inorganic salts. Winogradsky published his more complete results a few months earlier and is quite properly given the credit. It seems clear, however, that this important paper of Jordan and Richards was done quite independently, and it remains the earliest paper on nitrifying bacteria in this country.

A summer or two at the Woods Hole Marine Biological Laboratory brought Jordan back into zoological fields and in touch with Charles Otis Whitman and his genetic studies. In 1890 Jordan accepted a fellowship with Whitman at the recently founded graduate institution, Clark University. For the next two years he devoted himself largely to the "Habits and Development of the Newt," the subject of his doctor's thesis.

Again a change of base was made when President Harper persuaded Whitman to join the new University of Chicago where productive scholarship was to be a paramount aim. Jordan went with him and spent the rest of his active life in happy association with that institution, mounting through the various grades in the academic hierarchy from instructor in zoology in 1892 to Andrew McLeish Distinguished Service Professor of Bacteriology from 1931 until his retirement in 1933.

The year after his arrival in Chicago (1893), Jordan offered a lecture and seminar course in sanitary biology, although his chief obligations and interests were still in zoology. In an old apartment building assigned to zoology, Jordan was fortunate in obtaining the kitchen, a room with a sink and running water. Through the years, gradual improvement in the physical environment was provided, first to the basement of the chemistry building, then in 1897 to the fourth floor of one of the new Hull Biological Laboratories, and in 1915 to a separate building, the Ricketts Memorial Laboratory. Additional courses in bacteriology and immunity were offered from year to year, and in 1900 bacteriology was removed from the sheltering cloak of zoology and joined with pathology under Ludvig Hektoen as chairman. In 1912 occurred another fission; bacteriology and hygiene became a separate department with Jordan as chairman. The following year the animal parasites were brought into the department under Wherry, and we observe what I consider the appropriate organization, a department covering the whole range of microbes, wherever taxonomy may place them, the study of the morphology and physiology of these organisms as individual species and in their several environments, including also the reaction of any hosts. The University of Chicago is one of the few institutions that has carried on with this type of organization. I disapprove of the common use of the term parasitology as applying only to organisms assigned to the animal kingdom.

Following Jordan's difficult decision to abandon zoology and devote his life to bacteriology (about 1893 or 1894 as Mrs. Jordan remembers), it was natural for him to follow a major interest of that day. Typhoid fever and related diseases were rampant, and modes of spread with public measures of prevention were in part known. Jordan's first paper from Chicago was on the "Identification of the Typhoid Fever Bacillus" (1894); this organism and its close relations remained a major interest for most of his life leading him into epidemiological typhoid studies in nearby cities and later into the moot subject of food-poisoning.

The most extensive study of self-purification of streams in this country certainly, and at that time in the world, resulted from the building of the Chicago Drainage Canal, the change in direction of flow of the Chicago River and the pumping of most of Chicago's vast mass of sewage into the Illinois River. This river after meandering slowly (15–18 days) through the state, empties its burden into the Mississippi River at Grafton some miles above the confluence with the Missouri River, and about forty-three miles above the intake water for the city of St. Louis. St. Louis alleged that its typhoid rate had increased materially after this change and brought suit against Chicago. Most of the bacteriologists in the whole area, the more prominent sanitary engineers of the country, and physicians of national fame became involved in the long suit resulting in 8000 printed pages of testimony, a 370 page digest of this testimony, a number of important scientific papers, and a decision of the United States Supreme Court dismissing the bill without prejudice on February 19, 1906.

Jordan was the chief bacteriologist involved in the studies for Chicago with H. L. Russell of the University of Wisconsin and F. R. Zeit of Northwestern University as major additional contributors; these men had many assistants. In brief, they exposed large numbers of typhosus and paratyphosus organisms in celloidin or parchment sacs or in both in protected crates at different points along the 357 miles from Lake Michigan to the Mississippi River at St. Louis. The organisms were mixed in the sacs with water taken at the particular area; the sacs permitted prompt dialysis, providing a close approximation of the actual conditions organisms would meet in normal passage down the river. Multiple samples were taken from the sacs, which were kept under the diverse conditions of water flow at different seasons of the year and at different cross sections of the canals and rivers. The samples were examined by the accepted bacteriologic methods. Celloidin sacs had been used in laboratory studies by many observers, but never before, I think, for a field study of this nature. "From the experiments recorded in this paper, it appears that under conditions that probably closely simulate those in nature, the vast majority of typhoid bacilli introduced into the several waters studied, perished within three to four days." "In only a single instance was any typhoid germ isolated after this period, and that case was on the ninth day."

The bacteriologic studies for St. Louis were carried on chiefly by A. N. Ravold, a practicing physician, connected with the medical department of Washington University, and consulting bacteriologist for the health department of St. Louis. His chief experiments involved the use of enormous quantities of *Bacillus prodigiosus*, a nonpathogen not commonly found in water, with about the same viability in laboratory tests as *B. typhosus*. These bacteria were dumped in large quantities into the drainage canal near its starting point. A very few were found later in samples at the intake at St. Louis and also in other parts of the river. To a bacteriologist, the studies of Jordan and his associates were much more direct and convincing and apparently the court also held this view.

In the decision of the United States Supreme Court written in a restrained yet pertinent manner by none other than Mr. Justice Holmes, other important testimony was cited which made a strong case.

1. "Grossly the addition of more than nine parts of Lake Michigan water has greatly improved the Illinois River. Formerly it was sluggish and ill smelling. Now it is a comparatively clear stream to which edible fish have returned. The case then depends on the unseen."

2. "That typhoid fever has increased considerably has been disproved." This was based on the testimony of such eminent physicians as George Dock and Victor C. Vaughan of the University of Michigan, Lewellys F. Barker of the University of Chicago, and William S. Thayer of Johns Hopkins University. They all agreed that many of the reported diagnoses were based on ill-founded clinical terms such as intermittent typho-malaria and that they could see no evidence from the typhoid statistics that the Chicago drainage canal had anything to do with typhoid fever in St. Louis.

3. In cross examination, Sedgwick, leading sanitary expert for St. Louis, admitted that "even if all the sewage from the sanitary district of Chicago were eliminated from the Illinois River basin . . . , the water entering the intake of the St. Louis water works would still certainly be polluted and dangerous to the people of St. Louis and the towns below."

We emphasize this case partly because in Holmes's summary, he correctly stresses the tremendous importance of interstate pollution of our rivers and lakes; "in the case of sovereign states this might well be a *casus belli*," partly because of Jordan's prominent part in the bacteriologic portion, and because in Theobald Smith's testimony he stated that "the study of Illinois River between Chicago and Grafton was the most extensive ever made." Holmes asserted: "It is a question of the first magnitude whether the destiny of the great rivers is to be sewers of the cities along their banks or to be protected against everything which threatens their purity." Manifestly, this is still a problem of the first magnitude and not only for the great rivers.

On the witness stand Jordan made a remarkably fine impression, restrained, competent, and alert. (I have seen him and his manifest pleasure in such controversies.) He thoroughly enjoyed cooking up sticky questions for the lawyers to throw at opposing experts. The importance of and the publicity stemming from this *St. Louis* vs. *Chicago* case brought Jordan into special prominence. In the next decade he was called upon to investigate typhoid epidemics in a number of cities in the northern Mississippi Valley. Most of these proved to be water-borne outbreaks, with a few from milk; in many instances there was a continuing high incidence and Jordan, with his frequent co-investigator, E. E. Irons, suggested the means of controlling the situation. Later, from 1913 to 1936, Jordan, as unnamed special agent of the *Journal of the American Medical Association*, made annual reports on the incidence of typhoid fever in the large cities of the United States and still later (1925–36), similar surveys of diphtheria. Jordan had thus become one of the recognized statistical epidemiologists of our country. Investigation of typhoid led Jordan into years of study of the related paratypho-sus organisms and the broad problems of food-poisoning. Many papers, two books on food-poisoning (1917 and 1931), and stimulation of graduate students in this direction were among the results. Studies on respiratory diseases, the common cold, influenza, etc., also brought forth numerous papers. His statistical study of world-wide *Epidemic Influenza* (1927) was a noteworthy contribution.

Jordan wrote readily and with a lucid, easy style. Possessed of an extensive personal library, a delightful home and family, he lived a well-ordered life, taking full advantage of the quarter system of the University of Chicago to enjoy many periods of travel and study in other lands. He relished library work more than that in the laboratory, especially during the latter half of his active service. His choice of problems rarely called for the use of experimental animals, obviously a deliberate decision. Almost two hundred papers and books bear his name and those of his associates. Many of these, especially in the early years, were the broadly general persuasive type needed at that time. Pure milk and pure water with the necessary legal and laboratory controls were increasingly demanded by the public. He was influential in the organization of the Society of American Bacteriologists, and was active in the affairs of this society during its early years; in 1905 he became its sixth president.

Jordan was urbane and restrained, but his penetrating mind and tongue went to the point and the point was far from dull, frequently on the sly quizzical side. His eyes were sharp though kindly. He had a high degree of initiative; more than one would suspect. One had to get beneath Jordan's Maine reserve in order to know the man. The even tenor of his life continued on a high, patrician level. He played a consistent game of golf, no long drives, but his direction was good and he avoided the traps. His tennis game, played on the family court in immaculate flannels, had the same fastidious qualities. In the winter, to keep fit, he chopped wood.

Jordan's scientific accomplishments were widely recognized, with nomination to special lectureships, such as that of the Harvey Society, honorary degrees, and election to the National Academy of Sciences. Long the excellent associate editor with Ludvig Hektoen of the *Journal of Infectious Diseases* and author through eleven editions of his exceptionally well-written *General Bacteriology*, he exerted wide influence. The long list of competent graduate students and young instructors who have come from the department under his leadership provide a living memorial.

No chronicle of early bacteriology should fail to include the work of H. Gideon Wells, although he was chiefly a pathologist, and his productive life extended well beyond our period. Wells appreciated quite early the part chemistry was destined to play in pathology and immunology; this led him to continue these studies, begun under Chittenden and Mendel at Yale, with Emil Fischer in Berlin. His long and warm fellowship in Chicago with Hektoen from 1899, increasing responsibilities in the department of pathology at Chicago University and as director of the Sprague Memorial Institute, gave him merited opportunities to work with his own hands and to stimulate others. Realizing the importance of studying immunologic reactions with pure proteins rather than with the crude mixtures commonly employed, he and Thomas B. Osborne of the Connecticut Agricultural Experiment Station at New Haven carried out for years experiments with compounds such as crystalline egg albumen and with pure vegetable proteins prepared by Osborne, employing the anaphylactic reaction in guinea pigs as the means of testing. Their findings supported the view "that the antigenic capacity of a protein depends on the entire large colloidal molecular structure while its specificity seems to reside in certain of the radicals of the molecule." These early studies came into richer fruition later at the hands of Landsteiner and Michael Heidelberger. Wells also investigated intensively the chemistry of the tubercle bacillus and chemotherapy of tuberculosis with Lydia De Witt and H. J. Corper and still later with Esmond R. Long. His abundant energy and capacity for organization carried him forward rapidly. His text *Chemical Pathology* (1907 *et seq.*) and his *Chemical Aspects of Immunity* were highly important contributions, valuable aids both in this country and abroad. Wells' unusually warm, engaging personality, buoyant spirit, and continuing enthusiasm endeared him to all, not only those closely associated with him in Chicago, but those who came in contact with him as he gave lectures and conferences far and wide. Well-deserved honors came to him both early and late.

Howard Taylor Ricketts joined the staff of the pathology department in 1902, published early important papers on fungus diseases of the skin and later carried out his classical studies on Rocky Mountain spotted fever with a description of the causative agent now generally classified as *Rickettsia*. We shall consider these investigations in the Rocky Mountain area where the disease demanded investigation.

NORTHWESTERN MEDICAL SCHOOL

Mention has been made of bacteriology in the early days of North-western Medical School when as the Chicago Medical College it and other medical institutions of Chicago were slowly assuming their modern organization. In the twentieth century Frederick Zeit, who had worked some years with Edwin Klebs at Rush Medical School, was appointed professor of pathology and bacteriology in 1902. He was more interested in pathology, but published papers on the effect of X-rays and electric currents on bacteria. During the long conflict between St. Louis and Chicago over the alleged pollution of the Mississippi River, Zeit joined Jordan and Russell in their bacteriologic studies; his major part was the study of pollution in different areas of Lake Michigan. Zeit was a kindly, friendly person, loved by his students—"a nice guy." During the streptococcus-pneumococcus controversy, he used to say to his students with fervor—"If a streptococcus can become a pneumococcus, then I have no further foundation for life."[13] Arthur Kendall succeeded Zeit in 1912; his researches, mostly beyond our time limit, were chiefly in the hydrolysis of proteins and the fermentation of carbohydrates by various bacteria. His observation, that protein hydrolysis is suppressed if a utilizable carbohydrate is present, is still unexplained.

Wisconsin

EDWARD A. BIRGE,
HARRY L. RUSSELL, LEWIS R. JONES,
WILLIAM D. FROST, AND EDWIN G. HASTINGS

Bacteriology in the University of Wisconsin is an example of its obscure birth in a college of letters and science as a small offering in an already recognized field, in this case, cryptogamic botany under William Trelease. Cultures on sterile slices of potato were studied, and the students were required to read Burrill's 1881 paper on bacteria, a presentation of the knowledge then available. This minor recognition of bacteria continued from 1882 to 1885, when Trelease left Wisconsin for the Shaw Botanical Gardens of St. Louis. By dint of proddings on the part of Trelease, some $400 worth of apparatus to advance the work in bacteriology had been ordered, but did not arrive until after his departure. It fell therefore to Edward A. Birge,[14] by this time professor of zoology, to unpack the treasure. As Birge told the medical students in a talk (1935) on the beginnings of the premedical course in Wisconsin

it was quite unthinkable that an equipment so large and valuable should stand idle, and so I was told to get busy and teach bacteriology, which accordingly, I proceeded to do. I regarded my part in it as a temporary affair, so the course was not listed for the first two years. But Professor Charles R. Barnes who succeeded Trelease in 1887 knew little and cared less about bacteria, so I who meanwhile had learned a little about them, was obliged to continue the course.

The first specific appointment in our science came in 1893 in the person of Harry Luman Russell[15] as assistant professor of bacteriology in the College of Agriculture with responsibilities also in the Experiment Station. As a member of the university class of 1888, Russell had come under Birge's instruction and had continued as a graduate assistant at Wisconsin for the next two years. During this period, a study of the bacterial content of the ice on Lake Mendota resulted in his first paper (1889). As was common in that period for those who could afford it, he had a year of rewarding study in Europe, partly in Koch's laboratory with a table next to one occupied by Emil Behring, and a longer period at the Marine Biological Laboratory at Naples, investigating the bacterial flora of the water and underlying mud of the Bay of Naples. He spent two weeks at the Pasteur Institute, but it was vacation period with the "master" away, so Russell's brief contacts were chiefly with Roux and Metchnikoff. Back in this country, a year at Johns Hopkins, majoring with William Welch, with a thesis, "Bacteria in their Relation to Vegetable Tissue (1893)," one of the good early papers in this field, brought the desired Ph.D. degree.

One of the best early descriptions of Russell may be found in a letter, as always in his own handwriting, by William Welch to Franklin P. Mall, April 20, 1892. Obviously, Mall was to be a member of the examining committee for Russell's Ph.D. degree, and Welch wished to warn Mall against asking embarrassing questions on human anatomy. The letter also indicates Welch's breadth of interest.

Dear Mall,

Russell is a very good man. His special training is in botany and more particularly the parasite diseases of plants, a field of work of great importance for this country with few experts to cultivate it. He is a well-trained man in bacteriological methods and comes up for his Ph.D. here this year, with pathology for his major. His thesis will relate to the bacterial diseases of plants and the question of plant immunity and I think will be thorough. His examination under me will be on vegetable and not animal pathology. Brooks has a high opinion of Russell. I doubt whether there are many such men in the country and he has a future before him. He is an energetic big fellow with a good capacity for work and a clear head.

After a year as fellow in biology at the University of Chicago, Russell was ready to take over the upbuilding of bacteriology at Wisconsin with ever broadening administrative functions to occupy his attention. Wisconsin was still a pioneer state; bacteriologists were also pioneers, and new applications in agriculture and public health met opposition. Abundant wheat from the western plains had made necessary a change in Wisconsin farm practices, so that a major task of the Experiment Station and the College of Agriculture was obtaining and spreading knowledge to the farmer in meeting the problems of the growing dairy industry. Since many of the difficulties involved bacteriology or more accurately microbiology, Russell needed all of his "good capacity for work and a clear head."

Following the lead of Pasteur, Storch in Denmark, and Weigmann in Germany, Russell began to study the relation of bacteria to milk and the complex fermentation processes in the souring of milk and in the production of butter and the delectable cheeses. Pasteur's method of preserving wines by destroying some of the wild organisms through mild heating was being applied to the preservation of milk. Russell soon joined hands with the chemist, Stephen M. Babcock, who had been wrestling with the problems of ripening of Cheddar cheese using chemical methods and had come to realize that this riddle required co-operative study with a microbiologist. Later Babcock became famous for his simple quantitative butterfat test. On the basis of four or five years work together, they recommended the use of lower temperatures, the so-called cold-curing of the cheese, an effective practice still in use. An easy Wisconsin curd test was also recommended to determine whether a given milk was suitable for the manufacture of this type of cheese. The mysteries of the contents of the silos, the beautiful towers with their silvery domes on every up-to-date Wisconsin farm, were attacked, but not with high success at this early period. Bacterial action rather than enzymes from the fodder has been proved to be more important.

As in other experiment stations such as Storrs in Connecticut and Geneva in New York, detailed experiments with the holding process of pasteurization of milk and other dairy products were carried out and the information of its desirability spread throughout the state and farther afield. Experiments with pure cultures as starters both in the production of butter and of cheese were carried on by the Agricultural Experiment Stations of Wisconsin and the other important dairy states with improvement in the resulting products.

The use of Koch's tuberculin as a hypersensitivity diagnostic test for tuberculosis in cattle has been discussed in the chapter on bacteriology in the federal agencies. In 1894 Russell published his applications of this test; he injected a number of the cows of the station with tuberculin "primarily as a demonstration of the value of this test for our course students." This inoculation revealed so large a percentage affected that the whole herd was similarly studied and the details carefully reported. Although at the time of the beginning of the tests there was no clinical evidence of tuberculosis in the herd (during the test period, one cow did show swelling of the udder; this cow was isolated and later showed physical signs of tuberculosis), 25 of the 30 cattle reacted positively, 22 to the first test, and 3 others to a later test. Henry, the dean of the College of Agriculture, and Russell decided not to temporize. All of the herd save two nonreactors were slaughtered and autopsied. The post-mortem studies showed that every reacting cow and also one non-reacting animal had tuberculous lesions. This demonstration, and similar tests carried out gratis in other herds, had important educational influence throughout the state.

The whole story is a dramatic one and involves all the forces in public health; the demonstrations that pulmonary tuberculosis in man is largely due to the human type while the bovine types are more important in causing tuberculosis of the lymph nodes, the intestine, and the bones, have had wide applications. At the beginning of the century, we saw many people with scrofulous necks on the street and in our clinics; now, thanks to the elimination of tuberculosis in most of our milk cattle and the pasteurization of most of our city milk-supplies, we rarely see the King's Evil in this country. Wisconsin was one of the early states (1932) to earn the so-called accredited status, that is, a state in which less than 0.5 of 1.0 per cent of its cattle give a positive tuberculin reaction.

State-wide service has always been a recognized duty in the state universities, and Russell was inevitably drawn into the troubles of the pea-canning industry. Factories handling large volumes of peas were having a high percentage of spoilage, so-called swells. Russell found that the processing was carried out at a temperature as low as 238° F. for 12 minutes and seldom exceeded 240° F. for 20 minutes. Many experimental tests brought a recommendation of at least 15 pounds pressure with a temperature of 242° F. for 18 minutes; this reduced the losses to a negligible number. He found that even 18 pounds pressure did not impair the physical state of the peas. Prescott, who was himself working at the same time on similar problems, states in *Food Technology*, "The earliest published record of the application of bacteriology to canning is that by Professor H. L. Russell in 1895, just a hundred years after Appert began his notable experiments."

Russell's interests extended in many directions. Through his work in combating bovine tuberculosis, he became a member of the State Livestock Sanitary Board, and a few years later (1903) he became the first director of a struggling State Laboratory of Hygiene established in combination with Dr. C. A. Harper, secretary of the State Board of Health. Russell deserves warm commendation for his emphasis on the broad biological possibilities of bacteriology and for stressing investigations along dairy, soil, and public health lines. It is, however, as strong administrator while dean of the rapidly expanding College of Agriculture (1907–30) that he left his more indelible mark.

Conflict is universal whether among viruses, butterflies, or within university circles. A controversy in which Russell took a firm stand has more than local significance; his success has aided all colleges of agriculture and indirectly other colleges. In many states the land grant colleges and their experiment stations have been located apart from the state universities, but in Wisconsin, to our great good fortune, they were both placed in Madison. This brought in the question of the role of colleges of agriculture in basic research. The senior college, that of Letters and Science under Dean Birge, strongly opposed the development of pure research in the College of Agriculture; Russell, however, was unwilling to have good investigators serve as chore boys. "It is quite as important for an Experiment Station," he wrote, "to have under investigation problems related to pure as well as applied science, for no one can tell what practical application may be made from these more or less theoretical researches." Clash and compromise continued for some years, but fortunately Russell's philosophy and practice gradually won out, and much good bacteriological investigation as well as striking advances in other fields have come from our College of Agriculture.

Russell had been working on soft rot of cabbage (1898) and in 1910 he induced Lewis R. Jones,[16] who in Vermont had been making significant advances in our knowledge of this disease, to come to Wisconsin to be head of a new department of plant pathology. Jones isolated *B. caratovorus* from soft rot of many truck garden vegetables showing that the rotting was due to an enzyme, pectinase, produced by the bacterium. Following up Erwin Smith's work on fusaria and their destructive action on many crops, Jones and his colleagues were led to emphasize not only host and parasite, but the importance of altered environment, such as temperature, moisture, etc., in many plant diseases. Selection of resistant strains of plants and their seed, as in cabbage, won success and wide praise for the members of the department. Under the generous, appreciative spirit of Jones, with excellent selection of colleagues, and many graduate students, this department became and has continued outstanding in the country. He had the rare gift, in controversial matters, of bringing important agreements to the fore, subordinating the less significant points in which clash was apparent. He believed that it is the way it is said, rather than what is said.

As Russell's program in bacteriology required additional colleagues, W. D. Frost,[17] trained in botany, came in 1895, and E. G. Hastings,[18] with a chemistry background, in 1899. They became competent bacteriologists, an illustration of the way our subject obtained its recruits from diverse fields in those early days, a practice, I am glad to see, not entirely outmoded. Frost helped to organize the courses in pathogenic organisms and in dairy bacteriology. He was skillful in developing laboratory techniques, as for example his microscopic plate method for the bacterial study of milk. He devoted his research time mainly to human and bovine streptocci in market milk. His most important contribution was probably his early study of antibiosis. After his retirement from the university, his continuing interest in tuberculosis led him to become executive director of Morningside, a small tuberculosis sanitarium at Madison.

Infectious diseases of cattle and abnormalities of milk were the subjects of much of Hastings' work. Over the years, he demonstrated the important fact that acid-fast organisms other than the bovine type of tubercle bacillus could render cattle sensitive to tuberculin. The avian bacillus, the human type of tubercle bacillus, Johne's bacillus, and noncultivable, feebly parasitic, acid-fast bacilli found in minor skin lesions of cattle may at times be involved in sensitization, so that the possibility of complete elimination of reactors becomes less likely and a questionable goal from the point of view both of bovine and human tuberculosis. This has proved to be a continually recurring problem. With associates, he studied Johne's disease in cattle and the johnin reaction, similar in principle to the tuberculin test.

As chairman of the increasingly strong department of agricultural bacteriology for thirty years, Hastings (1872–1953) was highly successful as teacher, administrator, and public servant; this last loomed large in his conception of the role of a faculty man in a state university. He organized and supervised the preparation and distribution of tuberculin, johnin, root-nodule bacteria, cheese cultures, and Bang's antigen, and encouraged their proper utilization. Among his honors, he cherished the presidency of the Society of American Bacteriologists in 1923.

Work in the important field of soil bacteriology was begun at Wisconsin under Russell and Hoffmann in the early years of the century, though advance was slight until after Russell became Dean, when E. B. Fred,[19] from 1913 on, gave it his strong shoulder, restless mind, and engaging personality. Rhizobia (first described by Beijerinck in 1888) that infect the roots of leguminous plants, producing nodules in which the organisms live in symbiosis with the plants, deriving most of their nitrogen from the atmosphere, were a major concern of Fred and his associates, especially I. L. Baldwin, and Elizabeth McCoy. With E. J. Graul, Fred made successful field tests that aroused the interest of the Wisconsin farmers in rhizobia inoculants. For years, beginning around 1916, the department sold to the farmers at cost pure cultures of the respective organisms, thus enriching the soil, augmenting the crops, and winning the support of the farmers for further investigation.

Fred's exceptionally active life (more hours per day than even his vigorous associates could take) included a second major field, microbial fermentation, which had had its origins early in his career. During World War I, a shortage of acetic acid and its derivitives, such as acetone, needed for the manufacture of smokeless powder and as solvents in compounding airplane dopes caused the government to look for additional sources. Because of E. B. Fred's earlier studies on lactic acid fermentation, a federal grant was made to him and to W. H. Peterson, as biochemist, for the study of bacterial fermentation of xylose, abundantly present in corncobs and wood. This successful application of the two sciences was followed over the years by fruitful investigations resulting in over a hundred papers by the major authors and their assistants covering a wide range of fermentation products from butyl alcohol to silage and sauerkraut, produced through the action of bacteria, yeasts, and molds. As always, additional return has come through the development of fine graduate assistants who have later occupied positions of importance both in industry and in the universities.

Interest in the problems of parasitism at the University is attested by the establishment of a course in animal parasites in 1906 by William S. Marshall of the zoology department. In his student days, he had worked in Leipzig under Rudolf Leuckart, commonly regarded as the father of modern parasitology. In 1912 the development of this field passed into the strong hands of brawny (about 6 feet, 5 inches, and well over 250 pounds), cheerful, ironical Arthur S. Pearse. His abrupt, pointed remarks awakened even the slothful. His competent investigation of parasitic crustacea and his broad study of parasitism in Nigeria were significant contributions.

In other microbiological areas, the department of veterinary science under F. B. Hadley and B. A. Beach from 1910 was especially interested in hog cholera and its serum therapy. Collaboration of this department in many of the investigations of the department of agricultural bacteriology continued through the years especially in bovine tuberculosis and in Johne's disease.

Russell's management of the College of Agriculture was firm, direct, and clear cut. He had no hesitation about making decisions. He made sure that there was no uncertainty as to the location of authority in his organization. He favored a "monarchial executive." L. J. Cole (longtime professor of genetics) probably spoke for most of his colleagues when he testified that the Dean was indeed strong willed in matters concerning the budget, but that once he was convinced of the importance of the plans submitted to him, he did not waver in vigorous and sympathetic support of fundamental research.[20] Russell always fostered productive scholarship and chose men primarily with that point uppermost. We can forgive some of his mandatory self-assurance in view of the results accomplished. By 1911 Russell listed eight new departments including genetics, plant pathology, and agricultural bacteriology with competent investigators in each field.

A cheerful comrade when climbing over the bluffs of the Wisconsin River, Russell was at heart a naturalist, a lover of the out-of-doors, and a confirmed traveler. Get away from the job periodically was his plea. The last few years while Russell was dean, he spent much effort on the organization of the Wisconsin Alumni Research Foundation, an institution that developed from the social conscience of the scientist, Harry Steenbock, and the initiative of Russell and many others. In 1930 when he resigned from the deanship, Russell became director of this Foundation that has meant so much to the University of Wisconsin and its possibilities in productive scholarship; it has served as a model for other institutions.

In 1907 President Van Hise obtained legislative approval and funds for the beginning of the long-hoped-for medical school. Charles R. Bardeen, professor of anatomy, was made dean. In the upbuilding of a productive faculty for the first two years of medicine, Mazyck P. Ravenel, who had done yeoman service in Pennsylvania confirming the findings of Theobald Smith that the bovine and human tubercle are different types with different pathogenicity, was brought to Wisconsin. He took over the teaching of medical bacteriology as well as the directorship of the State Laboratory of Hygiene made vacant by the appointment of Russell as dean of the College of Agriculture.

In 1914 a decision to withdraw bacteriology altogether from the College of Letters and Science was reached, and the responsibilities were placed in the colleges where the major applications existed. E. G. Hastings was continued in efficient charge of bacteriology in the College of Agriculture; Ravenel went to take over bacteriology in the University of Missouri, leaving W. D. Stovall in charge of the State Laboratory of Hygiene; Paul F. Clark was brought from the Rockefeller Institute to take over medical bacteriology, now definitely placed in the medical school. This organization continued from that date throughout and beyond the period of our survey. Events and persons are much too close for further comment.[21]

CHAPTER XIV

Other Areas of the Central Valley

No man is an Island, entire of itself—
every man is a piece of the continent, a part
of the main; If a clod be washed away by the sea,
Europe is the less, . . .   JOHN DONNE

The teaching, study, and applications of bacteriology in the other central valley states developed usually somewhat later than in the three instances detailed and represent slight variations on one or another of these examples. These advances were highly important in each area and were characteristic of the period and stage of development. The detailed histories are usually centered around some of the universities or the development of public health and medicine in the state. The histories of medicine in the several states make little reference to bacteriology and rightly so, since each history deals chiefly with the period before any considerable emphasis was placed on this science. We must realize that, commonly in all laboratories, the development followed recognized lines, and any studies added only small details to the whole warp and woof.

Ohio

As a part of the Northwest Territory readily accessible to many pioneers, population increased so rapidly that Ohio was admitted to the Union as a free state early in the nineteenth century (1802). A number of enterprising colleges grew up, and the usual excessive number of competing proprietary medical schools.[1]

WESTERN RESERVE UNIVERSITY

WILLIAM O. HOWARD AND ROGER G. PERKINS

The story of early bacteriology at Western Reserve Medical College, Cleveland, has been told with zest by E. E. Ecker[2] of that institution; he, quite properly, awards no crowns to those who were merely following the trends of the times. Noting our dependence on European microscopes, he records the order of a microscope in 1869 for E. W. Morley, professor of chemistry, from Powell and Leland of London at a cost including freight of $336. He also records the manufacture of microscopes in Cleveland in 1838 by Charles A. Spencer, who later moved to Buffalo joining in the formation of the important Spencer Optical Company.

Although a few didactic lectures and demonstrations had been presented earlier, it was not until 1894 that an excellently trained man, William T. Howard[3] (Johns Hopkins and Munich), was appointed professor of pathology and bacteriology; and both fields came promptly to life. The appropriate courses were presented, and in bacteriology, studies on ulcerative endocarditis, *Bacillus aerogenes capsulatus*, mucoid streptococci, actinomycosis, the etiology of smallpox and the pneumonias followed each other in prompt succession. A horse was immunized against diphtheria toxin and was bled for antitoxin as early as February, 1895. In 1901 Howard became active as bacteriologist of Cleveland and increasingly interested in bacteriologic testing of water supplies and public health problems. In 1914 he was called back to Baltimore as assistant commissioner of health.

Roger G. Perkins, also from Hopkins, joined Howard in 1899, and gradually assumed the duties in bacteriology with increasing responsibility and full professorship in 1910, including also the city laboratory where he became chief in 1914. Perkins' chief contributions were a study of diphtheria carriers in Cleveland and extensive experimentation with *Bacillus mucosus capsulatus*. Farther afield, Perkins studied public health problems as a member of the Red Cross Commission to the Balkans during World War I. Perkins (1874–1936) was well liked by both students and colleagues; he was an active out-of-doors man, enjoyed travel and mountain climbing. At the Pasteur Centenary in Paris in 1923, he and his son reported themselves as just back from their recent ascent of the Matterhorn.

With the departure of Howard for Baltimore (1914), Howard Karsner took over pathology and Ecker joined him in 1918 as instructor in immunology, giving a course in this subject in connection with general pathology. Their productive careers are beyond our determined limit.

OHIO STATE UNIVERSITY

CHARLES B. MORREY AND W. A. STARIN

Instruction in bacteriology in Ohio State University began as elsewhere quite humbly about 1886 as a short series of lectures, direct translations from Fränkel's textbook, by H. J. Detmers, trained in veterinary medicine in Germany; these were designed for the senior veterinary students. About 1899 A. M. Bleile of the physiology department took charge of this work with his specially trained assistant, Charles B. Morrey,[4] who had spent a year studying bacteriology in Vienna and at the Pasteur Institute in Paris. Not until 1903 did bacteriology become independent of physiology with Morrey in charge; it remained a one-man department until 1906 when Eugene F. McCampbell was added to the staff. Morrey became increasingly involved in administrative duties first as executive officer of the State Board of Health and then as dean of the Medical School from 1917 to 1927. With the appointment of W. A. Starin in 1910 came the more active development of bacteriology, although most of this is beyond our time limits. Starin showed that gelatin, although a protein, is not antigenic; with associates he worked with *Clostridium botulinum* and other pathogenic anaerobic sporeformers.

In the University of Cincinnati, William B. Wherry (1875–1936) carried on effectively in bacteriology and public hygiene for many years. His outstanding contribution was a description in 1914 of the first demonstrated case of tularemia in man, the beginning of our understanding that this disease is not restricted to rodents but may be transmitted to man (see Chapter XVI).

Indiana[5]

ROBERT E. LYONS

As at the University of Michigan, although a decade later, bacteriology was introduced into Indiana University by a chemist, Robert E. Lyons, who spent several years in Europe, including Heidelberg, Wiesbaden, Copenhagen, and Paris in his wandering studies into the new field. He gave the first course in 1896–97 with advanced work as demand arose. In 1903, a two-year medical school was instituted on the Bloomington campus with bacteriology still under Lyons. In 1905 Wilfred H. Manwaring was appointed professor of pathology and bacteriology with L. W. Famulener as assistant. A year or two later the second year of the medical curriculum was transferred to the Medical Center in Indianapolis where the clinical facilities were superior. After Manwaring's resignation in 1907, bacteriology was continued with pathology in the competent hands of Virgil H. Moon, and we soon get beyond our period of observation. In Burton Myers' *History of Medical Education in Indiana*, bacteriology is barely mentioned even in the later years and only in association with pathology. Both L. F. Rettger, later professor of bacteriology at Yale, and I. M. Lewis, subsequently long-time head at the University of Texas, were students at Bloomington under Lyons.

PURDUE UNIVERSITY

P. A. TETRAULT

At Purdue University, J. C. Arthur, professor of botany, offered a twelve-week course in bacteriology in 1894. His publications were chiefly in mycology. A rapidly changing list of persons, each with short tenure, is given by P. A. Tetrault in his summary history of bacteriology at Purdue. Severance Burrage in public health and R. A. Whiting in veterinary bacteriology should be mentioned. Conditions seem to have become more stable after P. A. Tetrault came to Purdue in 1912 with new quarters provided in 1916. His productive work was largely in the bacterial decomposition of cellulose.

Minnesota[6]

FRANK F. WESBROOK, WINFORD P. LARSON, ARTHUR T. HENRICI, H. O. HALVORSON

An outbreak of smallpox, 1000 cases with 250 deaths, and a dynamic leader, Charles N. Hewitt, who had settled for medical practice in Red Wing after the Civil War, combined to induce the establishment of the Minnesota State Board of Health in 1872, the fourth in the country. He persuaded Theobald Smith to come west to help establish the State Hygienic Laboratory in 1892. As elsewhere, bacteriology began its climb towards recognition in several departments, more especially in the department of pathology under J. Clark Stewart, first professor of pathology (1889–95).

In 1896 Frank F. Wesbrook (1868–1918) was made director of the

Upper left   Thomas Jonathan Burrill, 1839–1916
                   Photograph taken about 1890, at the age of fifty-one.

Upper right   Ludvig Hektoen, 1863–1951
                   Photograph taken about 1935, at the age of seventy-two.

Lower left   Edwin Oakes Jordan, 1866–1936
                   Photograph taken about 1900, at the age of thirty-four.

Lower right   Howard Taylor Ricketts, 1871–1910
                   Photograph taken about 1905, at the age of thirty-four.

Minnesota Board of Health. He was a person of powerful physique, manifest distinction, and cordial human interest. He became the first professor of pathology and bacteriology at the University of Minnesota (1895–1913), director of the laboratory of the State Board of Health for the same period, a strong supporter of the American Public Health Association, its president in 1905, and an active charter member in the Society of American Bacteriologists. He was a proponent of the several aspects of bacteriology related to the moot questions in public health in his period. He was skillful in devising simple laboratory methods, as, for example, the hanging agar drop for watching bacterial fission. Along with most of our early bacteriologists he turned his attention to several bacteriologic families such as *Bacillus anthracis* and the aerobic spore-formers, rabies and its distribution in Minnesota, and infectious anemia of horses, both virus diseases, and, for several years, to the diphtheria group. He suggested a scheme of relation between the diverse morphological types of diphtheria bacilli when grown on Löffler's blood-serum and the toxicogenic powers of the organism. As this required close observation of individual organisms, it served a useful purpose in public health laboratories, but the supposed correlation has not proved true. Like many other competent bacteriologists, he later suffered elimination from the active field by advancement to administrative positions, in his case, by a return to his native Canada to become the president of the University of British Columbia.

Succeeding Wesbrook, came friendly, approachable Winford P. Larson (1880–1947) as head of the newly organized department of bacteriology and immunology from 1913. He was a competent, well-appreciated man who attracted an excellent group of associates, especially Arthur T. Henrici, strong in medical mycology, and H. O. Halvorson, in physiology of bacteria.

Henrici (1889–1943), the older of this interesting pair, comes briefly within our period. Many bacteriologists, partly it must be confessed because of the difficulties of the field and because of over specialization, have been reluctant until recently to give adequate attention to medical mycology and to the tremendously important industrial and antibiotic aspects of the other fungi. We are happy to salute Henrici as a bacteriologist who early in his career (1914) began the study of yeasts; with his characteristic thoroughness and patience he continued until he had become familiar with the important fungi. His clear-cut exposition of the molds, yeasts, and actinomycetes has helped many bacteriologists who would otherwise have become lost in the woods, or more exactly among the many different types of spores.

Although the Mayo Clinic has been especially noteworthy in fields other than bacteriology, we must not overlook the early significant studies of Louis Wilson in the etiology of Rocky Mountain spotted fever and his wisdom in the later upbuilding of the Mayo Foundation. Edward C. Rosenow, while in Chicago, emphasized with Frank Billings the importance of focal infections. When Rosenow came to the Mayo Clinic in 1915, he continued his studies in this field with stress on elective localization, especially of viridans streptococci (alpha-hemolytic) in many diseases of obscure etiology, including several such as poliomyelitis, encephalitis, and influenza in the filterable virus group. All recognize that some organisms do find more favorable growth conditions in certain tissues, as for example *Bacillus typhosus* in Peyer's patches and in the gall bladder. It is commonly agreed, however, that this conception was overemphasized during this period, yet all who knew Rosenow personally are convinced of his intense sincerity and honesty both in his studies and in the clashes that were occasionally rough.

Iowa[7]

STATE UNIVERSITY OF IOWA

WALTER L. BIERRING AND HENRY ALBERT

For several years prior to 1890, brief elective courses in bacteriology were offered by the professor of botany, Thomas H. Macbride. His major interest was in the higher fungi, yeasts, and molds; he avoided all pathogenic microorganisms. A few years later the professor of anatomy, Lawrence W. Littig, gave bacteriology a boost. He had studied in Koch's laboratory while enjoying a number of the European clinics, and had brought back the first oil immersion lens in Iowa. With this he demonstrated the tubercle bacillus in sputum and several other pathogenic bacteria to interested students.

The first professor of pathology and bacteriology at Iowa was Walter L. Bierring (1893–1903). He, too, had studied for several years in Europe, including periods in Vienna, Heidelberg, and at the Pasteur Institute in Paris. His account of his personal experiences in the European laboratories gives a graphic story of the bacteriologic revolution in pathology which he proceeded to introduce into his courses in Iowa, even to the offering of what he called Pasteur courses to enterprising physicians of the region.

In 1903 Bierring was transferred to the field that later became the department of internal medicine, and Henry Albert was appointed in his stead. A year later Albert was made also the director of the newly established laboratory of the State Board of Health; this became his major interest. His multiple duties, extending to 1921, beyond our period, permitted little time for investigation, but he did make a couple of interesting studies on morphology and staining reactions of the diphtheria bacillus. In 1938 official recognition of the importance of bacteriology both as a medical and a university subject was granted by a reorganization of the work with full department status and William M. Hale as chairman.

IOWA STATE COLLEGE, AMES

L. H. PAMMEL, R. E. BUCHANAN, MAX LEVINE

In the Iowa State College at Ames, bacteriology had, as usual, its first recognition as part of a parent subject, in this case cryptogamic botany under E. A. Bessey in the early eighties. About 1888 L. H. Pammel, who had worked in botany under Trelease at Wisconsin, gave the first designated course in bacteriology with a gradually increasing amount of laboratory work for students in agriculture and in veterinary medicine. Pammel's research interests were chiefly in plant pathology; he described (about 1895) *Bacillus campestris* now *Xanthoma campestris* (Pammel-Dowson), an organism that causes black rot of cabbage and other crucifers.

R. E. Buchanan entered this institution as a student in 1900 and because of his interest was immediately "adopted" by Pammel. While still an undergraduate, he became involved in the problems of plant taxonomy and nomenclature that were close to Pammel's heart, and these have, as we know, occupied Buchanan's mind from that day to this. Buchanan was graduated in 1904 and immediately became instructor in bacteriology, teaching large classes of veterinary students. Interweaving his teaching duties with graduate studies at Ames and through leaves of absences at the University of Chicago with Jordan, Buchanan received his Ph.D. degree in the summer of 1908 with a thesis on the nodule bacteria of leguminous plants. He was at once appointed associate professor of bacteriology at Ames and shortly thereafter became head of the department when it was made independent of botany. Under his leadership the growth has been strong especially in bacterial physiology and in taxonomic problems.

Max Levine, student under Sedgwick at Massachusetts Institute of Technology, was added to the staff in 1913 to give emphasis to the sanitary disposal of industrial wastes. Both Buchanan and Levine have written abundantly and well. Buchanan has always been a hard worker, friendly, but too busy to spend time in "bull sessions" even though they were on a high scientific plane. A typical somewhat straight-laced Scotch Presbyterian, he has preferred library studies rather than experimental laboratory work. Although officially one of the emeriti, he continues to be exceedingly active; you will find him at many meetings contributing to the debate; he is a world traveler and you are as likely to run into him in foreign lands as on the campus at Ames. As editor of the seventh edition of *Bergey's Manual* he continues to aid all bacteriologists. As a stripling of thirty-five years, he was the youngest of the presidents of the Society of American Bacteriologists.

Kansas[8]

UNIVERSITY OF KANSAS

M. A. BARBER AND NOBLE SHERWOOD

From Kansas, we fortunately have the entertaining recollections of its early bacteriologist, M. A. Barber, who lived so long and so well (1868–1953). He began in cryptogamic botany with his first professional appointment as an assistant at Harvard, while studying for his Ph.D. degree. Then he went back to Kansas where the bacteria exerted their pull; later, especially in the Philippine Islands, the helminths got their turn in 1911–15, and finally a large share (1915–39) of his long active life was spent with the United States Public Health Service and the International Health Board of the Rockefeller Foundation studying the malarial parasites in many lands. His publications are abundantly cited in the definitive work on *Malariology* edited by Mark Boyd; larvicides and incidence surveys were two of the phases in which he worked most. Referring to his youth Barber states that,

We had little or no bacteriology in that country [southeastern Kansas] in the 1870's but plenty of bacteria. Even among widely scattered homesteads the ravages of typhoid were alarming. Often some member of a family would come home ill with fever, then would follow a crop of cases in the family or in the immediate neighborhood. Pigs were blamed for the diseases, but never, as I remember, a contagion transferred from person to person. Newly turned soil was popularly accused of causing malaria, but not typhoid.

. . . .

Early in the 1890's a few types of non-pathogenic bacteria were a part of the study of cryptogamic botany in the University of Kansas. About 1896 we began to offer courses in which the study of pathogenic bacteria was included—following the sub-tilis-to-anthracis route probably traversed by more than one institution of that time. . . . After the beginning of the 1900's the progress of bacteriology and preventive medicine followed in Kansas much the same course as in most of the states of that part of the country.

Of the several methods of obtaining pure cultures, more accurate than the ordinary plating techniques, that of single cell picking by microcapillary pipettes devised by Barber (1907) has been used with great success and has passed through many mechanical improvements in the machines employed. His study of cell-division rates and growth curves starting from known single cells was important and typical of Barber's careful studies in diverse fields. The medical school was offi-cially organized in 1899 with bacteriology as a required course given by Barber. In 1906 a department of pathology and bacteriology came into being, and bacteriology was offered both in the college at Lawrence and in the medical school in Kansas City.

Following Barber at Kansas, robust Noble Sherwood began his duties as assistant in bacteriology in 1910, reaching full professorship in 1918, passing beyond our period, and reaching official but not actual retire-ment in 1952. He has been especially active in studying and writing in the broad field of immunology.

Lands South of the Mason-Dixon Line

Broadly speaking, bacteriology came into its own in the South even more slowly than in the North. The complex causative factors, mixed in with slavery, cotton culture, a terrific war, and the disastrous, shameful reconstruction, still in process, have been critically discussed by many social historians as in Merle Curti's *Growth of American Thought*. The College of William and Mary, second oldest in the country, and other institutions of higher learning such as Jefferson's University of Virginia emphasized chiefly the liberal arts until towards the close of our period. As in the North, the study of natural history was only slowly enriched by subdivision into its parts.

Three world-devastating microbic diseases in which our southern states were heavily involved and to which they made extensive contributions are yellow fever, hookworm disease, and malaria. The dramatic revelations in the spread and control of yellow fever have been presented in some detail. Less circumstantially we have given the findings of C. W. Stiles and the campaign of the Rockefeller Commission in preventing the spread of the hookworm. The local efforts, both community and state, in the gradual reduction of this debilitating disease deserve credit. Education and the raising of the economic level have been major factors. The world importance of malaria cannot be exaggerated. In our own country it spread northward in human carriers and after the opening of the West (now the Middle West) it became the great endemic disease.

Drawing from the excellent history of malaria in the United States by the distinguished malariologist M. A. Barber, we find much about this disease in the southern states.

In the Southern States malaria is still prevalent, especially in the valleys of the larger rivers. There is no doubt, however, that malaria has decreased in the South as well as in the North, although the diminution has been less marked and has proceeded at a slower rate. Bass states that malaria was rife in New Orleans and the territory surrounding it between 1890 and 1900. Large numbers of cases were treated in the New Orleans Charity Hospital, where at present they are so few that it is difficult to get enough material for teaching purposes. Dr. Henry R. Carter has noted a decrease in North Carolina and Virginia.

Barber's summary runs as follows:

Malaria was once very prevalent in the northern United States. During the past 50 or 60 years it has greatly diminished and is no longer a serious problem there. In the Southern States malaria has also decreased, but in many localities the rate is still high and constitutes an important sanitary problem.

The liability of a serious increase of malaria in the North is not great so long as the present economic status of that region persists; in the South the danger of a recrudescence of the disease is much greater, as the events of the past few years have demonstrated.

The factors concerned in the diminution of malaria in the United States are interdependent; their importance has varied with time and locality, but all have been closely related to the agricultural development of the country.

Texas[9]

I. M. LEWIS

Bacteriology has grown up in the several institutions of Texas largely after our period of observation. At the University of Texas beginning courses were given about 1903–5. I. M. Lewis (1878–1943), trained at Indiana University chiefly in botany with a minor in bacteriology under Manwaring, came to the University in 1909 and, save for a period in the Sanitary Corps of the army, remained at Texas throughout his life. He was essentially a self-made product, primarily a devoted teacher, who left a strong imprint of himself on both students and colleagues. He had a strong sense of individual responsibility and showed meticulous attention to details. He was one of the old fashioned, now forgotten, bacteriologists; he made all his own media, reagents, and stains (such a misuse of time), worked early and late, was an omnivorous reader in the several languages of science, was skillful in devising simple laboratory equipment, and was devoted to his profession and to his students. He was a shy introvert, a characteristic somewhat exaggerated doubtless by his deafness. Of the graduate students that have over the years come from afar to the Wisconsin campus, those from Lewis' laboratory have shown unusual enthusiasm for their modest, unselfish teacher.

4

OUR WESTERN LANDS

CHAPTER XV

Rocky Mountain Area

HOWARD TAYLOR RICKETTS

*Let us first understand the facts and then
we may seek the cause.*   ARISTOTLE

*We all labour against our own cure,
for death is the cure of all diseases.*
                    THOMAS BROWNE, *Religio Medici*

Following Lewis and Clark and the later pioneers over the plains we shall proceed rapidly westward stopping only once in the Rocky Mountains. A mysterious disease had existed in this area apparently from early days, occurring chiefly in the spring and in the sparsely settled mountain regions. An old Indian chief who had lived many years in the Bitter Root Valley tells that in the spring of the year the valley was visited by evil spirits and that certain canyons were particularly hazardous. Because of the rarity of the disease, it attracted little attention until the period of white settlement (1890–95). The first adequate description was given in 1899 by E. E. Maxey[1] of Boise, Idaho. He defined it as "an acute endemic, non-contagious, but probably infectious, febrile disease, characterized clinically by a continuous moderately high fever, severe arthritic and muscular pains and a profuse petechial or purpural eruption in the skin, appearing first on the ankles, wrists, and forehead, but rapidly spreading to all parts of the body." The death rate varies markedly from around 5 per cent in Idaho to from 65 to 90 per cent in western Montana. A similar peculiar difference exists between cases occurring in more closely adjoining areas; for example, while on the west slope of the Bitter Root Valley the disease is severe with a high death rate, on the eastern slope the cases are few and mild. Most observers regarded the disease as a distinct infection, cause and mode of spread unknown.

A number of serious studies were made after 1900, especially by Wilson and Chowning for the Montana State Board of Health and by John F. Anderson of the United States Public Health Service. A protozoan parasite *Piroplasma hominis* had been implicated, but C. W. Stiles of the Public Health Service, after a more complete study, emphatically refuted these findings. Folklore, the seasonal incidence, and the almost unfailing history of recent tick bites in cases of human infection had led to the common name, tick fever of the Rocky Mountains.

Into this environment with its involved enigma came on April 21, 1906, a modest, well-trained young man, Howard Taylor Ricketts,[2] from the University of Chicago. A graduate of Northwestern Medical School in 1897, Ricketts, while he was a fellow in cutaneous pathology in Rush Medical College, had attracted Ludvig Hektoen's favorable attention by a thorough study of blastomycosis of the skin. Following Hektoen's suggestion, Ricketts spent a year of study in Berlin, Vienna, and Paris, and then accepted an instructorship in pathology with Hektoen at the University of Chicago in 1902. Also to Missoula came for a brief time W. W. King, detailed from the United States Public Health Service to study the same disease. These men worked independently, but shared the same laboratory and frequently the same material. A happy degree of collaboration resulted. Since the experimental guinea pigs were few and the supply of blood from patients limited, and since a favorable route of possible artificial infection was unknown, the two men drew lots for route of injection. Happily both won; both the subcutaneous and the intraperitoneal injections of the blood into the guinea pigs proved successful, and each was able to publish independently his important observations.

Each also succeeded in producing the typical disease in monkeys and in transferring it from infected to normal guinea pigs by means of the wood tick, *Dermacentor andersoni*, Stiles. A typical experiment follows: a small female tick was placed on a guinea pig that had become ill following the injection of blood from a sick patient. After having fed on the infected guinea pig for two days, the tick was removed, placed in a ventilated pillbox for two days more and then attached to the base of the ear of a guinea pig. After an incubation period of three and one-half days, the temperature of the animal gradually rose to 106.4° F., near which point it remained for seven days, when it gradually returned to normal. The monkey injected with blood from the same patient came down with an infection more like the human disease. When a fresh supply of guinea pigs arrived, Ricketts found it possible to alternate injections, monkey to guinea pig and again to a monkey, thus providing a source of material for continued study of the disease beyond its brief season of natural prevalence. Subsequently guinea pig to guinea pig inoculations proved possible by obtaining blood earlier in the course of the infection. All the infected animals ran similar courses of fever with frequent development of a hemorrhagic eruption characteristic of the disease in man, and the essential anatomical changes also agreed with those in man. However, all cultures from blood or organs proved negative. That this experimental disease was actually Rocky Mountain spotted fever and not some other similar infection was further demonstrated by an active immunity developed both in guinea pigs and in monkeys. Recovered animals remained well when injected with infectious material that produced the typical disease in normal animals.

Ricketts continued with a beautifully built-up series of experiments, some thirty papers in all, giving us much of what we know today about Rocky Mountain spotted fever. By 1909 the following important results had been repeatedly demonstrated:

1. Although the number was small, infected wood ticks were found in the so-called infected districts.

2. Adult ticks, both male and female, may acquire the disease by feeding on an infected animal and may transmit it to a normal susceptible animal for several weeks thereafter. Larval and nymphal ticks may also acquire the infection and prove infective when they become adults.

3. The infected female tick may transfer the infection to her young through the egg, a transovarian passage as in Texas fever.

4. The virus is widely distributed in the infected mammal and in the infected tick. The disease, however, is chronic in the tick, not highly destructive.

5. Blood cells from infected animals retain the virus in spite of re-

peated washings. Many attempts to pass the virus through Berkefeld filters failed, indicating that the organism should be visible under the microscope.

6. Continued attempts to cultivate any organism from the disease in man or experimental animals failed.

7. Active immunity following recovery is strong, of long duration, and in the case of the female guinea pig is transmissible passively to the offspring. This immunity of the young does not depend on the ingestion of the mother's milk. It was found possible to obtain an immune serum from horses repeatedly injected with virus.

8. With suitable stains, diplococcoid bodies and sometimes short bacillary forms were found with considerable constancy in the blood of patients of the artificially infected animals and in all tissues of infected ticks. Specific relations were shown by the agglutination of these organisms with Rocky Mountain spotted fever antiserum. Suspensions of organisms continued to produce the disease in guinea pigs and in monkeys. Those from the western slope of the Bitter Root Valley proved to be more virulent than those from Idaho where the disease was mild.

9. A serious difficulty arose when similar microbes were found in some noninfectious ticks. These would not produce the disease but they were agglutinated by the specific "spotted fever" immune sera and not by normal serum. How then could the Henle-Koch postulates be fulfilled?

10. Ricketts met this difficult block by many studies and finally with an assumption that subsequent work has proved true, that the organism in question is a common parasite of many varieties of ticks and lives symbiotically without injury to the tick.

11.Wild rodents, notably the ground squirrel, the ground hog, and the rock squirrel were susceptible to Rocky Mountain spotted fever and were the usual animals involved in the disease. Only rarely was it transmitted to man by a tick with the virulent organisms.

12. Successful vaccination was accomplished by the injection of suspensions of ticks rich in virulent organisms after these had been killed either by desiccation or by chloroform.

In a summary paper of 1907, Ricketts called attention to transmission experiments carried out a year before his own. L. P. McCalla and

H. A. Brereton of Boise City, Idaho, obtained a tick from the chest of a man very ill with spotted fever and applied it to the arm of a man who had been in the hospital for two months and a half, and had lost both feet from gangrene due to freezing. On the eighth day the patient became ill and passed through a mild course of spotted fever with a characteristic eruption. The experiment was repeated by placing the tick on a woman's leg, and she likewise was infected with spotted fever. These transfers of spotted fever from man to man (with their consent) by means of the tick received no publicity and were reported only to local societies. Ricketts records his pleasure in giving these men the credit so justly due.

His unusually successful series of experiments and the similarity of Rocky Mountain spotted fever to typhus fever, next to malaria man's greatest disease enemy, made Ricketts eager to try similar methods in the more widespread disease. Accordingly, in 1909, his chief, Dr. Hektoen, arranged a leave of absence from the University of Chicago for the autumn, the season in which typhus fever is prevalent in Mexico. Actually he did not reach Mexico City until early in December, only to find that Nicolle in Tunis, Africa, and Anderson and Goldberger in Mexico had just transmitted typhus to monkeys. Nicolle had been unable to infect monkeys initially, but he infected a chimpanzee by injecting blood from human patients. Injections of blood from this chimpanzee to lower apes, *Macacus sinicus*, proved successful, and finally he transferred the disease from one monkey to another by means of the body louse, *Pediculus vestimenti*. Anderson and Goldberger had been successful in transmitting typhus to monkeys directly by injecting the blood from patients.

In spite of some understandable chagrin at coming in just too late, Ricketts went to work, aided by Russell Wilder, and confirmed these findings. Ricketts and Wilder added further knowledge by observing organisms similar to those seen in the Rocky Mountain disease, both in the blood of typhus patients, in the lice that had fed on these patients, and in the feces of the infected lice. They found that monkeys could be infected by rubbing such feces into minor incisions. This is considered the common method of transfer to man, first the bite, the itching, and then the scratching of the infected feces into the skin wound.

The gist of the story was now clear with countless details added by dozens of investigators both before and subsequent to these studies.

One always feels unhappy in describing a major scientific achievement so briefly, because such a tale necessitates the omission of the important failures and partial gains that have made final success possible.

Following Ricketts' untimely death in May, 1910, from typhus fever while working in Mexico City, an act of homage was presented at the National Bacteriological Institute of that city with appropriate ceremonies and a memorial volume. In Chicago the Pathological Society published a volume of Ricketts' more important papers. His early textbook (1905–6) covering *Infection, Immunity and Serum Therapy* was extremely useful; it served well all students of the period. A memorial service was held at the University of Chicago, and later the Ricketts Laboratories were built for the use of the department of pathology and bacteriology.

Ricketts is described as a modest, quiet, unassuming young man, with a winning charm. He was physically vigorous, a former fullback at the University of Nebraska, a terrific worker, completely absorbed in what he was doing. The lights in his laboratory at the University of Chicago burned late into the night. "When hot on the trail," his wife not infrequently had to come to the laboratory to remind him that he had worked right through the dinner hour. His absorption in his work and his persistence amounted at times to obstinacy, and forgetfulness of other obligations. One day at lunch his wife told him that their daughter Elisabeth was running a fever. She suggested that he take the daughter's temperature. He did, and reported that it was normal and there was nothing to worry about. He had hardly arrived back at the laboratory when his wife called saying that Elisabeth had a temperature of 102°F. By George! He remembered. It was for guinea pigs that the normal temperature was 102°F. He agreed that a man could get too absorbed in his work. As do all persons devoted both to their professions and to their families, he felt keenly the conflict between his desire to push on with his scientific studies and his affectionate longing to be a good husband and father.

Financial struggles during student days had taken him through diverse jobs, collecting turtles for his biology teacher, cashier at an amusement park, and combined medical attendant and cook on airplane trial grounds of the Indiana sand dunes. These had contributed to his stamina, his ingenuity in "making do," and to sympathy with human foibles especially among his typhus fever patients in Mexico.

Russell Wilder, who at the time of the typhus investigations was a third-year medical student tells that "Ricketts was a delightful chief to work for, always kind, generous to a fault." Ricketts treated him as an associate and not as an assistant; in their work and papers together, equality of interest and of purpose rather than degree of training was the emphasis. "Once we injected blood into the anterior chamber of the eye of a *Macaccus rhesus* monkey. When I suggested this, he called it the best idea that either of us had had since coming to Mexico City. That you may recall was in 1910 and long before virus cultures had been made successfully." Wilder was alone with Ricketts in the American Club in Mexico City when the illness that proved fatal fell upon him. Ricketts died some fourteen days later, after his fever left him, with acute dilatation of the heart. He was only thirty-nine when he died; so much he accomplished in so brief a life. Would that we could more adequately compensate the families that pay the full price for dedicated professional service.

The name *Rickettsia prowazeki* for the typhus organism was suggested by another able investigator, DaRocha Lima, of Hamburg, Germany, in honor of both Ricketts and Prowazek who lost their lives while working on typhus. This name has been commonly accepted and *Rickettsia ricketts i* for the Rocky Mountain fever organism. The generic name Rickettsia has been approved for all similar organisms inciting related diseases the world over.

Although the story now passes beyond our period, Americans have contributed so considerably to its unraveling that it seems appropriate to include a glimpse of later achievements: diagnoses of these rickettsial diseases have been improved by specific serum reactions and by observation of scrotal reactions in injected male guinea pigs; the Rickettsia have been grown in various types of tissue cells (Zinsser and Castaneda and others) and also by the yolk-sac injection of embryonated hens eggs (Cox); [3] such cultivated organisms have been the basis for fairly successful preventive vaccines; great advance has been made in delousing populations by the use of DDT, thus preventing the major disease, epidemic typhus fever; at least three antibiotics, aureomycin, chloramphenicol, and terramycin, have been used with considerable success in treatment. Brill's disease, a mild form long known in New York City, has been proved to be a sporadic typhus of the louse-borne type; a murine typhus spread among the rats and to man by the rat flea has been differentiated. How one would enjoy telling with pride such a success story in greater detail.

CHAPTER XVI

California and the Coast

*It can hardly be a matter for surprise
that our race has not succeeded in solving
any large part of its most difficult problems
in that first millionth part of its existence.
Perhaps life would be a duller affair
if it had, for to many it is not knowledge
but the quest for knowledge that gives the
greatest interest to thought—to travel hopefully
is better than to arrive.* SIR JAMES JEANS

The winning of the Far West includes such a long series of turbulent clashes that one has difficulty in thinking of humble unicellular organisms playing any considerable part. But though silent and unseen, the amazing rapidity with which these organisms multiply and their astounding capacity for work did several times place them in leading roles.

As in the earlier settlements of the East, many nations were involved in the aggressive claims for these lands. The Louisiana Purchase from France in 1803, the Lewis and Clark Expedition 1804–6, the revolt of Texas from Mexico and subsequent annexation of the Lone Star to our Star-Spangled Banner (1845), the 1846 settlement of the boundary with Britain and Canada by intelligent compromise on the forty-ninth parallel rather than "Fifty-four forty or fight," the Mexican War which resulted in the addition of California and the great Southwest to the United States (1848), the Gadsen Purchase of 1853, and finally the purchase of Alaska from Russia (1867), the last of the contending nations, settled the major claims. The later clashes became tied in with the much wronged original owners of the land, the Indians.

While the "clear and unquestionable claims" advanced by Jefferson and "manifest destiny" repeatedly invoked in later public documents were pushing the many political issues, thousands of adventurous pioneers, fur-traders, and land-seekers were pushing westward along the Santa Fe Trail in the South and the Oregon Trail in the North. The finding of gold in California in 1848 brought a middle route, the California Trail, into heavy use. With our congenital desire for expansion, the West was now on its boisterous way to its present lusty life. Medicine and infectious disease during the different periods, Spanish, Mexican, and the Gold Fever, described by Henry Harris[1] in his entertaining well-documented *California's Medical Story* (1932), share in all of this turbulence. They provide us with another example of the rise of bacteriology under pioneer conditions. Of the "Doctor Adventurers," the one most noteworthy from our bacteriologic point of view was Dr. Victor J. Fourgeaud,[2] trained under the master of diphtheria, Pierre Brétonneau of Tours, France. Fourgeaud described an epidemic of diphtheria in the San Francisco Bay region in 1856, expressing the views of his former teacher that the disease is a specific infection and contagious. His complete brochure, published in 1858, is regarded by medical historians as an important early contribution to our knowledge of this disease.

California was admitted to the Union in 1850 and Oregon in 1859, both as "free" states. Washington was split off from Oregon much later (1889). As in other parts of the country, the early interest in microbes was chiefly as disease-inciting agents; anticontagionism and inertia were apparent as elsewhere. The California State Board of Health was organized in 1870 with Thomas M. Logan as its chief, but not until 1880 do we find in a medical journal specific mention of a bacterial pathogen, in this case the anthrax bacillus. The same year Williams presented a paper "On the Supposed Identity of the Poisons of Diphtheria, Scarlatina, Typhoid Fever and Puerperal Fever." But in 1882 we find two articles on "Listerism" and a paper by our peripatetic, army bacteriologic pioneer, George Sternberg, on "Organic Germs in Relation to Disease." The jogging advance in the stagecoach of progress was receiving jolts from the microbes.

Coccidioidomycosis

WILLIAM OPHÜLS

Emmet Rixford and T. C. Gilchrist[3] in 1896 gave us an excellent first account of "Two Cases of Protozoan (coccidioidal) Infection of the Skin and Other Organs" (Pseudo-tuberculosis). Two fatal cases in San Francisco of this new disease are described with photographs of the lesions, both gross and microscopic, and successful experimental inoculations, but with failure to cultivate the organism. In 1900 William Ophüls,[4] professor of pathology in Stanford University Medical School in San Francisco, another of our well-trained German scientists, continued the story by publishing with H. C. Moffitt, papers on "A New Pathogenic Mould," formerly described as a protozoan, *Coccidioides immitis pyogenes*. The organism cultivated on ordinary agar by Moffitt and Ash, was pathogenic for experimental animals, dogs, rabbits, and guinea pigs with lesions similar to those in man. A similar organism had been demonstrated in tissues by Posadas and by Wernicke in a patient in Argentina (1892); all the cases recorded in this country had at some time resided in California, six of the twelve had peculiar skin lesions, four had had primary lesions in the lung.

These papers merit especial attention because of the wider spread of this dust-borne disease in our arid regions and because of the two forms of this so-called San Joaquin fever; the primary coccidioidomycosis, which is commonly an acute, benign, self-limiting, respiratory infection, and the progressive, chronic, malignant, disseminated disease involving cutaneous, visceral, and osseous tissues. In the southwestern part of the country a large proportion of the population shows a hypersensitive skin reaction to coccidioidin, indicating the endemic character of the disease.

The Plague in California

W. H. KELLOGG AND J. J. KINYOUN

A violent outburst occurred in California during the spring of 1900 —an explosion of nerves and fears rather than many cases of the plague. However, there were cases of this disease, the Black Death of earlier centuries made familiar to the lay reader by Boccaccio (1345) and by Pepys (1665) for the plague year in London. The causative organism of this infection had been demonstrated by Yersin (1894), and numerous workers had shown that the disease is primarily one of rodents. Ogata (1897) and especially Simond (1898) had presented some evidence that the disease was spread to man by the agency of the infected rat flea. The success of the antiplague work in San Francisco based on this hypothesis became important evidence in support of this point. General acceptance followed the publication of the remarkable reports of the India Plague Commission (1906–17).

On March 6, 1900, a Chinese had died in San Francisco without benefit of medical attention; in order to provide a burial permit, an autopsy was performed by the assistant city physician, Frank P. Wilson. Because of the pathologic findings, he suspected bubonic plague. This was reported to W. H. Kellogg,[5] bacteriologist of the City Board of Health, who demonstrated in smears from an enlarged lymph node organisms having the size, shape, and staining reactions of the plague bacillus. As the city had no facilities for animal tests, the glands were submitted to the federal quarantine officer, J. J. Kinyoun, who on March 8 injected the material into rats, guinea pigs, and a monkey. Three days later one rat and two guinea pigs died with typical enlarged lymph nodes and spleen; the monkey became ill and died on March 13. Thus the cause of death was confirmed bacteriologically both by Kinyoun and by Kellogg; the Chinese *had* died of bubonic plague. As a matter of fact the health authorities had been expecting the plague because the disease had been on the march from India and China since early in 1894.

Then the storm broke. Appropriate preventive procedures were put into operation, but city and state authorities took different positions. Some said there was plague; some, including Governor Gage and members of the State Board of Health, said there was no plague. A campaign of vilification such as we had not seen in medical controversies in this country was waged by pen, cartoon, and political attack. Business was being injured was the cry and, of course, a truthful one. Kellogg was relieved of his job (he later made a good comeback and became secretary of the State Board of Health), and Kinyoun would have been fired had he not had a federal position. Local litigation, conflict between state and national authority, and interstate quarantine came into the picture. Controversy was so intense over the humiliating scandal that a neutral commission was appointed by federal authority to determine the truth. Simon Flexner from the University of Pennsylvania for pathology, F. G. Novy from the University of Michigan for bacteriology, and Lewellys F. Barker from the University of Chicago for clinical medicine, each with experience with plague, went to San Francisco, studied six cases and came to the unanimous conclusion that the cases were the plague. Novy took cultures of the organism back to Ann Arbor and gave them to a medical student (C. B. H.) to make some

Haffkine plague vaccine; the student developed pneumonic plague with the organisms demonstrable in his sputum, but he made a good recovery and later practiced medicine in California for many years.

This particular California epidemic lasted four years with 121 cases and 113 deaths. San Francisco was declared free from plague in February, 1904. No further cases occurred until May, 1907, a year after the earthquake-fire. From May, 1907, to November, 1908, 160 cases with 78 deaths occurred. Rat-proofing and the establishment of regions free from infected rats gradually crushed the epidemic, but occasional sporadic cases have continued to occur in widely scattered areas.

A startling discovery came out of these studies, the finding of plague in infected ground squirrels, placing California as one of many world foci of sylvatic or rural plague. No one knows whether these rodents were infected by fleas from rats dying during the 1900 epidemic or whether, as Karl Meyer and others maintain (Pollitzer),[6] the disease in our western rodents is a much older condition. This seems more probable. But we do know that the rodent disease is there and in all the neighboring states and that there have been a few cases of plague in man traced to wild rodents. The complete elimination of the rodent disease is essentially impossible. Rodents are prolific, adaptable, and the rat is a world traveler. Continuous rather than spasmodic efforts are necessary for control. The notion that any infectious disease is completely conquered is, as far as any evidence I know of, a delusion. Wishful thinking commonly leads the newspapers to transform a marked restriction of a disease into a complete victory.

Tularemia

GEORGE MC COY AND EDWARD FRANCIS

Still another discovery of moment takes its origin from a few of the thousands of autopsies of wild squirrels made by George McCoy[7] of the United States Public Health Service in the efforts to determine the geographical distribution of plague in these animals. This beautifully exact study (1911) detailed the finding of a plague-like disease of ground squirrels distinguishable from that caused by *Bacillus pestis* only with difficulty, chiefly because the lesions did not contain that organism. This disease he readily transferred to a wide variety of other rodents by injection of the infected tissues, but he failed to cultivate any organism. The next year (1912), however, McCoy and Chapin were successful in cultivating an organism on coagulated egg yolk and with this they reproduced the characteristic infection in other rodents. They named it *Bacterium tularense* from Tulare County, California, where it was found, but they had no notion of any relation of this organism to disease of man.

In 1914 Wherry and Lamb[8] gave an excellent description of ulcers of the conjunctiva of the eye of a meat-cutter from which they obtained material that produced lesions in a series of experimental guinea pigs and rabbits, but they were unable to cultivate any microbe. After learning of the work of McCoy and Chapin, they tried coagulated egg yolk as a medium and were successful in growing an organism apparently identical with *Bacterium tularense*.

Through a highly productive series of investigations begun towards the end of our period, about 1919, by Edward Francis[9] of the United States Public Health Service, we have come to recognize that rabbit fever, deer-fly fever, and several other locally named diseases are actually one and the same infection, now more properly called tularemia. This occurs primarily as a fatal infection of wild rodents; it is secondarily transmitted to man by blood-sucking flies or ticks or by self-inoculation while handling infected animals. It has world distribution; in the United States 2000 to 3000 cases are reported annually with a mortality of about 5 per cent. With considerable enthusiasm, Francis describes this infection as the only one in man that has been worked out from beginning to end by American investigators. And this all started from the acute observations of a modest, meticulously dependable man, George McCoy, carrying out a rather disagreeable routine job. I am reminded of the outstanding achievements of one, Theobald Smith, in the routine work of the antitoxin laboratory in Boston. What is a routine job? It varies with the vision of the man, does it not?

Bacteriology at the University of California and the State Hygiene Laboratory

A. R. WARD, WILBUR A. SAWYER,

FREDERICK P. GAY, AND KARL F. MEYER

Meanwhile the need of instruction in bacteriology became increasingly apparent in agricultural as well as in medical schools. Of several pioneer schools, the Toland Medical School, after the usual clashes and commotion, combined with the University of California.[10] For the confusing story of the many persons who paid their passing respects to bacteriology in different departments of the University of California,

I must refer the inquirer to the paper of L. S. McClung and K. F. Meyer, "The Beginnings of Bacteriology in California."[11] As elsewhere the early instruction in bacteriology was slight; here it tied in with lectures on hygiene, physical culture, and later the student health service. We shall largely ignore the departmental organization and try to present merely a few of the more important contributions.

A. R. Ward, in the division of veterinary medicine, was the first (1902) appointee with specialized training in bacteriology. He gave courses including laboratory work in bacteriology, and in 1906, when the State Laboratory of Hygiene was established, Ward became the first director. The moving spirit in the establishment of this laboratory was George F. Reinhardt, professor of hygiene in the University of California; largely through his influence, housing and staff were provided by the University. The services offered were similar to those in other state laboratories. Because of the earthquake and fire of that year, instruction in bacteriology in the medical school was transferred to the Berkeley campus with three students registered. Ward resigned in 1910 and Wilbur A. Sawyer[12] became director of the state laboratory until 1915 when he became the active executive head of the State Board of Health. During all of this period, he held faculty positions in the University.

Sawyer devoted much study to latent and carrier cases as sources of infectious diseases, including two unusual typhoid carriers. One (1912) was a winch-driver on a lumber steamer *Acme* who had nothing to do with food-handling. Over a period of some forty-three months, 26 cases with 4 fatalities came from this vessel, so that it became known among the sailors as the "fever ship," resulting in difficulty in obtaining a crew. Clever detective correlation of cases, personnel, and ships by Sawyer pointed to H. O. as the probable carrier. He had had typhoid fever four years previously, but stool and urine cultures were repeatedly negative; persistent efforts, however, finally yielded positive results. H. O., unlike Typhoid Mary, was intelligent and highly co-operative, but neither a long course of typhoid vaccines nor subsequent removal of his gall bladder was successful in clearing up the carrier state. Although stools and urine cultures were negative in 41 successive examinations over a period of fourteen months, *Bacillus typhosus* was finally isolated from his stomach contents containing bile.

This case shows the occasional necessity of prolonged study and reinforces the findings of the Spanish-American War epidemics as to the importance of personal contacts, even though no food-handling is

involved. "If the staff of the Marine Hospital in San Francisco had discovered typhoid bacilli in the stools of their patient, H. O., in January
1908 and had in some way prevented his spreading typhoid among the
sailors, this one hospital would have saved for itself the expense of
treating 21 typhoid patients, and 4 deaths would have been prevented."
How shall society deal fairly with cases such as that of this active able-
bodied man who intermittently discharges typhoid bacilli?

The other epidemic (1914), involving 93 persons infected by a typhoid carrier at a public church dinner, also opened many eyes. By the
usual elimination procedures all but chicken pie and Spanish spaghetti
were thought to be guiltless. Because of many instances of food-poisoning through chicken pie and because we have all burned our tongues on
escalloped spaghetti, the former was considered the more likely
vehicle. Many of the food-handlers came down with the typhoid fever
so they could hardly have been carriers of the organism that produced
the disease in themselves. Stool and urine samples from all of the other
food-handlers were sent at once to the state hygienic laboratory for
study. Meanwhile, careful histories of this group showed that one
woman, Mrs. X, had kept a boarding house from which through a
number of years had come a number of obscure cases of typhoid fever.
Although Mrs. X gave no history of previous typhoid fever, the laboratory promptly returned a statement of positive stool culture. All clear
so far, but how could so many persons have become infected? Mrs. X
had prepared the Spanish spaghetti at home. The ingredients, including
the sauce, were prepared the day before the dinner. On the morning of
the dinner, the spaghetti and the sauce were mixed in a large dishpan
and covered with cheese. The weather was warm, conducive to bacterial multiplication. At the hall, the mixture was placed in pans and
browned. The question was—would such heating penetrate the mass
and kill possible typhoid germs?

Repeated laboratory experiments using the same methods of preparation of spaghetti with *Bacillus typhosus* added before the browning
process gave positive cultures after varying times and temperatures.
Even when the material was kept at temperatures ranging from 207 to
214°C. (405 to 417°F.) for half an hour, and the surface of the spaghetti was dark brown with the points sticking up definitely charred,
cultures taken from a depth of .5 inch showed a few colonies of *B.
typhosus* and cultures from a depth of 2.5 inches showed abundant
colonies. Manifestly, heat penetrates masses of food like the Spanish
spaghetti very slowly. Ordinary browning as in this epidemic merely

provides incubator conditions for organisms in the interior of the food masses.

In 1910 bacteriology at the University of California acquired new impetus by the appointment of Frederick P. Gay[13] of Harvard to the chair of pathology in the medical school. In addition to excellent earlier training with Flexner at the University of Pennsylvania and in the Philippines, Gay had had rich experience in bacteriology and immunology for three years (1903–6) with Nobel prizeman Jules Bordet at the Pasteur Institute in Brussels. Accordingly he was requested to give some undergraduate instruction in bacteriology at Berkeley and to organize the course in medical bacteriology badly in need of attention.

Gay's active research interests were shown in a series of papers alone or with associates, especially G. Y. Rusk and Edith J. Claypole. These dealt chiefly with detailed studies of the then recently described complement fixation reaction of Bordet and Gengou, on the origin and nature of antibodies, and on biologic specificity. His extensive study of typhoid fever both experimental in the rabbit with the production of the carrier state and the monograph (1918) on the disease in man, its pathogenesis and prevention, are meritorious. A valuable aid to our one-language Americans was Gay's translation of *Studies in Immunity* by Jules Bordet and his collaborators (1909), including a number of papers by Gay himself. In 1923 Gay was called to Columbia University Medical School to succeed Zinsser, who had gone to Harvard. The studies of Ivan C. Hall of the department on anaerobic sporeformers, especially *Clostridium tetani* and its toxins, also deserve attention.

Karl Friederich Meyer[14] (1884——), a strong personality, was born in Switzerland and had early training in that country, in South Africa, and in Pennsylvania. He came upon the bacteriologic stage of California in 1913 and occupied its center for many years, long after our terminal date. On the Berkeley campus he succeeded John G. Fitzgerald, who became director of the newly established Connaught Laboratories in Toronto. But no single campus could contain Karl Meyer, and although most of his active life extends beyond the purview of these chronicles, we shall present a brief summary.

Meyer has always gone out into the field both in this and other countries, and he has not infrequently arrived at the center of an outbreak of disease before the constituted health authorities, much to their chagrin. Indeed, most of the early bacteriologists went out into the field, became involved in difficult epidemic problems, but with the extensive development of health boards and laboratories, those in university laboratories are now permitted to give advice and not infrequently a deal of work, but they are not welcomed in the field, a much to be regretted result of our wealth and high degree of specialization. Meyer's eager mind, supreme confidence, deep voice, and powerful physique have aided him in these conflicts.

In 1915, in addition to his duties in Berkeley he joined the staff of the Hooper Foundation under able George H. Whipple; he also took a firm hand in studying the problems of the canning industry, important not only in California. He has contributed to many microbiologic clashes, probably with most effect in plague, especially sylvatic plague, the importance of which he pounded into our reluctant minds. His interest in medical history and biography and his remarkable collection of portrait photographs deserve praise and preservation. He has won many honors. In 1921, when Whipple was called to build a medical school *de novo* in Rochester, New York, Meyer became director of the active Hooper Foundation with its ivy-covered laboratory building and friendly old-world atmosphere. (I do hope this building and this institution will not be crowded out by the new invasive growths of this frighteningly wealthy age.)

Bacteriology on the other campuses of the University received little attention until after our chosen period; for example, Courtland Mudge was not brought to the Davis campus until 1922, and his appointment, even then, was not in bacteriology, but in the Dairy Industry Division. In the State Experiment Station, however, significant studies in plant pathology were reported by 1908. These included investigation on walnut blight caused by *Pseudomonas juglandis*, lemon rot caused by a fungus, *Pythiacystis citrophthora*, and peach blight also caused by a fungus. Charles B. Lipman contributed a number of studies on the antagonistic effect of ions in relation to bacterial growth and metabolic processes.

Stanford University

HANS ZINSSER AND WILFRED H. MANWARING

Bacteriology received its early tentative recognition at Stanford University at the hands of the professor of botany, George James Pierce, shortly after his arrival on the campus with his bride in 1897. He had studied in Bonn, Munich, and Leipzig, having received his Ph.D. degree from the last-named institution. It is recorded that a serious outbreak of typhoid fever was curbed after the young botanist traced the source of the disease to a bacillus carrier in a lumber camp in the Sierras.

In 1908 the Cooper Medical College of San Francisco became part of Stanford University, and in 1910 the youthful effervescent Hans Zinsser[15] was brought "from one of our largest medical schools, Columbia, to found a department of bacteriology in earthquake ruins in what was then our youngest and smallest," in "a quiet country village and the isolation of the farm." They were totally unprepared for him at Stanford, and he began work in a small made-over room with no equipment, a space graciously squeezed out by the anatomy department. But shortly, "it was a gay exciting busy laboratory, with the lure of a rapidly developing field. Zinsser's own laboratory was a hopeless litter to anyone but himself. He maintained that a neat laboratory was an indication of laziness. Actually, he was interested in too many things . . . to devote himself to one." In spite of the lack of facilities, by 1913 Zinsser published two papers on toxins and one with Stewart Young, physical chemist, on the striking similarity of precipitation phenomena in colloid chemistry and in the specific precipitin reactions of immunology. This chemical approach to immunologic problems that Zinsser stressed had been begun earlier in Europe, especially by Bordet (1899) and by Arrhenius and Madsen (1902). In this country its further development has been promoted by many, including Gideon Wells in Chicago, Karl Landsteiner and Michael Heidelberger in New York.

Zinsser was followed at Stanford by a person of a very different type, a most restrained, diffident bacteriologist, Wilfred H. Manwaring. He had had unusually wide experience in European laboratories and at Hopkins, Indiana University, and the Rockefeller Institute in this country before going to the Far West. His major contributions were in several phases of immunology, especially by demonstration through elaborate transfusion methods that, in the dog, the liver is directly responsible for the production of anaphylaxis. He was president of the American Association of Immunologists in 1926. In 1920 Manwaring was succeeded as head of the department by the competent Edwin W. Schultz, but that is beyond our period.

BOTULISM

ERNEST C. DICKSON[16]

That explosive outbreaks can occur even in the ivory towers of our universities is instanced by a sudden severe epidemic of food-poisoning that followed a sorority supper at Stanford University in November, 1913. Of 24 girls at the supper, 12 became severely ill and one died with signs and symptoms of bulbar disturbances characteristic of botulism. With so many similar cases at one time, the diagnosis was not difficult. The one common article of diet was a salad made from string beans canned in the home of one of the girls during the previous summer. As is usual in such cases, by the time illness developed the salad was gone, so no direct studies of the food could be made. But two cans from the same home pack were left on the cellar shelves. One of these seemed unspoiled, but the other can was swollen, and upon being opened showed manifest fermentation with a bad odor. Bacteriologic studies showed a large anaerobic sporeformer similar in heat resistance but not, however, *Clostridium botulinum*.

Two reasons present themselves for mentioning this epidemic. The first is that this was the first well-studied epidemic in this country caused by growth of the botulinum organisms in vegetable tissues. Only one such epidemic was known in Europe; most cases had come from contaminated meat, especially sausages (*botulus* means sausage). The second reason is that following this outbreak, experimental studies were begun by Ernest C. Dickson of the Stanford Medical School, showing that *Clostridium botulinum* injected into commercially canned beans will grow there anaerobically over a period of months producing the typical toxins of these organisms. His work showed that vegetable proteins will support the growth of *Cl. botulinum*, that the toxin is thermolabile, and on that basis, home-canned vegetables of high protein content should be freshly heated before they are served. This was the precursor of much work on the different types of *Cl. botulinum*, of Dickson's excellent monograph of 1918, and of our appreciation that this disease, though fortunately rare, occurs over wide areas with a larger number of the cases in California than in our other states.

Many other persons became involved in the highly successful, prolonged study of botulism and the canning processes necessary to destroy anaerobic sporeformers. Among these Ray Lyman Wilbur and William Ophüls should be mentioned and later (1919), after an outbreak of the disease traced to ripe olives canned in glass, Karl F. Meyer, J. Russell Esty, and J. C. Geiger, as chief epidemiologist for the United States Public Health Service.

CANNING

J. RUSSELL ESTY

The canning of food both in home and in factory has been tremendously important throughout the world, but the basic early experiments come from France at the time of the French Revolution. Although important studies have been carried on in many areas, since much of the underlying experimental work in this country was conducted in California, I am quoting from an excellent history of bacteriologic studies on commercially canned foods by one of California's effective investigators of these problems, J. Russell Esty.[17] This was prepared for the historical symposium of the Society of American Bacteriologists in San Francisco in 1953; because of Esty's death it never reached an editorial chair.

In 1795 the French Government offered a 12,000 franc prize to the citizen who could devise a method of preserving fresh food for transport during military or naval movements of great distance and duration. Nicholas Appert worked on the problem for fifteen years. His simple theory was that if food is sufficiently heated and then sealed in a container that excludes air, it will keep. He filled bottles with various foods, sealed them with cork stoppers and cooked them in boiling water. Samples of his preserved vegetables and fruits were put on sailing vessels and sent around the world. They retained their wholesomeness, and in 1809 he was awarded the prize by Emperor Napoleon Bonaparte himself.

Appert's procedures were set forth in his treatise *Art of Preserving All Kinds of Animal and Vegetable Substances*, which was published in 1810. It became the basic reference work for subsequent developments in canning, and is still the fundamental procedure of canning as practiced today. In 1810 also, Peter Durand introduced and patented the "Tin Canister" made of iron coated with tin. In 1813 Bryan Donkin and John Hall in England, using Appert's method, sent tins of foods to authorities of the British Army and Navy for trial. In 1819 William Underwood established a cannery in Boston and packed fruits, pickles, and condiments in bottles, and Thomas Kensett and Ezra Daggett packed salmon, lobsters, and oysters in New York. In 1825 Kensett was granted the first American patent on the tin container.

The war between the states in 1861–65 stimulated the use of canned foods, and canners greatly increased their output. By 1870 there were about 100 canneries in the United States, and by 1900 the number had increased to 1800. During World War I an enormous amount of canned foods was consumed by our armies and navies. By 1920 the annual total pack of commercially canned foods in the United States was approximately four billion containers. During World War II two-thirds of the food supply used by the fighting forces of the United States and its allies was sent to them in cans. Since then record packs have been made annually to supply the military and consumer demands. The commercial canning industry in this country (1953) comprises about 3500 canneries located in 47 states and territories and produces some 400 different canned food items. The 1951 production amounted to about 20 billion pounds of food packed in over 19 billion containers and was valued at approximately 2.5 billion dollars.

In 1809 Appert knew that his process preserved food but not why. It was not until 1860, fifty-one years later, that Louis Pasteur demonstrated that food spoiled because of the growth of ever present bacteria and that microorganisms in raw foods are destroyed by heat. Concurrently, through the pioneer bacteriological studies of H. L. Russell in Wisconsin in 1894 on the cause of spoilage in canned peas and S. C. Prescott and W. L. Underwood in Massachusetts in 1895 on canned corn, it was shown that sterilization of a food is related to the heat resistance of the specific microorganisms present in the particular food. It should be noted that at the first annual meeting of the Society of American Bacteriologists on December 29, 1899, in New Haven, Connecticut, a detailed account of bacteria detected in sour corn was presented by S. C. Prescott.

In 1913 the canning industry established for the National Canners Association a research laboratory in Washington, D. C. to work out answers to canners' technical problems and to place canning methods on a scientifically sound basis. Later a similar laboratory was established in San Francisco with Esty as director; the special function of this division was the study of the canning of low-acid foods and the heat resistance of spores of thermophilic bacteria. This represents a highly effective co-operation among university men, public health officers, and the agencies of an important industry.

Wine

E. W. HILGARD AND F. T. BIOLETTI

One cannot take leave of California appropriately without a toast to its bounteous land and effervescent spirit in one of its choice wines, which are so dependent on well-selected and well-managed yeasts. From Bacchus through Hippocrates to the present day, the fruit of the vine and the industry that provides us with the products thereof have received both paeans of praise and threats of calamity.

The production of wine in California is its second largest agricultural industry, exceeded only by that of the citrus fruits; in the several important wine counties, 85 per cent of our native wines are produced and over 80 per cent of all wines consumed in this country. Vine culture brought to Mexico from Spain in the time of Cortez spread northward into California, then a part of Mexico, and was encouraged in the chain of Franciscan missions from the time of Father Junipera Serra in 1769. Commercial vine growing began almost a century later. Agaston Haraszthy,[18] a remarkable Hungarian who settled in San Diego in 1849, has been called the father of California viticulture. After travel in all the important wine areas of Europe, he brought back thousands of cuttings of some fourteen hundred varieties of vines.

But both the vines and the wines have destructive diseases. Of the former, the native American plant louse, *phylloxera*, has decimated great areas of vineyards both in this country and in Europe. Probably our greatest contribution to wine production (obviously not bacteriologic) is that of American vine roots which are relatively resistant to this pest; today most of the vines both in this country and in Europe are grafts of choice European varieties on American phylloxera-resistant roots.

The early studies in fermentation as well as the arts of preservation of foods by this process stem from Europe and lands farther east. Bacteriologists quite properly think at once of the immense amount of fundamental work on fermentation by Louis Pasteur extending over twenty years (1857–77) and his application of temperatures around 150° F. for the destruction of microorganisms causing spoilage of wine (1866) and of beer (1876), and the subsequent application of the method to the protection of milk. In California and in all the wine-producing countries, studies both microbiological and chemical have been made of the diseases both of vine and of wine. Many facts have become available through these studies, but wine making is still an art controlled only partly by scientific methods, with trained taste buds as the final judge.

Eugene W. Hilgard, first dean of the College of Agriculture in the University of California (1874), began experiments on fermentation of must in a small cellar on the Berkeley campus as early as 1880. In 1897 Frederic T. Bioletti, at that time a graduate student in botany, gave some instruction in wine making and later courses in zymology. This work was soon moved from Berkeley to the Davis campus; Bioletti continued his interest and his publications and became a recognized leader in the field until his retirement in 1935. Several men such as A. P. Hayne, E. H. Dwight, Charles S. Ash, H. C. Holm, and W. V. Cruess have through the years added their contributions with the following points

Upper left   Karl Friederich Meyer, 1884——
                    Photograph taken about 1930, at the age of forty-six.

Upper right   Wilbur Augustus Sawyer, 1879–1951
                    Photograph taken about 1923, at the age of forty-four.

Below   Frederick Parker Gay, 1874–1939
                    Photograph taken about 1928, at the age of fifty-four.

repeatedly emphasized. The rise in temperature during fermentation must be kept down to 90° F. or lower by some method of cooling or the yeast becomes inactivated so that the fermentation is stuck. Aeration helps to keep the temperature down and also invigorates the yeast. Dwight and Ash made pure cultures of wine yeasts, finding that masses of known favorable organisms introduced into the must induced more uniform and rapid fermentations. The wild yeasts isolated from the ripe grapes were not as effective as several pure cultures introduced from Europe. These yeasts gave wines of fresher flavor and bouquet, and the must fermented with these culture yeasts cleared more rapidly. One true wine yeast isolated in the studies of Holm's zymology course was named *Saccharomyces bioletti* in honor of his contribution. The principal pure cultures supplied by the University's zymology laboratory to wineries were and still are, however, the so-called Burgundy and champagne Ay strains obtained from P. Pacottet of France.

In 1916 Cruess and his associates showed that by adding grape concentrates in small doses during fermentation with several strains of yeasts, wines of 18 to 19.9 per cent alcohol by volume could be obtained so that dessert wines could be produced without adding brandy. Also Cruess and Bioletti reported that wine yeast, *Saccharomyces ellipsoideus*, is much less sensitive to sulphur dioxide, now so frequently used to eliminate or inhibit the undesirable wild yeasts and acetic and lactic acid producing bacteria that interfere with the production of delicious wines.

St. Paul wrote to Timothy (I Tim. 5:23), "Drink no longer water, but use a little wine for the stomach's sake and thine often infirmities." The thirteenth century Latin manuscript of Arnald of Villanova[19] was translated into German by Wilhelm von Hirnkofen and published in 1478, thus becoming the earliest printed book on wine. This in turn has recently been translated into English by Sigerist; from this delightful work, I quote the following:

Wine not only strengthens the natural heat but also clarifies turbid blood and opens the passages of the whole body. It strengthens also the members. And its goodness is not only revealed in the body but also in the soul, for it makes the soul merry and lets it forget sadness. It sharpens it to investigate subtle and difficult matters. It gives it also audacity and generosity, and well prepares the instruments of the spirit so that the soul may operate with them. If wine is taken in right measure, it suits every age, every time and every region. It is becoming to the old because it opposes their dryness. . . . Wine strengthens by its own virtue the substance of the heart and thus keeps people young.

Early Bacteriology in Oregon and Washington

A. E. MACKAY, HARRY J. SEARS, AND JOHN WEINZIRL

Many factors, including the greater distance from the early Spanish influence and from the tremendous forces of the gold rush, made for slower development in the lands north of California. The scholarly detailed studies by Olaf Larsell[20] in *The Doctor in Oregon* give us examples, as in all our pioneer areas, of conscientious missionaries, of early medical practitioners with little or no training, and of occasional blatant quacks. Epidemics of smallpox, cholera, typhoid fever, and diphtheria came and went as elsewhere with similar histories; the same lack of knowledge of sources and modes of infection and methods of control and the same heavy losses persisted.

Medical schools typical of the period came into being as for example the Willamette Medical Department first in Salem (1867), later in Portland where it was eventually merged with the University of Oregon Medical School (1913). Larsell cites A. E. Mackay, trained in Toronto, as giving the first lectures and demonstrations in microscopy at the University of Oregon Medical School in 1889. "He demonstrated the tubercle bacillus and other microorganisms with his microscope, the only one in the city at the time, and obtained cultures of other bacteria for study and demonstration to his students." The gradual development of bacteriology took its slow course in several departments chiefly under Mackay. In 1912 the department of pathology was formed with Mackay's student Ralph Matson as assistant professor responsible for bacteriology. Matson's brief term of a year was followed by several others who also served briefly until 1918 when bacteriology was granted departmental status under Harry J. Sears. Sears, coming from the Berkeley campus of California after earlier training under Zinsser at Stanford, developed the department admirably, and we are soon brought up to modern times and the logarithmic growth of bacteriology, an exciting period that we must leave with reluctance.

At the University of Washington, John Weinzirl as the first person who had had specific training in bacteriology, was appointed to the botany department in 1907. His studies on ptomaine poisoning both with Rosenau at Harvard and independently helped in burying that colorful but inaccurate term. A separate department of bacteriology was established in 1915, near the end of our period of scrutiny.

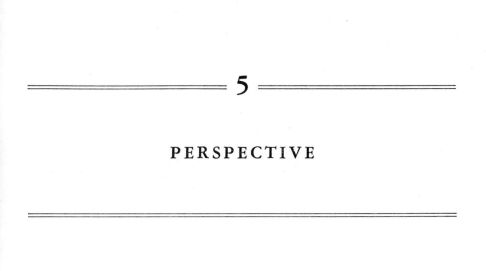

5

PERSPECTIVE

CHAPTER XVII

Our Means of Communication and Our Early Leaders

The march of the human mind is slow.   EDMUND BURKE

In addition to universities and official bodies such as boards of health, scientific societies, since the time of Plato's Academy and doubtless before, have been potent agencies in supporting and spreading knowledge. In our broad country, with its federal form of government and peoples from all lands, these societies have been invaluable in providing opportunity for interchange and fertilization of ideas, for scientific controversy, and for publishing journals. Commonly, such private associations have paved the way for similar, expanding governmental services. As in the world of living things, societies have been born and have died, have fused to make stronger units, and by fission have split (like bacteria) into untold numbers. The freedom of speech that has prevailed in these associations and the ease of publication are terribly important. In these days of stupendous governmental support and control with extensive classified restriction, much of it absurd and defeating the main purpose, many begin to realize that we have been losing some of the freedom upheld by our Bill of Rights and the earlier freer climate of opinion.[1] These societies and their early leaders have caught the fire, if not from Prometheus, at least from close to Olympus, and have passed it on with determination and enthusiasm. They shall serve us as inspiration.

The Royal Society of London, chartered by King Charles II in 1662, was highly important in serving the scientific interests of American colonists down to our Revolution. At least fifteen prominent colonials, including Cotton Mather, Roger Williams, and Benjamin Franklin, were members and a number of them sent contributions to the *Philosophical Transactions*.

1727[2] The oldest continuing scientific society in this country, the American Philosophical Society, originated in Benjamin Franklin's Junto, merged later with three other groups and acquired more formal organization in 1743. The transactions of this society have shown broad coverage including papers by Joseph Leidy in microbiology.

1780 Boston, not to be outdone by Philadelphia, established the American Academy of Arts and Sciences with John Adams as its leader, after his return from France. The first volume of *Memoirs* was published in 1785. The oldest of the state academies of arts and sciences is that of Connecticut which started in 1799.

1795 The Agricultural Society of South Carolina was incorporated in 1795, the first state geologic survey in North Carolina in 1823, and many natural history and "learned agricultural societies" were founded in the early decades of the nineteenth century. By 1830 the need for national scientific societies became apparent and some of the local organizations joined together for greater strength. Most of the men in science at that time were amateurs; many even on the college faculties were clergymen devoting part time to a hobby.

1818 *American Journal of Science and Arts* was a highly important pre-Civil War journal edited by Benjamin Silliman of Yale. This journal continues to thrive; it emphasizes chiefly geology and the earth sciences rather than biology.

1827 A long-lived influential journal is the *American Journal of the Medical Sciences* which began publication as the *Philadelphia Journal of the Medical and Physical Sciences*. In the earlier decades before many of our libraries subscribed to foreign journals, it was strong in presenting translations and reviews of foreign publications. Recently, presentation of "Summaria" in "Interlingua" deserves commendation.

1847 Of the societies with specific purposes, local groups of physicians began to organize early, and the American Medical Association, established in 1847, published its *Proceedings* 1846–47, *Transactions* 1848–72 and the *Journal* of the Association from 1883. State Medical Societies (the oldest continuing society, that of New Jersey 1766–) and their journals have also served as means of communication in medicine including bacteriology. The *New York Medical Journal*, the *Medical Record*, and the *Boston Medical and Surgical Journal*, even in the seventies published occasional articles showing some awareness of the coming microbic revolution.

1848 A potent influence in stimulating research in all the sciences has been the American Association for the Advancement of Science. Its published *Proceedings* from the outset down to 1861 (resumed again after the war), its weekly journal *Science* from 1883, and the *Scientific Monthly* (formerly *Popular Science Monthly*, 1872, now absorbed successfully by *Science*) have been outstanding in breadth of interest and high quality of the articles.

1863 The important National Academy of Science was founded under the pressures of the Civil War catastrophes.

1868 and 1878 Two early journals with broad interests, including microbiology, still continue publication. The *American Naturalist*, instituted by Alpheus Spring Packard in 1868, was taken over by the American Society of Naturalists when that was formed in 1883. The American Microscopical Society has published its widely varied *Transactions* since 1880 (named *Proceedings* since 1895).

1872 The American Public Health Association published reports and papers 1873–1910, the *American Journal of Public Hygiene* 1891–1910; this was continued as the *American Journal of Public Health and the Nations Health* 1911–. The influence of this society has been paramount in its field; it has had many working committees reporting especially along lines of improved and standard methods.

1886 Association of American Physicians. Because of the surging growth of bacteriology in the early years of this society, an unusually large proportion of the papers in its *Transactions* was devoted to pathogenic bacteria. The names of Abbott, Prudden, T. Smith, Sternberg, Trudeau, and Welch appear frequently both as authors and in discussion.

1896 The *Journal of the Boston Society of Medical Sciences* (Vols. 1–5) became (under the efficient editorship of Harold C. Ernst) the *Journal of Medical Research*, 1901–24, and then from 1925 the *American Journal of Pathology and Bacteriology*, the official organ of the American Association of Pathologists and Bacteriologists.

1896   The *Journal of Experimental Medicine* was begun under the en-
        thusiastic editorship of William Welch; to insure continuity of
        publication, it passed in 1905 (Vol. 6) to the Rockefeller
        Institute with Simon Flexner and Eugene L. Opie as editors.
        Although its field includes the whole gamut of experimental
        medicine, quite naturally many of its published papers have been
        in medical microbiology.

1899   The Society of American Bacteriologists was founded by per-
        sons interested in the many aspects of bacteriology; medical,
        industrial, engineering, soil, dairy, public health, and the promo-
        tion of the broad science of bacteriology have been emphasized.
        It began as an offshoot of the American Society of Naturalists
        with A. C. Abbott of Pennsylvania, H. W. Conn of Wesleyan,
        and Edwin O. Jordan of Chicago as the organizing committee.
        Its first president, William T. Sedgwick of the Massachusetts
        Institute of Technology, emphasized that bacteriology or micro-
        biology was sufficiently important to stand by itself rather than
        to be merely the handmaiden of medicine and agriculture. That
        precept has typified the activities of the society. With the estab-
        lishment of its *Journal of Bacteriology* in 1916 with C.-E. A.
        Winslow as editor, the society widened its admission require-
        ments to include any recommended persons interested in the
        field.

*Presidents of this society from
the beginning through our
period.*

*Institution of major appointment
at time of presidency.*

1900—W. T. Sedgwick	Massachusetts Institute of Technology
1901—W. H. Welch	Johns Hopkins University Medical School
1902—H.W. Conn	Wesleyan University
1903—Theobald Smith	Harvard University and Massachusetts State Board of Health
1904—F. G. Novy	University of Michigan Medical School
1905—E. O. Jordan	University of Chicago
1906—Erwin F. Smith	United States Department of Agriculture
1907—James Carroll	Medical Corps United States Army
1908—H. L. Russell	University of Wisconsin College of Agriculture
1909—J. J. Kinyoun	Health Department, District of Columbia
1910—V. A. Moore	College of Veterinary Medicine, Cornell University
1911—F. P. Gorham	Brown University
1912—W. H. Park	New York City, Bureau of Laboratories

Presidents of this society from the beginning through our period.	Institution of major appointment at time of presidency.
1913—C.-E. A. Winslow	City College of New York
1914—C. E. Marshall	Massachusetts College of Agriculture
1915—D. H. Bergey	University of Pennsylvania
1916—T. J. Burrill	University of Illinois
1917—L. F. Rettger	Sheffield Scientific School, Yale University
1918—R. E. Buchanan	Iowa State College
1919—S. C. Prescott	Massachusetts Institute of Technology

1901   The American Association of Pathologists and Bacteriologists[3] founded in 1901, has had an important productive history with "the advancement of the knowledge of disease" as its purpose. In this respect, it has quite properly emphasized aspects of pathology unrelated to microorganisms, thus leaving many aspects of microbiology, such as soil and industrial problems with no direct relation to disease in man, to the slightly older Society of American Bacteriologists.

Presidents of this society from the beginning through our period.	Institution of major appointment at time of presidency.
1901—W. T. Councilman	Harvard University Medical School
1902—W. T. Howard, Jr.	Western Reserve University Medical School
1903—Ludvig Hektoen	University of Chicago
1904—Eugene Hodenpyl	Columbia University Medical School
1905—Simon Flexner	Rockefeller Institute for Medical Research
1906—James Ewing	Cornell University Medical School
1907—W. H. Welch	Johns Hopkins University Medical School
1908—A. S. Warthin	University of Michigan Medical School
1909—Harold C. Ernst	Harvard University Medical School
1910—F. B. Mallory	Harvard University Medical School
1911—E. R. LeCount	Rush Medical College
1912—Richard M. Pearce	University of Pennsylvania Medical School
1913—H. U. Williams	University of Buffalo Medical School
1914—J. J. Mackenzie	University of Toronto Medical School
1915—Leo Loeb	Washington University Medical School, St. Louis
1916—John F. Anderson	U. S. Hygienic Laboratory
1917—William H. Park	New York City, Bureau of Laboratories
1918—Eugene L. Opie	Washington University Medical School, St. Louis
1919—Oskar Klotz	University of Pittsburgh Medical School

1903   The Society for Experimental Biology and Medicine and its promptly published *Proceedings* has aided greatly in keeping the specialized groups on speaking terms with one another.

1904   The *Journal of Infectious Diseases* was founded by the John Rockefeller McCormick Memorial Institute for Infectious Diseases with Ludvig Hektoen and Edwin O. Jordan as its capable editors for many years. It is now published for the John Rockefeller Memorial Fund of the University of Chicago.

1909   *Phytopathology* is the official journal of the American Society of Phytopathology.

Presidents of this society from the beginning through our period.	Institution of major appointment during presidency.
1909—L. R. Jones	University of Wisconsin, College of Agriculture
1910—F. L. Stevens	North Carolina Agricultural Experiment Station
1911—A. D. Selby	Ohio Agricultural Experiment Station
1912—G. P. Clinton	Connecticut Agricultural Experiment Station, New Haven
1913—F. C. Stewart	New York Agricultural Experiment Station, Geneva
1914—Haven Metcalf	United States Department of Agriculture
1915—H. H. Whetzel	Cornell University
1916—Erwin F. Smith	United States Department of Agriculture
1917—M. T. Cook	Rutgers University
1918—E. M. Freeman	University of Minnesota, College of Agriculture
1919—C. L. Shear	United States Department of Agriculture

1909   *Mycologia* superseded the *Journal of Mycology* (1885–1908) and the *Mycological Bulletin* (1903–8). Since 1931, when the Mycological Society of America was formed, *Mycologia* has become its official journal.

1914   The American Association of Immunologists, established in 1914, began the publication of its *Journal of Immunology* in 1916 under the able editorship of Arthur Coca.

Presidents of this society from the beginning through our period.	Institution of major appointment during presidency.
1914—G. B. Webb	Colorado Foundation for Research in Tuberculosis
1915—J. W. Jobling	Vanderbilt University Medical School

1916—Richard Weil   Cornell University Medical School
1917—J. A. Kolmer   University of Pennsylvania Medical School
1918—W. H. Park   New York City Bureau of Laboratories
1919—Hans Zinsser   Columbia University Medical School

1914   The *Journal of Parasitology* was initiated by Henry B. Ward; it became the official organ of the American Society of Parasitologists when that society was formed in 1924.

1916   *Soil Science* was founded by Jacob G. Lipman; it has given the broad coverage that our invaluable top soil demands.

The preponderating influence of the men and institutions of the northeastern seaboard in the development of microbiology in the United States is brought out sharply by observing the geographical distribution of the presidents of the several important societies during their early growth period. Very few of the men are found elsewhere. One, G. B. Webb, in immunology, 1913, was in the western mountain area; two were south of the Mason-Dixon Line, F. L. Stevens in North Carolina in phytopathology, 1910, and J. W. Jobling, who worked most of his active life in New York City, was in 1915 serving Vanderbilt University Medical School.

Of scientific and philanthropic societies with specialized functions, the number is legion. Many of these are devoted to the investigation, treatment, and prevention of one disease whether it is statistically highly important or not. This leads us to consider a recent critical article by Marion Sanders,[4] giving voice to questions that have been troubling many of us during several decades. In her survey of such societies, she presents clearly the duplications both of function and effort, the increase in overhead, the large office organizations, the overemphasis of emotional appeal rather than the approach to the problems on a statistical basis of the needs; she calls attention to the development of allegiance to the organization rather than the initial purpose.

Shall we continue to support the great number of such single purpose organizations or shall we adopt more largely the Community Chest ideas for philanthropy and the public support of medical and scientific needs on the basis of statistical information? Obviously this is a complex question that involves us in a deeper one; how far can we support paternalism on the part of our many governmental units and at the same time maintain our cherished individual initiative? A further difficulty that many of us have observed is that some of the richer societies have had more money in recent years than could be properly expended, because of the dearth of adequately trained personnel. Even though one can readily present adverse comments on unnecessary overhead and plush carpets, some of these private organizations (it would be invidious in this broad survey to name any one) have had, over decades, impressive histories of achievement.

Books on bacteriology conform to the usual practice—"of the making of books there is no end." Early American publications in this field have been listed through 1915 by L. S. McClung,[5] archivist of the Society of American Bacteriologists. He employed the term bacteriology not as we have done, but in a stricter taxonomic sense omitting animal parasites, and also more loosely, including texts in pathology, and even practical therapeutics, if the book included a chapter or a section concerned with bacteria or bacteriologic techniques. Of the approximately 250 titles in his survey, about 50 would come under the head of popular teaching, especially important in the early period, a similar number of laboratory guides, useful chiefly in the courses for which they were written, a goodly number of addresses and short notes, and about 50 more complete texts varying in breadth and depth and number of editions to satisfy the demand.

In the several sections of these chronicles, I have mentioned the books that have seemed to me important from a national point of view. When one realizes the labor involved, one wonders why anyone ever attempts to write a book, including this one. The recent broad-scale annotated guide to the history of bacteriology by Thomas H. Grainger and the bibliography of communicable diseases with critical abstracts and personal notes by Arthur L. Bloomfield will be helpful to give us a deeper understanding of the shoulders on which we stand.

Americans have done world service in making medical literature available. Through the initiative of John Shaw Billings, the *Index Catalogue of the Library of the Surgeon General's Office of the United States Army* was begun in 1880; it still continues its marvellous cumulative indices. The *Quarterly Cumulative Index Medicus* is also an invaluable necessity. England has provided the *Zoological Record* and the *Index Veterinarius*, equally important in their respective fields. A more recent *Bibliography of Agriculture* stems from the United States Department of Agriculture. Still more recently, we have been making more successful efforts to provide abstracts and translations of the literature from Russia and other little known areas. We need occasional shocks.

CHAPTER XVIII

Epilogue–From a Laboratory Window

We thank with brief thanksgiving
Whatever gods may be
That no man lives forever,
That dead men rise up never;
That even the weariest river
Winds somewhere safe to sea.   SWINBURNE

Of the twelve different laboratories assigned to my use in several parts of the world during the half-century of my professional life, each has had its distinctive characteristics, different outlooks either restricted or broad, and differing odors and equipment. Of them all, my early laboratory at Wisconsin, a room in the attic of Science Hall, high above the nearby maples and on a level with the tops of the elms farther up the hill, had unique values of its own and the broadest prospects. It faced south with a large arched window and a skylight, hot in the summer, but delightful in the winter when the sun was describing a low arc above the horizon. The hourly tramp of students up and down the hill gave rhythmic encouragement to the mind; the experimental animals in the adjacent areas immediately outside the door provided opportunities both for mind and hand; on occasion, ammoniacal odors gave acrid evidence that the animal cages needed cleaning; we had little help in those days. Two other features of this office-laboratory should be mentioned; the long climb—148 steps up from the street level and no elevator until after many years—eliminated casual visitors and the great steel I beams extending from the low eaves to the high peaks of the roof gave shattering reminders to the unwary when misdirected movement brought the soft head into contact with the hard metal. Memories of

some near knockout blows, the isolated position of the room, and the
extensive view have induced me to choose this laboratory, rather than
some with superior equipment, as a vantage point from which to scru-
tinize microbiology and some of the failures and successes of microbiologists.

This is no attempt to explain genius; rather it is a bringing together
of a few road signs that may help the "mine run" of young microbiologists.

> *Doing easily what others find difficult is talent;*
> *Doing what is impossible to talent is genius.*   AMIEL

Much good counsel has come from the prophets of all ages, specifically
from our wiser scientists from Aristotle down. Can this survivor of an
earlier generation of bacteriologists provide any additional glimmers
that may be useful? Perhaps from such a high window, as from a moun-
taintop, one may see the far horizons and from the same spot one may
see more sharply the pebbles on the ground or possibly, an anemone.

Since the discoveries and applications of microbiology were largely
responsible for much of early preventive medicine, may we first look
far beyond the elms to determine some of the effects of this revolution
on the world scene. The reduced death rates from communicable diseases, especially in infancy, although an immediate boon to mankind,
have, when coupled with continuing high birth rates, given us explosive
overpopulation, especially in areas such as India where the rice bowl
is frequently empty and manure is used for fuel instead of to replace the
used-up elements in the topsoil. This has become a world problem of
terrifying magnitude, more explosive than an atom bomb. So much attention is being directed to this catastrophy and with some slight success that one hopes for a partial solution within the century.[1] If not;
wars, famine, and disease will certainly take over.

A related hot question is what shall we do with the thousands over
sixty-five years of age? And here in these United States, "a land flowing with milk and honey," the federal government has been spending
billions to purchase excess farm products with an additional cost of
millions of dollars each year to house the excess.[2] And meantime, millions of men, women, and children in other areas are starving or living
on bare subsistence diets, some of the latter even in our own land.

Predation and parasitism are essentially universal, stemming from
the struggle for existence, adaptation to environment, and the com-

pelling demand for food beginning with the most primitive prebacteria a billion or more years ago, down through the infinitely slow, evolutionary ages to man of today. This struggle for existence has been so bred into us through the ages that we seem unable to avoid violent conflict even when the food supply is more than ample. Commonly, persons want more and more of whatever it is they are after—food, money, power, praise, even when the "cup runneth over," an interminable struggle, frequently ruthless. Because the prospect is so awful and so revolting to many, we strive to ignore violent predation, the preying of the larger on the smaller organisms, and also insidious parasitism, the smaller living at the expense of the larger.

Small organisms both plant and animal reproduce prodigiously; most of them go into the maw of the next larger species in the pyramid of life, leaving only a few to carry on the race. Each must ceaselessly feed, fight, breed, and die. Consider the billions of microbes in our intestinal tracts. There is increasing evidence that such parasites are desirable for the development of a successful mechanism against pathogenic invaders. "Parasitism may be regarded not as a pathological manifestation but as a normal condition having its roots in the interdependence of all living organisms."[3] Conflict is inherent in life. How much of this is an appropriate struggle for life and for growth and how much sheer selfish greed are always moot questions. Only after millions of years has the body developed a fairly satisfactory compromise with parasites and among opposing physiologic mechanisms.[4] Man in society needs to consult his body and the lowly parasites to learn wisdom, the necessity of compromise, and the facts of the interdependence of all living creatures, great and small.

Another distressing view, and one even more difficult to cope with, is that man, this worst predator with the gun, carries on the conflict ruthlessly with his own species even in the realm of his religions where ideals and altruism should rule. The wars of religion have been as fierce and as pitiless as the worst of those for land or for gold, even up to yesterday with the partition of India. Millions through all ages have prayed for peace, yet relentless wars have ravaged them and their lands. And here in this country we have not been guiltless. Are not all the major religions essentially the same in their underlying philosophies? Norman Cousins in his stimulating book *Who Speaks for Man*[5] gives the phrasing of the Golden Rule, man's hoped for attitude-towards-man, as taught in nine religions of the world. The Bahai Cause, Buddhism,

Christianity, Confucianism, Hinduism, Islam, Judaism, Shintoism, and Zoroastrianism all express the same idea save that three of them express it in the negative form—do not, rather than do. "The purpose of religious controversy should be, not to convert the opponent, but to persuade him that his religion is essentially the same as our own" (Ananda K. Coomaraswamy).

Why cannot our intellects control the emotions when these lead to such cruelty and to such stupidity? That question and a score of others pour in upon me as I look beyond the horizon. Why? Why is anything? Science makes little attempt to meet these unknowable questions save to say quite willingly, I do not know. Different peoples and different individuals have through the ages adopted many hypotheses. For the most part these gropings into the unknown are sincere strivings frequently tied in with religion and with science. Striving, even under dire misfortune, is the great glory of mankind. The scientist would say to all, make as many hypotheses as you like; but remember they are only hypotheses. They will change as our knowledge increases. If others adopt different ones, is it not their right? Should they be slain for so doing?

And the conflict between science and religion continues. In my college days, we were taught from the scholarly two-volume treatise by Andrew D. White[6] about the conflict of science and theology throughout Christendom. A hundred years ago Darwin, Wallace, Huxley, and others startled the world with "Brother thy tail hangs down behind." Informed persons have accepted the overwhelming mass of evidence supporting the evolutionary thesis, but a few years ago we had the searing experience of the Scopes trial.[7] Bryan's polemic began here on the Wisconsin campus; I was among those present. Fanaticism is only smoldering and is frequently tied to blind though sincere faith. Although our eyes are at rest when viewing the horizon, the mind is not. Neither the bacteriologist, the astronomer, nor the philosopher is able to pierce the mists. Thoughts crowd in even to the imminent possibility of complete annihilation of all but some of the autotrophic bacteria that can survive on CO_2 and simple inorganic compounds.

I hope I may be forgiven for this digression from our immediate theme; many hours at the microscope do not blind a person to broader world problems. Since in all the sciences, and in other fields too, we commonly make progress only when we narrow the point of attack, may we come back now to our more restricted field and the friendly microscope, with light and field well controlled. Just below the window,

I see and hear the students, so optimistic and gay, the very essence of spring whether it be May or November. I hear someone singing, "Oh what a beautiful mornin'."

Of the papers and books on the art and methods of investigation that I have enjoyed, three[8] recommend themselves especially. *The Way of an Investigator* by Walter Cannon, formerly professor of physiology in Harvard Medical School, is warmly personal, full of stimulating examples, and quite largely autobiographical. *The Art of Scientific Investigation* by W. I. B. Beveridge, professor of animal pathology in Cambridge University, will be exceptionally helpful to all those dealing with infectious disease problems that require animal experimentation. *An Introduction to Scientific Research* by E. Bright Wilson, professor of chemistry in Harvard University, bears the stamp of the physical chemist; it is highly quantitative in its approach, exact, and exacting. Whatever your age, if you will spend three long weekends, one with each of these books, both your thinking and the quality of your work will be improved.

Walter Cannon, the exuberant, dedicated, somewhat naive and highly successful physiologist, lists the following traits as important for success in a career of investigation: curiosity, imaginative insight, critical judgment, thorough honesty, a retentive memory, patience, good health, and generosity. He makes no attempt to weigh the relative merits of each characteristic and avers that, "training and practice will help for early inadequacy." He gives examples of the trails over which curiosity has led him and others, the role of hunches during a sleepless night (keep a pencil and paper at the bedside), and especially serendipity, the happy faculty of recognizing unforeseen accidental bypaths, not infrequently more important than the original road. He emphasizes also the choice of able associates, from "Deans to *Dieners*," in the adventures of exploration. He cries for freedom of action without which the investigator is sure to lack the inspiration and the zest that grow in an independent atmosphere. Scientific disagreements, depending on how they are met, may be either baneful or beneficial. In examining ways of going astray, he stresses the errors of untested assumptions, the error of omitted controls, and frequently faulty technique—a constant error. The neglect of multiple causes is always with us and the drawing of unwarranted conclusions. We all fall into the error of *post hoc, ergo propter hoc.*

Beveridge gives specific meaty kernels of advice. He urges attention to the history of science, the art of skim-reading, critical review of the relevant literature, all of which should lead to useful guesses or hypotheses. Experiments could then be devised to test the most likely of these hypotheses. Randomization of the control groups, frequently neglected, is essential and the determination by lot rather than by any method involving human discrimination. These elements in experimentation have been more completely recognized since the work of R. A. Fisher.[9] As does every critical writer and every observer of his own life and that of his fellows, Beveridge finds many instances of the importance of chance. He begins with the well-known story of Pasteur's researches in fowl cholera. After a two weeks' vacation, Pasteur found that his cultures, formerly virulent, now failed to grow and also failed to infect birds. He was about to discard the whole lot, but decided to chance a second injection with fresh virulent organisms. To the surprise of all, the animals withstood the inocula that killed normal birds. This was the beginning of the broader conception of vaccination. Beveridge gives ten fascinating examples of chance in his chapter on that subject and seventeen more in the Appendix. Many more could be dug from the records. He places a high value on hypotheses as instruments in research, particularly if these are suggested by the imagination or what he terms "intuition." Cannon's word for this trait is "hunch"; it has been called inspiration, action of the subconscious mind, or simply daydreams. The flash, the notion, the idea may come when we are consciously thinking of the problem or at some odd time when seemingly the mind is at rest or considering totally different matters. Again Beveridge cites examples from his experience and from the literature.

Bright Wilson, partly because of the field in which he works, gives greater attention to the careful design of the experiments, the design and construction of the apparatus, and the analyses of results. In whatever field, all could profit by reading these chapters. He, too, stresses the importance of sampling, of personal bias as a frequent factor in errors, failures in technique, and the great difficulty in devising suitable controls when, as commonly, several factors are involved. He gives startling examples, especially in biology and medicine, of the pits into which we have fallen through inadequate controls.

With keen appreciation of the wisdom of these authors, I am selecting a few points that have especially impressed me during the past five decades, as I have watched the rise and fall of many able men and their contributions.

The Master-word in Microbiology

Osler in his brilliant essay, "The Master-word in Medicine,"[10] builds up increasing suspense as he proposes to give his students the master-word, the magical touchstone, "the open sesame to every portal . . . the true philosopher's stone which transmutes all base metal of humanity into gold. With this talisman the blind shall see by touch, the dumb shall speak with their fingers" and all shall lay hold on hope. Finally, after delightful wanderings, he proclaims the powerful master-word— work.

Whatever the field, work, persistence, and devotion to the task is the password. In the generations I have known personally, I think of no microbiologist who has achieved signally without this countersign. Drive is a word frequently employed, but to me it is a word tinged with an aggressiveness that uses elbows and smacks of high-pressure campaigns for money or power. I have known many highly successful microbiologists who have not shown this militant "drive," but they have worked consistently and their direction has been excellent. Edwin O. Jordan, Oswald T. Avery, W. H. Park, L. R. Jones, in their varying fields, and a score of others come to mind at once.

Aside from the master-word, we must have direction and continuity; these have been especially exemplified through the long life of Theobald Smith. And one thinks with regret of poor Noguchi with his tremendous fire and energy, but so unfortunate in his directions. Closely associated with direction is the choice of subject. Theobald Smith advised the choosing of a subject "close at hand," partly because of the greater facility in obtaining material. Most men have followed this example; only occasionally, the compelling influence of a dramatic disease has drawn men to distant parts (Ricketts *et al.*).

Persistence to the point of obstinancy in working on the chosen subject is commonly necessary even when one is almost overcome with fatigue or with boredom in piling up the evidence. Theobald Smith called his period of work on Texas Fever four years of slavery. When I asked Weinberg, who worked so successfully on the pathogenic anaerobes for years, whether he ever got bored, he replied with a dramatic French gesture, which I must leave to your imagination, that "just to think of these organisms frequently gives me nausea and vomiting." One recent sample especially pleases me. In congratulating John Enders for his Nobel Prize on the cultivation of poliomyelitis virus in nonnervous tissue, I expressed my enthusiasm that he had persisted in these studies even after two good men, Sabin and Olitsky,[11] had twice cultivated the virus in nervous tissues from human embryos, but had failed with other tissues from the same sources. At that time, most persons in the field had accepted the idea of a highly specific affinity of this virus for the nervous system. Enders replied that he feared that he was just too obstinate to accept that idea and to drop the quest. That indeed is what it takes, together with a realization of the values of "gradualness."[12]

Species Differences as Well as Variety or Strain Differences, Both in Host and in Parasite

Differences in species susceptibility were realized as soon as man began to observe his own illnesses and those of animals around him. Obviously some diseases afflicted both man and other animals. "First he [Apollo] shot the mules and the swift dogs, and then he shot a sharp arrow against the men and smote them. And the crowded pyres of the dead burned on, unceasing."[13] Much later, with the experimental approach to problems of infection, species differences became even more apparent (J. A. Villemin, Theobald Smith and tuberculosis). Although Koch repeatedly warned his students that mice were not men, he fell into this pitfall himself. His interpretation of the Koch phenomenon and his efforts to immunize with tuberculins show that he did not quite realize the many differences between experimental tuberculosis in the guinea pig and the naturally occurring disease in man. Then, too, his insistence on the identity of the bovine and the human tubercle bacilli, years after Villemin and Theobald Smith had demonstrated the differences, gave proof of his undue reliance on his own judgment.

When an experimental disease is similar both histologically and clinically to that in man, we are prone to make unwarranted assumptions. A recent example of this can be found in experimental poliomyelitis. Infection by the intranasal route was so easy to carry out in the rhesus monkey; the virus was so frequently found in the nasopharynx of human carriers; and the importance of the nasal route had been shown for epidemic meningitis. What more natural assumption than that the nasal route is the common portal of entry in man! But later evidence showed that this was an erroneous assumption. Similar instances could be cited almost indefinitely.

Not only must we bear in mind species differences of the experimental hosts, but differences in variety, age (Coxsackie virus studies), sex, and differences on the basis of changes in environment, nutrition, and on different routes of infection (Sabin and Olitsky and others).[14] Altered virulence of the infective agent when grown on artificial media was a difficulty recognized early; antigenic differences based on the presence or absence of flagella, capsules, or internal phase differences have given investigators headaches as well as opportunities (T. Smith, Rettger, *et. al.*).

In plant studies too, a similar error has occurred in the cross-inoculation of leguminous plants with rhizobia. Investigators used test or so-called indicator plants for certain plant groups under the impression that all plants were mutually interchangeable with the same strain of rhizobia. The concept of the definitive individuality of plant species was lost sight of just as has repeatedly been the case in animal studies.

The physical conditions under which the animals or the plants have been kept, temperature, light, etc., as determining factors in the infection have not infrequently been neglected. (Hippocrates, Trudeau and tuberculosis, Baldwin *et al.* and Rhizobia, and Thom and soil pathogens.)

Similarity of Lesions Produced by Different Agents or by Secondary Invaders or by Both

Even the experienced pathologists may be led astray; witness much of the early work on hog cholera (Welch, Theobald Smith) and the secondary invaders; bacteria have been described as the etiologic agent in practically every virus disease before the demonstration of the specific virus. These experiences have reinforced the necessity for using specific antigen-antibody reactions; even these are not without hazards, making many controls necessary. The infectious granulomata with their several different infectious agents such as the tubercle bacillus, *Treponema pallidum*, *Histoplasma capsulatum*, and other fungi have provided many examples of such error and confusion. The close similarity of the gross and microscopic pathology in fungus and tuberculous infections should be emphasized and the need of demonstrating the parasite.[15] Many infectious agents and a variety of chemical agents can produce similar confusing motor-neuron damage (the strange Durban Epidemic of 1937 is one example of the latter, Note 2).

The Fallacy of Pure Cultures

To the bacteriologists, the pure culture has been the *sine qua non* of much of his knowledge; impure cultures have been an anathema. In recent years we have gone well beyond our earlier conceptions of the single species; the presence or absence of flagella, capsular polysaccharides, antigenic components within the body of the organism, subtle phases, and even an invading bacteriophage are all elements in specificity (Smith and Reagh, Neufeld, Avery *et. al.*). The young bacteriologist in the laboratory citadels should bear in mind that we have at times permitted the idea of the pure culture to swing us too far to the right. In the field outside of the laboratory whether we are dealing with diseases of plants, of lower animals, or of man, many diseases are mixed infections. The tubercle bacillus is the causative agent of tuberculosis, and one can produce the disease experimentally with pure cultures of that organism. But in the natural disease the pus-producing cocci are also important. To be sure we find pure cultures of *Bacillus typhosus* in the bile from the gall bladder and from gallstones. Pure cultures of a number of invasive bacteria such as beta-hemolytic streptococci or *B. anthracis* are obtainable from the blood stream, and in endocarditis pure cultures of cocci (different species) are readily obtainable from the heart valves. But frequently, disease represents a synergistic result of two or more organisms, as for example, in the terrible 1918–19 epidemic of influenza.

In the black rot of cabbage also, the way is prepared for a secondary infection, soft rot. The organism, *Phytophthora infestans*, that caused the potato famine in Ireland in the 1840's and many disasters both before and since, prepares the way for secondary invaders. The number and variety of degrees of association and synergism is endless (Marshall[16]). The virus diseases provide us with baffling instances. Tobacco rosette disease is caused by two unrelated viruses, one that is transmitted by its aphid vector only if the other virus is present in the host. Many diseases of the lower animals are also of this mixed-infection character, for example, scours, due to *Escherichia coli* and a virus; so-called shipping fever of cattle due to a member of the *Pasteurella* genus and a hemabsorption virus is another example; and so on to the end of a long chapter. Among nonpathogens, the wide variety of cheeses provide us with similar but more savory examples. In the laboratory we have provided a restricted series of conditions only distantly approximating those in the field. It is difficult enough, especially in diseases of man, to reproduce the disease with pure cultures so we rarely try to work in the laboratory with the mixed infections of the field and the hospital.

Health and Hobbies

Long years of good health and suitable opportunities are obviously desirable. A couple of hobbies will commonly be helpful, one for out-of-doors and one for a winters evening, but beware not to ride your hobbies too hard, after you have "arrived." Sacrifice at least one journal to a clipping file or an old-fashioned commonplace book. If possible, develop a new method or adapt one that is known to a new purpose. *Die Methode ist Alles* was an aphorism of the distinguished physiologist, Ludwig. A glance at the history of bacteriology or any science will show how apt this is.

Chance

And finally and always there is *chance*. Even Theobald Smith in talking with his friend Eugene Opie said that he would not care to go through life again since chance had been so important for him and might not be so favorable another time. Everywhere we look, accident, luck, and the occasion loom as tremendously influential, more so than we like to admit. And I am referring to minor events that happen to each individual. An unusually capable graduate student or an intelligent animal caretaker may be the stimulant. M. J. Rosenau said that one day when he asked his helper to bring him a certain group of guinea pigs for further serum injections, the man responded, "those animals that have had previous injections all die" (i.e. anaphylactic shock). In the broad field of medicine, chance observations, frequently reflected in folklore, have given us much. Oliver Wendell Holmes[17] summarizes the debt of medicine to the layman as follows: "It learned from a monk how to use antimony, from a Jesuit how to cure agues, from a friar how to cut for stone, from a soldier how to treat gout, from a sailor how to keep off scurvy, from a postmaster how to sound the Eustachian tube, from a dairy-maid how to prevent small-pox and from an old market woman how to catch the itch-insect." Many such instances have been brought together entertainingly by George M. Gould.

A job with an active prominent man is an open sesame to further opportunity (observe the Welch rabbits).[18] Ask any older person when he is feeling friendly and appropriately humble, and he will tell you the same story. It was Pasteur who said, "In the field of experimentation, chance favors only the mind prepared for discoveries by patient study and presevering effort." "Discovery should come as an adventure, rather than as the result of a logical process of thought. Sharp prolonged thinking is necessary that we may keep on the chosen road, but it does not necessarily lead to discovery," were the words of Theobald Smith. Maintain the enthusiasm of the amateur. One cannot avoid chance, but one can within limits choose one's institution, seek opportunities and productive associates, and a laboratory with many problems actively under investigation.

Now that we are aware that even the humble bacteria mate on some sort of random propinquity basis, it may not be out of place to suggest that the bacteriologist should use a more selective method. William Osler used to advise his students to "put your affections in cold storage for a few years, and you will take them out ripened, perhaps a bit mellow, but certainly less subject to those frequent changes which perplex so many young men." That advice is not in style today, but it is still good practice to postpone marriage until you have earned your degrees and have a job. But whether you marry early or late, choose a wife who will be able to grow with you as you advance in experience and position. On the other hand, a goodly number of successful bacteriologists of each sex have preferred the independence of single blessedness. One thinks immediately of the pioneers, Welch and Prudden, and a little later, Park, Dochez, and Avery; and on the distaff side, such productive scholars as Anna Williams, Alice Evans, and Sara Branham.

In the wars and confusion of this century, the great man of our age, Winston Churchill, has this to say, "What hope can there be for the future of the world unless there is some form of world government which can make its effort to prevent renewal of the awful struggle through which we have just passed." Obviously we cannot say that such a government will work but it must be tried.

And the distinguished writer John Masefield, poet laureate of England, at a celebration at the University of Shefield,[19] England, gave voice to our deep admiration, our love towards universities.

> *There are few earthly things more splendid than a University. In these days of broken frontiers and collapsing values, when the dams are down and the floods are making misery, when every future looks somewhat grim and every ancient foothold has become something of a quagmire, wherever a University stands, it stands and shines; wherever it exists, the free minds of men, urged on to full and fair enquiry, may still bring wisdom into human affairs.*
>
> *There are few earthly things more beautiful than a University. It is a place where those who hate ignorance may strive to know, where those who perceive truth may strive to make others see; where seekers and learners alike, banded together in the search for knowledge, will honour thought in all its finer ways, will welcome thinkers in distress or in exile, will uphold ever the dignity of thought and learning and will exact standards in these things. They give to the young in their impressionable years, the bond of a lofty purpose shared, of a great corporate life whose links will not be loosed until they die. They give young people that close companionship for which youth longs, and that chance of the endless discussion of the themes which are endless, without which youth would seem a waste of time.*
>
> *There are few things more enduring than a University. Religions may split into sect or heresy; dynasties may perish or be supplanted, but for century after century the University will continue, and the stream of life will pass through it, and the thinker and the seeker will be bound together in the undying cause of bringing thought into the world. To be a member of one of these great societies must ever be a glad distinction.*

Notes

CHAPTER I—*Beginnings in Other Lands*

1 C-E. A. Winslow, Century of progress through sanitation, *Am. J. Pub. Health*, *43* (1953), 15–19.
2 Agnes Repplier, from essays.
3 Louis Pasteur, *Oeuvres de Pasteur*, vol. 7, Réunies par Pasteur Vallery-Radot (Paris, 1922–39), p. 215.
4 Thomas Henry Huxley, *Science and culture*, (London, 1881), pp. 1–23.
   J. C. Fisher, Publication of basic research in industry, *Science*, *129* (1959), 1653–57.
   John R. Pierce, Innovations in technology, *Sci. Am.*, *199* (1958), 117–30.
5 Nicholas Appert, *Canning* (Paris, 1810), English translation (London, 1811).
6 W. Guttmann, *Baltische Wochenschrift*, *51* (1890), 603. Cited by E. Nocard, Application des injections de tuberculine au diagnostic de la tuberculose bovine, *Ann. Inst. Pasteur*, 6 (1892), 44–54.
   Bernhard Bang, Selected works in the original language (Copenhagen, 1936). The major tuberculin article is in English.
   J. Arthur Myers, *Man's greatest victory over tuberculosis* (Springfield, Illinois, 1940), p. 331.
7 Charles Darwin, *Origin of species* (London, 1859).
8 F. H. Garrison, *History of Medicine*, ed. 2 (Philadelphia, 1917), p. 20.
9 F. H. Garrison, The history of drainage, irrigation, sewage-disposal and water-supply, *Bull. N. Y. Acad. Med.*, 5 (1929), 887–938. Excellent, with photographs.
   George Rosen, *History of public health*, (New York, 1958), pp. 25–29.
10 Hippocrates, *Works of Hippocrates*, 2 vols., trans. by Francis Adams, Sydenham Society (London, 1849).
11 Thucydides, 2 vols., trans. by B. Jowett, (Oxford, 1881), p. 127.
12 Homer, *The Iliad*, 2 vols., classics in translation, trans. by A. H.Chase and W. G. Perry, Jr. (Madison, University of Wisconsin Press, 1952), p. 16.
13 Lucretius, *De rerum naturae*, trans. by William Ellery Leonard (Madison, University of Wisconsin Press, 1916).
14 Varro cited by Dobell. Clifford Dobell, *Antony van Leeuwenhoek and his little animals* (New York, Harcourt, Brace and Company, Inc., 1932). To be enjoyed by all microbiologists.
15 Erwin H. Ackerknecht, *A short history of medicine* (New York, 1955).

16 J. F. C. Hecker, *The epidemics of the middle ages*, trans. by B. G. Babington (London, 1844).

17 Boccaccio, *Decameron*, from 1st day to 17th, translator not known (London, 1909 republished).

18 Fracastorius, *Contagion*, trans. by W. C. Wright (New York, 1930).

19 Harry Beal Torrey, Athanasius Kircher and the progress of medicine, *Osiris*, *5* (1938), 246–75.

20 See Clifford Dobell, *Antony van Leeuwenhoek* . . . , pp. 365–70.

G. L. Hendrickson, in Winslow, *Conquest of epidemic disease* (Princeton, Princeton University Press, 1943), pp. 151–52.

21 William Bulloch, *History of bacteriology* (Oxford, 1938).

Francesco Redi, *Esperienze interno alla generazione degl'insetti* (1667), trans. by Mab Bigelow (Chicago, 1909).

L. Spallanzani, For this reference and others on the overthrow of doctrine of spontaneous generation, see Bulloch, pp. 67–125.

John Tyndall, Observations on the optical deportment of the atmosphere in reference to the phenomena of putrefaction and infection, *Brit. Med. J.*, *1* (1876), 121.

22 Clifford Dobell, *Antony van Leeuwenhoek* . . . .

23 Louis Pasteur, *Oeuvres de Pasteur*, vols. 1, 2.

24 F. L. Schaffer and C. E. Schwerdt, Crystallization of purified M.E.F. poliomyelitis particles, *Proc. Nat. Acad. Sci.*, *41* (1955), 1020–23.

N. W. Pirie, *Meaninglessness of the terms life and living. Perspectives in biochemistry* (Cambridge, 1937), pp. 11–22.

Paul F. Clark, Alice in virusland, *J. Bact.*, *36* (1938), 223–41.

Arthur Kornberg, *Pathways of enzymatic synthesis of nucleotides and polynucleotides, chemical basis of heredity* (Baltimore, Johns Hopkins Press, 1957), p. 848.

Arthur Kornberg, Enzymatic synthesis of deoxyribonucleic acid, *Harvey Society Lectures*, *53* (1958), 83–129.

S. A. Miller, Production of some organic compounds under possible primitive earth conditions, *J. Am. Chem. Soc.*, *77* (1955), 2351–61.

V. R. Potter, The present status of the deletion hypothesis, *Univ. Mich. Med. Bull.*, *32* (1957), 401–12. In this illuminating essay, Potter has attempted a modern definition of life based on nucleoprotein behavior.

John Keosian, On the origin of life, *Science*, (1960), 479–82.

25 Rudyard Kipling, Mystery of man, *J. Am. Med. Assn.*, *81* (1928), 1228.

26 Charles A. Browne, *Man and teacher, Justus von Liebig. Liebig and after Liebig* (Lancaster, Pennsylvania, 1942), pp. 1–9.

27 Louis Pasteur, *Oeuvres de Pasteur*, vols. 1, 2.

28 Eduard Büchner, Alkaholische Gärung ohne Hefenzellen, Zweite Mittheilung, *Ber. Deut. Chem. Ges.*, *30* (1897), 114–24; 1110–13.

29 Thomas Sydenham, *Works of Thomas Sydenham*, 2 vols., trans. by R. G. Latham (London, 1848).

30 William Bulloch, *History of bacteriology*.

31 Jacob Henle, Von den Miasmen und Kontagien, trans. by George Rosen, *Bull. Inst. Hist. Med.*, *6* (1938), 907–83.

D. W. Montgomery, Strange history of vesicle in scabies, *Ann. Med. Hist.*, *9* N.S. (1937), 219–29.

32 E. H. Ackerknecht, Anticontagionsism between 1821 and 1867, *Bull. Inst. Hist. Med.*, *22* (1948), 562–93.

33 William James, *Gifford lectures* (New York, 1902).

34 F. H. Garrison, *History of medicine*, ed. 4 (1929), p. 18.

CHAPTER II—*Early Centuries in America*

1 John D. Hicks, *The federal union* (Boston, 1937), p. 21.

   Noah Webster, *A brief history of epidemic and pestilential diseases* (Hartford, 1799).

2 Richard Shryock, The origins and significance of the public health movement in the United States, *Ann. Med. Hist. N. S.*, *1* (1929), 645–65. Illuminating.

3 R. C. Williams, *United States Public Health Service, 1798–1950* (Washington, D. C., 1951).

4 Eleanor Macdonald, A history of Massachusetts department of public health, *Commonwealth*, *23* (1936), no. 2, April, May, June.

5 R. C. Williams, *U. S. Pub. Health Service.*

6 H. S. Cumming, *U. S. quarantine system during the past 50 years, Half century of public health*, in M. P. Ravenel ed. (New York, 1921), p. 119.

7 Lemuel Shattuck, *Report of the Sanitary Commission of Massachusetts* (Boston, 1850; reprinted Cambridge, 1948), pp. 61–71. "Remarkable in its clarity and completeness and in its vision of the future."—C-E. A. Winslow.

   Wilson G. Smillie, *Public health, its promise for the future* (New York, 1955), pp. 21–60.

8 N. Webster, *A brief history . . . epidem. dis.*, p. 203.

9 Cooper Curtice, *Trans. Amer. Med. Assn.*, *2* (1849), 495.

10 Lemuel Shattuck, *Mass. San. Com. report*, p. 70.

11 John Duffy, *Epidemics in colonial America* (Baton Rouge, 1953).

   Cotton Mather, letter to John Woodward, Dec. 16, 1716, Boston.

12 O. T. Beale, Jr. and Richard H. Shryock, *First significant figure in American medicine* (Baltimore, 1954).

13 Janet Whitney, *Abigail Adams* (Boston, 1949), pp. 17–18.

   J. B. Blake, Smallpox inoculation in colonial Boston, *J. Hist. Med.*, *8* (1953), 284–300.

14 N. Webster, *A brief history . . . epidem. dis.*, p. 57.

15 Edward Jenner, *An inquiry into the causes and effects of the* Variolae vaccinae, *a disease known by the name of the cowpox* (London, 1798).

CHAPTER III—*Critical Epidemiology Before the Birth of Bacteriology*

1 Pierre Bretonneau and others, *Five memoirs on diphtheria*, trans. by R. H. Simple, Memoir on contagion, pp. 173–87, Sydenham Society (London, 1859).

   Bretonneau et ses correspondants, *Contagion de la dothienentérie*, 2 vols. (Paris, 1892), pp. 135–39.

2 P. L. Panum, *Observations made during the epidemic of measles on the Faroe Islands in the year 1846* (New York, 1940).

   C-E. A. Winslow, *The conquest of epidemic disease* (Princeton, New Jersey,

1943). An excellent historical and philosophical discussion; the changing concepts.

3　John Snow, Report on the cholera outbreak in the Parish of St. James, Westminster, during autumn of 1854. Presented to this vestry by the Cholera Inquiry Committee (London, 1855).

4　William Budd, *Typhoid fever* (London, 1874). *Lancet*, Nov. 15, 1856. (Reprint, New York, 1931.) This publication followed earlier articles including outbreak of fever at the clergy orphan school.

5　O. W. Holmes, Contagiousness of puerperal fever, *Am. J. Med. Sci.*, N.S., *6* (1843), 260–64 (Copied from *N. Eng. Quart. J. Med. Surg.*, April, 1843. Reprinted with additions, 1861 [*Medical essays* of O. W. H., Boston]).

6　John Harris, Oliver Wendell Holmes's great contribution to American obstetrics, Wisconsin Medical History Seminar, 1933.

In this scholarly essay on the history of puerperal fever (unfortunately never published) Harris quotes liberally from many of the early authors including Charles White of Manchester, England, and his several editions (1773 *et seq.*), Alexander Gordon of Aberdeen (1795 *et seq.*), and Robert Collins (1826 *et seq.*). After much study, Harris considered that Gordon was the first to recognize the part of the nurse and the physician in the spread of puerperal fever. He found no evidence that White appreciated these important personal factors in transmission and considered the Adami essay on White an example of special pleading.

George J. Adami, *Charles White of Manchester and the arrest of puerperal fever* (London, 1922).

Ian A. Porter, *Alexander Gordon, M.D. of Aberdeen* (Scotland, 1958). This recent essay on Gordon and his contributions to epidemic puerperal fever tends to confirm Harris' findings.

7　Robert Collins, *A practical treatise on midwifery* (Philadelphia, 1838), p. 192.

8　John Harris, Semmelweis, Wisconsin Medical History Seminar, 1947–48.

F. P. Murphy, Philipp Ignaz Semmelweis, an annotated bibliog., *Bull. Hist. Med.*, *20* (1946), 653–707.

W. J. Sinclair, *Semmelweis, his life and his doctrine* (Manchester, 1909).

9　Charles Meigs, *Females and their diseases* (Philadelphia, 1848).

Hugh L. Hodge, Cases and observations regarding purpueral fever, as it prevailed in the Pennsylvania Hospital in February and March, 1833, *Am. J. Med. Sci.*, *12* (1833), 325–52.

10　O. W. Holmes, *Medical essays* (Boston, 1855).

11　Austin Flint, Account of epidemic fever which occurred at North Boston, Erie County, New York, during the months of October and November, 1843, *Am. J. Med. Sci.*, N. S., *10* (1845), 21–35.

Austin Flint, Relations of water to the propagation of fever, *Am. Pub. H. Assn.*, *1* (1873), 165–72.

Austin Flint, Logical proof of the contagiousness and noncontagiousness of diseases, *N. Y. Med. J.*, *19* (1874), 113–33.

12　L. Woods, Cases of typhoid fever dependent upon contaminated drinking water, *Boston Med. Surg. J.*, *96* (1877), 192–93. Excellent.

L. A. Stimson, Bacteria and their septic influence, *N. Y. Med. J.*, *22* (1875), 113–45.

13 Ely Van de Warke, Typhoid fever poison, *Pop. Sci. Mon.*, *14* (1878–79), 514–23.

14 C. S. Caverly, Notes of an epidemic of acute anterior poliomyelitis, *J. Am. Med. Assn.*, *26* (1896), 1–5.

15 The great epidemics, *Harpers Magazine*, *13* (1856), 62, 205, 359, 784.
Facts and opinions about the cholera, *The Nation*, *2* (1866), 520–21.

CHAPTER IV—*Period of Great Epidemics in America*

1 Lemuel Shattuck, *Report of the Sanitary Commission of Massachusetts* (Boston, 1850; Reprinted Cambridge, 1948), pp. 61–106.

2 Stephen Smith, *The city that was* (New York, 1911).
Stephen Smith, et al., *Citizens report of sanitary conditions of New York* (New York, 1865).

3 John D. Hicks, *The federal union* (Boston, 1937), p. 562.

4 Henry R. Carter, *Yellow fever* (Baltimore, 1931). Remarkably complete.
Henry R. Carter, *New Orleans Med. Surg. J.*, *52* (1900), 617.

5 Benjamin Rush, *Yellow fever*, ed. 2 (Philadelphia, 1794).
Mathew Carey, *A short account of the malignant fever lately prevalent in Philadelphia*, ed. 4 (Philadelphia, 1794).
William Currie, *A view of the diseases most prevalent in the United States* (Philadelphia, 1811).
W. S. Middleton, Yellow fever epidemic of 1793 in Philadelphia, *Ann. Med. Hist.*, *10* (1928), 434–50. Gives prescription for thieves' vinegar.
H. H. Powell, *Bring out your dead* (Philadelphia, University of Pennsylvania Press, 1949).

6 Edwin O. Jordan, *Epidemic influenza* (Chicago, 1927).
Public Health Report, *Report on the pandemic of influenza 1918–19* (London, 1920).

7 Benjamin Rush, *Yellow fever*, p. 146.

8 J. M. Woodworth, *Am. Pub. Health Assn. Rep.*, *4* (1880), 167–68.

9 George Sternberg, The pneumonia-coccus of Friedländer, *Am. J. Med. Sci.*, N. S., *90* (1885), 106–22.
Antoine Magnin, *Bacteria*, ed. 1, trans. by George Sternberg from the French (1880).
George Sternberg, *A Manual of bacteriology* (New York, 1892).
F. L. Paxson, *Recent history of the United States* (Boston, 1922), p. 245. The failure of the medical corps was only part of the general lack of preparedness. The complete breaking down of the quartermaster and commissary departments was witnessed at Tampa.

10 Carlos J. Finlay, "The mosquito hypothetically considered as the agent of transmission of yellow fever," read before the Royal Academy of Havana, 1881.
Carlos J. Finlay, Yellow fever; its transmission by means of the culex mosquito, *Am. J. Med. Sci.*, *102* (1891), 264–68. This is a restatement of his notions and his experiments in attempting to immunize persons by permitting contaminated mosquitoes to bite them.
Carlos J. Finlay, *Selected papers on yellow fever*, Secretaria de Sanidad y Beneficincia (Havana, 1912).

George M. Sternberg, *Report on the etiology and prevention of yellow fever* (Washington, D. C., 1890).

Howard Kelly, *Walter Reed and yellow fever* (Baltimore, 1906).

Walter Reed et al., *Papers by various authors of the Yellow Fever Commission*, Senate Doc. 822, Washington, D. C., 1911.

Henry R. Carter, *Yellow fever*.

George K. Strode et al., *Yellow fever* (New York, 1951).

Albert E. Truby, *Memoir of Walter Reed* (New York, 1943).

Carlos E. Finlay, *Carlos Finlay and yellow fever*, in Morton C. Kahn, ed. (New York, 1940).

11   Louis-Daniel Beauperthuy, Yellow fever, *Gaceta Official de Cumana*, 57 (1854). Discussed with enthusiasm by Agramonte, *Boston Med. Sur. J.*, *158* (1908), 927–30. Josiah C. Nott, Yellow fever, *New Orleans Med. J.*, *4* (1848), 563–601.

12   Patrick Manson, On the development of *Filaria sanguinis hominis* and on the mosquito considered as a nurse, *Linn. Soc. Zool.*, *14* (1878), 304–11.

13   Walter Reed et al., *Papers by various authors . . . Yellow Fever Commission*, Washington, D. C., 1911.

14   Adrian Stokes, J. H. Bauer, and N. P. Hudson, Experimental transmission of yellow fever to laboratory animals, *Am. J. Trop. Med.*, *8* (1928), 103–64.

15   Max Theiler, and H. H. Smith, The use of yellow fever virus modified by *in vitro* cultivation for human immunization, *J. Exp. Med.*, *65* (1937), 787–800.

16   John M. Woodworth, John C. Peters, and Ely McClellan, *The cholera epidemic of 1873*, U. S. Ex. Doc. No. 95, Washington, D. C., 1875.

17   J. S. Chambers, *Conquest of cholera, America's greatest scourge* (New York, 1938), pp. 42–43.

18   Woodworth et al. *Cholera . . .* , pp. 568, 607–9, 617, 620–21.

19   J. S. Chambers, *Cholera . . .* , pp. 199, 205, 208.

20   Woodworth et al., *Cholera . . .* , p. 100.

21   Jacob Henle, Von den Miasmen und Kontagien, trans. by George Rosen, *Bull. Inst. Hist. Med.*, *6* (1938), 907–83.

22   Phyllis Allen Richmond, Animalcular theory. Etiological theory in America prior to the Civil War, *J. Hist. Med.*, *2* (1947), 489–520.
Phyllis Allen Richmond, American attitudes toward the germ theory of disease, *J. Hist. Med.*, *9* (1954), 428–54.

23   John Kearsley Mitchell, *Cryptogamous origin of malarial and epidemic fevers* (Philadelphia, 1849).

24   Daniel Drake, *Principal diseases of the interior valley of North America*, ed. 1 (Cincinnati, 1850), pp. 723–28.

25   R. Pollitzer, Carrier question in cholera, *Bull. W. Health Org.*, 7 (1952), 359–69.

26   Robert Koch, Cholera and its bacillus, *Brit. Med. J.*, *2* (1884), 403, 453, 674.
Robert Koch, Die Cholera in Deutschland während des Winters 1892 bis 1893, *Zeit. f. Hygiene*, *15* (1893), 18–165.

27. Richard Shryock, The origins and significance of the public health movement in the United States, *Ann. Med. Hist.* N. S. *1* (1929), 645–65.

28   Lemuel Shattock, *Mass. San. Com. Report*, pp. 81, 89.

29   James M. Newman, Report on sanitary police of cities, *Trans. Am. Med. Assn.*, *9* (1856), 413–81, esp. 432, 442–44.

30 Henry I. Bowditch, *Public hygiene in America* (Boston, 1877), p. 1. Excellent early study.
31 Erwin H. Ackerknecht, Malaria in the upper Mississippi Valley, *Bull. Hist. Med. Supp., No. 4* (1945), 4–15.
32 R. C. Buley, Pioneer health prior to 1840, *Miss. Valley Hist. Rev., 20* (1933–34), 510.
33 Henry I. Bowditch, *Public hygiene in America*, p. 177.
   Walter Reed, Victor C. Vaughan, and Edward O. Shakespeare, *Origin and spread of typhoid fever in U. S. military camps during the Spanish War of 1898* (Washington, D. C., 1900–1904), abstract of report (Complete report, 2 vols., 1904.)
34 Mark F. Boyd *et al.*, *Malariology*, 2 vols. (Philadelphia, 1949). Survey from a global standpoint. Sixty-five authors.
35 Erwin H. Ackerknecht, *Malaria . . .*, p. 127.
36 Hippocrates. *Works of Hippocrates*, 2 vols., trans. by Francis Adams, Sydenham Society (London, 1849), p. 133.
37 Richard Shryock, *P. health in U. S.*, p. 656, Note 12.
38 Esmond R. Long, Tuberculosis in modern society, *Bull. Hist. Med., 27* (1953), 302–4.
39 René and Jean Dubos, *The white plague* (Boston, 1952), esp. pp. 84, 229.

CHAPTER V—*Early Sanitation and Public Hygiene*

1 Edwin Chadwick, *Sanitary condition of labouring population* (London, 1842).
   John Simon, *London sanitary conditions 1850–51* (London, 1851).
2 Lemuel Shattuck, *Report of the Sanitary Commission of Massachusetts* (Boston, 1850; Reprinted Cambridge, 1948).
3 Mazyck P. Ravenel, ed., *A half century of public health* (New York, 1921).
4 Franklin H. Top, ed., *History of American epidemiology* (St. Louis, 1952).
   Wilson G. Smillie, *Public health, its promise for the future* (New York, 1955).
5 *Am. Med. Assn. Transactions 1* (1848), pp. 305–10.
6 James M. Newman, Report on sanitary police of cities, *Trans. Am. Med. Assn., 9* (1856), 431–81.
7 John H. Griscom, *The sanitary condition of the laboring population of New York* (New York, 1845).
   John Bell, *Report on the importance and economy of sanitary measures to cities* (New York, 1859).
   Stephen Smith *et al.*, *Citizens report of sanitary conditions of New York* (New York, 1865).
8 Milton J. Rosenau, *Preventive medicine and hygiene* (New York, 1913).
9 Morris Fishbein, *A History of the American Medical Association 1847–1947* (Philadelphia, 1947), pp. 888–89.
   H. E. Sigerist, *American medicine* (New York, 1934), p. 132.
10 Abraham Flexner, *Medical education in the United States and Canada*, Bull. 4, Carnegie Foundation Adv. Teaching (New York, 1910).
    Abraham Flexner, *Medical education in Europe*, Bull. 6, Carnegie Foundation Adv. Teaching (New York, 1912).

CHAPTER VI—*Johns Hopkins University, the Medical School*

1 Richard Shryock, *The unique influence of the Johns Hopkins University on American medicine* (Copenhagen, 1953).

2 Eugene L. Opie, *Bardeen memorial laboratories* (Madison, Wisconsin, 1957), pp. 8–17.

3 Simon Flexner and James Thomas Flexner, *William Welch and the heroic age of American medicine* (New York, 1941), p. 101.

William H. Welch, *Collected papers*, 3 vols. (Baltimore, Johns Hopkins Press, 1920). Of the 398 papers (many not previously published), 31 are in bacteriology and 17 in preventive medicine.

4 A. Parker Hitchens and Morris C. Leikind, *J. Bact.*, 37 (1939), 485–93. Frau Hesse had learned from her mother to use agar-agar in soups and jellies. Koch tried it in culture media and referred to it briefly in his 1882 paper on tuberculosis. O. Brefeld had used agar earlier, *Naturforschenden Gesellschaft zu Halle*, 12 (1873), 1–50.

5 References to these and other technics in immunology can be found in any text in this field and in the more complete texts in bacteriology.

Hans Zinsser, *Infection and resistance* (New York, 1914).

6 W. H. Welch and G. H. F. Nuttall, A gas-producing bacillus (*B. aerogenes capsulatus*, nov. spec.), capable of rapid development in the blood vessels after death, *Johns Hopkins Hosp. Bull.*, 3 (1892), 81–91.

C. G. Bull and I. W. Pritchett, Identity of the toxins of different strains of *Bacillus welchii* and factors influencing their production in vitro, *J. Exp. Med.*, 26 (1917), 867–83.

M. Weinberg *et al.*, *Les microbes anaerobies* (Paris, 1937).

7 Flexner and Flexner, *William Welch . . .*, p. 456.

8 Mark F. Boyd *et al.*, *Malariology*, 2 vols. (Philadelphia, 1949), p. 13.

9 Eugene L. Opie, Hematozoa of birds, *J. Exp. Med.*, 3 (1898), 79–101.

W. G. MacCallum, Hematozoan infections of birds, *J. Exp. Med.*, 3 (1898), 117–36.

10 William T. Councilman and Henri A. Lafleur, Amoebic dysentery, *Johns Hopkins Hosp. Reports*, 2 (1891), 395–548.

11 George H. F. Nuttall, On the role of insects, arachnids and myriapods, as carriers in the spread of bacterial and parasitic diseases of man and animals, *Johns Hopkins Hosp. Reports*, 8 (1900), 1–154.

George H. F. Nuttall, *Blood immunity and blood relationship* (Cambridge, Cambridge University Press, 1904).

12 W. W. Ford, Toxins and antitoxins of poisonous mushrooms, *J. Infect. Dis.*, 3 (1906), 191–224.

W. W. Ford, Antibodies to glucosides, with special reference to *Rhus toxicodendron*, *J. Infect. Dis.*, 4 (1907), 541–51.

W. W. Ford and J. J. Abel, On the poisons of *Amanita phalloides*, *J. Biol. Chem.* 2 (1907), 273–88.

13 W. T. Howard, *Public health administration and the natural history of disease in Baltimore, Maryland, 1797–1920* (Washington, D. C., 1924), p. 132.

14 Milton J. Rosenau, *Preventive medicine and hygiene* (New York, 1935), p. 1125.

15 T. Caspar Gilchrist, Blastomycetic dermatitis, *Johns Hopkins Hosp. Reports, 1* (1896), 269–86.

16 B. R. Schenck, On refractory subcutaneous abscesses caused by a fungus possibly related to the sporotricha, *Johns Hopkins Hosp. Bull., 9* (1898), 286–90. Organism later named *Sporotrichum schenckii.* First described case of sporotrichosis.

CHAPTER VII—*Massachusetts, Boston, and Public Hygiene*

1   Eleanor J. Macdonald, A history of Massachusetts department of public health, *Commonwealth, 23* (1936), No. 2.

2   Henry I. Bowditch, Address on hygiene and preventive medicine, *Transactions of the International Medical Congress of Philadelphia* (Philadelphia, 1876), pp. 21–48.
    Henry I. Bowditch, *Public hygiene in America* (Boston, 1877).

3   J. H. Griscom, *The sanitary condition of the laboring population of New York* (New York, 1845).

4   Eleanor J. Macdonald, Hist. Mass. dept. p. health, p. 14.

5   Samuel C. Prescott, *When M. I. T. was "Boston Tech."* (Cambridge, The Technology Press, 1954).

6   E. O. Jordan, G. C. Whipple, and C-E. A. Winslow, *William Thompson Sedgwick, a pioneer of public health* (New Haven, Yale Press, 1924). With his complete bibliography.

7   W. T. Sedgwick, *Principles of sanitary science and the public health* (New York, 1902).

8   George C. Whipple, *State sanitation*, Vols. I and II (Cambridge, Harvard Press, 1917).
    George C. Whipple, Fifty years of water purification, in *Half century pub. health* (New York, 1921), pp. 161–80.

9   Jordan *et al.*, *Sedgwick* . . . .

10 Walter Reed, Victor C. Vaughan, and E. O. Shakespeare, *Origin and spread of typhoid fever in U. S. military camps during the Spanish War of 1898* (Washington, D. C., 1900–1904), abstract of report. (Complete reports, 2 vols., 1904.)

11 Samuel Prescott, unpublished essay in Archives of Soc. Am. Bact., 1930.
    Samuel Prescott, Unpublished manuscript in Archives of Soc. Am. Bact. (1954), also, personal recollections of Paul F. Clark. The Boston Bug Club was an informal provocative group that arose *de novo* with only a semipermanent secretary. It spread its influence to Providence and Worcester and eventually even to the metropolis of New York City. Talk included shoes and ships and sealing wax and on occasion whether bacteria had wings.

12 George C. Whipple, *Typhoid fever its causation, transmission and prevention* (New York, 1908).

13 Theobald Smith, Investigations into the nature, causation, and prevention of southern cattle fever; a comparative study of bovine tubercle bacilli and of human bacilli from sputum, *Medical Classics, 1* (1937), 341–669. Complete bibliography.
    Paul F. Clark, Theobald Smith, student of disease, *J. Hist. Med., 14* (1959), 490–514.
    Theobald Smith *Parasitism and disease* (Princeton, Princeton University Press, 1934).

14 Theobald Smith and F. L. Kilbourne, Investigations into the nature, causation and prevention of Texas or southern cattle fever, *Bur. Anim. Ind. Bull.*, *1* (1893), 151–52.

15 S. Arloing, *Leçons sur la tuberculose* (Lyons, 1892), p. 512.

S. Arloing, Variabilité du bacille de la tuberculose, *Revue Tuberculose*, *5* (1908), 1–42.

16 J. A. Villemin, *Compt. Rend. Acad. Sci.*, *61* (1865), 1012–15.

J. A. Villemin, *Études de la tuberculose* (Paris, 1868), p. 538.

17 C. A. Brandly and A. W. McClurkin, *Ann. N. Y. Acad. Sci.*, *66* (1956–57), 181–85. This has been a moot question with a virus adding to the confusion. Recent studies have shown that *Entamoeba coli* and colostrum are still important. A good summary by R. C. Reisinger in his studies on the pathogenesis of infectious diarrhea of newborn calves (unpublished M.S. thesis, University of Wisconsin, 1957).

18 Philip Hillyer Smith, personal letters and statements.

Philip Hillyer Smith, Theobald Smith, *The Land*, *8* (1949), 363–68.

Hans Zinsser, Biographical memoir of Theobald Smith 1859–1934, *Nat. Acad. Sci.*, *17* (1936), 261–303.

19 A definitive biography is being written by Drs. Frederick B. Bang, Frederick F. Ferguson, and Norman R. Stoll.

20 Roland Thaxter, On the myxobacteriaceae, a new order of schizomycetes, *Bot. Gaz.*, *17* (1892), 389–406.

21 James H. Wright, Biology of the microorganism of actinomycosis, *J. Med. Res.*, *13* (1905), 349–404.

CHAPTER VIII—*Rhode Island*

1 Wilson G. Smillie, *Public health, its promise for the future* (New York, 1955), p. 479.

2 Charles V. Chapin, *Municipal sanitation in the United States* (Providence, 1901).

Charles V. Chapin, The fetish of disinfection, *J. Am. Med. Assn.*, *47* (1906), 574–80.

Charles V. Chapin, *Sources and modes of infection* (New York, 1910).

Charles V. Chapin, Studies in air and contact infection at the Providence City Hospital, *Am. J. Pub. Health*, *2* (1912), 135–40.

Charles V. Chapin, *A report on state public health work based on a survey of state boards of health*, Am. Med. Assn. (Chicago, 1915).

Charles V. Chapin, Evolution of preventive medicine, *J. Am. Med. Assn.*, *76* (1921), 215–22.

3 C. A. Fuller, The sanitary inspection of oyster-grounds in the United States, *J. Am. Med. Assn.*, *56* (1911), 733–36.

C. A. Fuller, *Oysters and sewage in Narragansett Bay*. Appendix report U. S. Commission of Fisheries (Washington, D. C., 1904).

CHAPTER IX—*Connecticut and State Agricultural Experiment Stations*

1 Herbert Joel Conn, Professor Herbert William Conn and the founding of the Society of American Bacteriologists, *Bact. Reviews*, *12* (1948), 275–96.

2 Herbert W. Conn, Bacteriology in our medical schools. *Science*, *11* (1888), 123–26.

3 H. W. Conn, *The outbreak of typhoid fever at Wesleyan University*, Connecticut State Board of Health Report (1895), pp. 243–64.

4 L. F. Rettger, History of bacteriology in Connecticut, unpublished paper in Archives of Soc. Am. Bact., 1937. An excellent résumé.

5 Alfred Charles True, *A history of agricultural experimentation and research in the United States, 1607–1925*, Misc. Pub. No. 251 U. S. Dept. Agr., 1937.

6 *Ibid.*, pp. 158–59.

7 *Ibid.*, p. 144.

8 Leo F. Rettger, History of bacteriology in Connecticut.

9 Leo F. Rettger and S. C. Harvey, Pullorum disease, *J. Med. Res.*, *18* (1908), 277–90.

   Leo F. Rettger, W. Kirkpatrick, and R. E. Jones, Review in *Storr's Monograph*, Bulletin No. 7, 1914.

   Leo F. Rettger and Harry A. Cheplin, *Intestinal flora and implantation of B. acidophilus* (New Haven, Yale Press, 1921).

10 C-E. A. Winslow, *Life of Hermann Biggs* (Philadelphia, 1929).

   C-E. A. Winslow, *The conquest of epidemic disease* (Princeton, Princeton University Press, 1943).

   C-E. A. Winslow and David Greenberg, Effect of putrefactive odors upon growth and upon disease resistance, *Am. J. Pub. Health*, *8* (1918), 759–68.

   John F. Fulton, C-E. A. Winslow, leader in public health. *Science*, *125* (1957), 1236.

   Ira V. Hiscock, Charles-Edward Amory Winslow, *J. Bact.*, *73* (1957), 295–96.

11 H. J. Conn, Professor Herbert William Conn and the founding of the Society of American Bacteriologists, *Bact. Reviews*, *12* (1948), 275–96.

12 L. A. Rogers, History of American type culture collection, unpublished paper in Archives of Soc. Am. Bact., 1948.

13 Ross G. Harrison, Observations on the living developing nerve fiber, *Proc. Soc. Exp. Biol. Med.*, *4* (1907), 140–43.

   Alexis Carrel and Montrose T. Burrows, Cultivation of tissues in vitro and its technic, *J. Exp. Med.*, *13* (1911), 387–96.

CHAPTER X—*The Great Metropolis and New York State*

1 Stephen Smith, *The city that was* (New York, 1911).

   Israel Weinstein, Eighty years of public health in New York city, *Bull. N. Y. Acad. Med.*, *23* (1947), 221–37.

2 Charles V. Chapin, *Municipal sanitation in the United States* (Providence, 1901).

3 John D. Hicks, *The federal union* (Boston, 1948), p. 562.

4 Lillian E. Prudden, *Biographical sketches and letters of T. Mitchell Prudden* (New Haven, Yale University Press, 1927), pp. 43–58.

   T. Mitchell Prudden, Progress and drift in pathology, *Med. Rec.*, *57* (1900), 397–405.

5 Wade W. Oliver, A bacteriological firmament is born, unpublished paper in Archives of Soc. Am. Bact., 1955. Interesting résumé.

   Marion E. Wilson, Early bacteriology in hospitals and medical schools in New York City, unpublished paper in Archives of Soc. Am. Bact., 1955. Good paper.

6 C-E. A. Winslow, *Life of Hermann Biggs* (Philadelphia, 1929).

7 Hermann M. Biggs and A. A. Breneman, The epidemic of typhoid fever in Plymouth, Pa., *N. Y. Med. J.*, *41* (1885), 576–79, 637–39.

8 H. L. Taylor, *Typhoid, Plymouth epidemic 1885*, Report of State Board of Health (Pennsylvania, 1886), pp. 176–95.

9 Hermann M. Biggs, History of an epidemic of dysentery at the Almshouse, Blackwell's Island, New York, *N. Y. Med. J.*, *45* (1887), 355.

   Hermann M. Biggs, Diagnostic value of the cholera spirillum, *N. Y. Med. J.*, *46* (1887), 548–49.

   Hermann M. Biggs, History of the recent outbreak of epidemic cholera in N. Y., *Am. J. Med. Sci.*, *105* (1893), 63–72.

   E. K. Dunham, Bacterial examination of the recent cases of epidemic cholera in New York, *Am. J. Med. Sci.*, *105* (1893), 72–80.

10 William Park and A. L. Beebe, Diphtheria and pseudodiphtheria, *Med. Rec.*, *46* (1894), 385–401.

11 J. C. G. Ledingham and J. A. Arkwright, *Carrier problem in infectious diseases* (London, 1912).

12 Geo. A. Soper, Typhoid carrier, *J. Am. Med. Assn.*, *48* (1907), 2019–22.

   George A. Soper, The curious career of Typhoid Mary, *Military Surgeon*, *45* (1919), 1–15.

13 R. B. Gibson and E. J. Banzhaf, Changes in proteins of blood plasma of horses in the course of immunization, *J. Exp. Med.*, *12* (1910), 411–34.

   W. H. Park, A. Zingher, and M. H. Serota, Active immunization in diphtheria and treatment by toxin-antitoxin, *J. Am. Med. Assn.*, *163* (1914), 859–60.

14 Paul Ehrlich, *Studies in immunity*, collected and trans. by Charles Bolduan (New York, 1906).

15 Philip H. Hiss and F. F. Russell, A study of a bacillus resembling the bacillus of Shiga from a case of fatal diarrhea in a child; with remarks on the recognition of dysentery, typhoid, and allied bacilli, *Med. News.*, *82* (1903), 289–95.

16 Hans Zinsser, *Infection and resistance* (New York, 1914).

   Hans Zinsser, *Rats, lice and history* (Boston, 1935), p. 296.

   Hans Zinsser, *As I remember him, the biography of R. S.* (Boston, 1940).

   Hans Zinsser, Now is death merciful, *Atlantic Monthly*, *165* (1940), 645.

17 Christian A. Herter, *Common bacterial infections of the digestive tract* (New York, 1907).

   Conrad Elvehjem, The role of intestinal bacteria in nutrition, *J. Am. Dietetic Assn.*, *11* (1946), 959–63.

   Karver L. Puestow, The role of bacteria in the gastrointestinal tract with changing concepts of intestinal function, *Am. J. Gastroenterology*, *25* (1956), 22–32.

18 Arnold H. Eggerth, Unpublished Soc. Am. Bact. symposium, Archives Soc. Am. Bact., 1955.

19 Peyton Rous, Simon Flexner, 1863–1946, *Obituary notices of fellows of the Royal Society*, *6* (1949), 409–45.

   Simon Flexner, Pathological changes caused by certain so-called toxalbumins, *Med. News*, *65* (1894), 116–24.

   Simon Flexner, Etiology of dysentery, *J. Am. Med. Assn.*, *36* (1901), 6–10.

Simon Flexner and J. W. Jobling, An analysis of four hundred cases of epidemic meningitis treated with the anti-meningitis serum, *J. Exp. Med.*, *10* (1908), 690–733.

Eugene L. Opie, Obituary of Simon Flexner, 1863–1946, *Arch. Path.*, *42* (1946) 234–42.

20 Peyton Rous, A transmissible avian neoplasm, *J. Exp. Med.*, *12* (1910), 696–705.

Peyton Rous, Virus tumors and the tumor problem, *Harvey Society Lectures, 31* (1935–36), 74–115.

21 Montrose T. Burrows, The cultivation of tissues of the chick embryo outside the body, *J. Am. Med. Assn.*, *55* (1910), 2057–58.

Montrose T. Burrows, The growth of the chick embryo outside the animal body, with special reference to the nervous system, *J. Exp. Zool.*, *10* (1911), 63–83.

Alexis Carrel and Montrose T. Burrows, Cultivation of adult tissues and organs outside the body, *J. Am. Med. Assn.*, *55* (1910), 1379–81.

Alexis Carrel, Present condition of a strain of connective tissue 28 months old, *J. Exp. Med.*, *20* (1914), 1–18.

22 A. R. Dochez and L. J. Gillespie, A biologic classification of pneumococcus by means of immunity reactions, *J. Am. Med. Assn.*, *61* (1913), 727–30.

23 Fred Griffith, Influence of immune serum on the biological properties of pneumococci, *Brit. Min. of Health Rep.*, *18* (1923), 1–13.

24 F. Neufeld, Über die Agglutination der Pneumokokken und über die Theorieen der Agglutination, *Zeit. f. Hygiene 40* (1902), 54–72.

Oswald T. Avery, H. T. Chickering, R. Cole, and A. R. Dochez, *Acute lobar pneumonia; prevention and serum therapy*, Rockefeller Institute, Monograph. No. 7, 1917.

M. Heidelberger and O. T. Avery, The soluble specific substance of pneumococcus, *J. Exp. Med.*, *38* (1923), 73–79.

M. Heidelberger and W. F. Goebel, Soluble specific substance of pneumococcus, *J. Biol. Chem.*, *70* (1926), 613–24.

O. T. Avery, C. M. MacLeod, and M. McCarty, Induction of transformation by a desoxyribonucleic acid fraction isolated from pneumococcus type 3, *J. Exp. Med.*, *79* (1944), 137–58.

Oswald T. Avery, Obituary, *Lancet, 1* (1955), 463.

25 John Auer and Paul Lewis, Acute anaphylactic death in guinea pigs; its cause and possible prevention, *J. Am. Med. Assn.*, *53* (1909), 458–59.

26 Martha Wollstein, An experimental study of parotitis (mumps), *J. Exp. Med.*, *23* (1916), 353–75.

Martha Wollstein, A further study of experimental parotitis, *J. Exp. Med.*, *28* (1918), 377–85.

27 Hideyo Noguchi, *Snake venoms* (Carnegie Institution of Washington, 1909).

Gustav Eckstein, *Hideyo Noguchi* (New York, 1931).

Paul F. Clark, Hideyo Noguchi, *Bull. Instit. Hist. Med.*, *33* (1959), 1–20.

Hideyo Noguchi, Transmission experiments on yellow fever, *J. Exp. Med.*, *29* (1919), 565–84.

Hideyo Noguchi, The etiology of trachoma, *J. Exp. Med.*, *48* (1928), 1–53.

P. H. Long, P. K. Olitsky, and C. P. Rhoads, Survival and multiplication of the virus of poliomyelitis in vitro, *J. Exp. Med.*, *52* (1930), 361–77.

G. A. LoGrippo, Concerning the nature of the globoid bodies, *J. Bact.*, *31* (1936), 245–53.

28 William J. Elser and Frank M. Huntoon, Studies on meningitis, *J. Med. Res.*, *20* (1909), 377–541.

29 Arthur Coca and Ella F. Grove, Studies in hypersensitiveness; atopic reagins, *J. Immun.*, *10* (1925), 445–70.

30 Veranus A. Moore, *Bovine tuberculosis and its control* (New York, 1913).

Simon H. Gage, Obituary of V. A. Moore, *J. Bact.*, *22* (1931), 1–5.

31 J. M. Sherman, 1954, and William Hagan, 1958, personal letters; Bacteriology at Cornell.

32 Robert S. Breed, Sanitary significance of body cells in milk, *J. Exp. Med.*, *14* (1914), 93–99.

H. J. Conn, Obituary of R. S. Breed, *J. Bact.*, *71* (1956), 383–84.

33 E. L. Trudeau, An experimental research upon the infectiousness of non-bacillary phthisis, *Am. J. Med. Sci.*, N. S., *90* (1885), 361–65.

E. L. Trudeau, Environment in its relation to the progress of bacterial invasion in tuberculosis, *Am. J. Med. Sci.*, N. S., *94* (1887), 118–23.

E. L. Trudeau. *An autobiography* (New York, 1916).

CHAPTER XI—*Pennsylvania, New Jersey, and Delaware*

1 Joseph Leidy, *Researches in helminthology and parasitology*, in Joseph Leidy Jr., ed., with bibliography (Philadelphia, 1904).

W. S. Middleton, Joseph Leidy, scientist, *Ann. Med. Hist.*, *5* (1923), 100–112. A highly appreciative biographical sketch.

2 W. W. Gerhard, On the typhus fever which occurred at Philadelphia in the spring and summer of 1836, *Am. J. Med. Sci.*, *19* (1836), 289–322; *20* (1837), 289–322.

W. W. Gerhard, Cerebral affections of children, *Am. J. Med. Sci.*, *13* (1833), 313–59; *14* (1834), 99–111.

W. S. Middleton, William Gerhard, *Ann. Med. Hist.*, N. S., 7 (1935), 1–18.

3 Joseph McFarland, Beginnings of bacteriology in Philadelphia, *Bull. Inst. Hist. Med.*, *5* (1937), 149–98.

4 A. C. Abbott, Relation between water supply and epidemics, *Johns Hopkins Hosp. Bull.*, *1* (1890), 55–56.

W. S. Middleton, letter to author.

5 George C. Whipple, *Typhoid fever, its causation, transmission, and prevention* (New York, 1908), pp. 246, 382.

6 David H. Bergey, Early instruction in bacteriology in the United States, *Ann. Med. Hist.*, s. *1*, v. *1* (1917), 426–27.

David H. Bergey, *Manual of determinative bacteriology* (Baltimore, 1923).

7 Frederick D. Chester, *Manual of determinative bacteriology* (New York, 1901).

8 Joseph McFarland, Beginnings of bacteriology in Philadelphia, *Bull. Inst. Hist. Med.*, *5* (1937), 149–98.

9 Paul F. Clark, personal recollections of the author and letters from Hitchens and others in the possession of Roger Porter, present editor of the *J. Bact.*

10 J. F. Siler, Milton W. Hall, and A. Parker Hitchens, Dengue, *Bull. 20, Acad. Sci.* (Manila, 1926).

P. M. Ashburn and C. F. Craig, Etiology of dengue fever, *J. Infect. Dis.*, *4* (1907), 440–75.

11 Mazyck P. Ravenel, The comparative virulence of the tubercle bacillus from human and bovine sources, *Lancet*, *2* (1901), 349–56, 443–48.

M. P. Ravenel, ed., *A half century of public health* (New York, 1921).

12 Selman A. Waksman and Robert L. Starkey, Bacteriology in New Jersey, unpublished papers in Archives of Soc. Am. Bact., 1955.

13 Frederick D. Chester, *Manual of determinative bacteriology*.

CHAPTER XII—*Important Contributions to Microbiology by Federal Agencies*

1 Frederic Jackson Turner, *Significance of the frontier in American history*, University of Wisconsin Extension, Syllabus No. 12, 1893.

Frederic Jackson Turner, *The United States, 1830–1850* (Cambridge, Harvard University Press, 1931).

2 W. C. W. Glazier, *Trichinae and trichinosis*, U. S. Pub. Health Bull. 1 and Treas. Doc. 84 (Washington, D. C., 1881).

3 A. M. Stimson, *Brief history of bacteriological investigations of the U. S. Public Health Service*, Sup. 141, 1938, p. 2.

4 Hermann M. Biggs, Diagnostic value of the cholera spirillum, *N. Y. Med. J.*, *46* (1887), 548–49.

Hermann M. Biggs, History of the recent outbreak of epidemic cholera in N. Y., *Am. J. Med. Sci.*, *105* (1893), 63–72.

E. K. Dunham, Bacterial examination of the recent cases of epidemic cholera in New York, *Am. J. Med. Sci.*, *105* (1893), 72–80.

5 R. C. Williams, *United States Public Health Service 1798–1950* (Washington, D. C., 1951), pp. 249, 177–81.

6 M. J. Rosenau and John F. Anderson, United States Public Health Service, *Hyg. Lab. Bull.*, *29* (1906).

M. J. Rosenau and John F. Anderson, Hypersusceptibility, including an abstract of discussion by Theobald Smith, *J. Am. Med. Assn.*, *47* (1906), 1007–10.

Milton J. Rosenau, *Preventive medicine and hygiene* (New York, 1913).

Milton J. Rosenau and Harold L. Amoss, Organic matter in the expired breath, *J. Med. Res.*, *25* (1912), 35–85.

M. J. Rosenau, Serendipity, *J. Bact.*, *29* (1935), 91–98.

Lloyd D. Felton, Obituary of M. J. Rosenau, *J. Bact.*, *53* (1946), 1–3.

S. B. Wolbach, Obituary of M. J. Rosenau, *Tr. Assn. Am. Phys.*, *59* (1946), 32–33.

R. C. Williams, *U. S. Pub. Health Service*, pp. 181, 250–51.

7 John F. Anderson and J. Goldberger, Experimental measles, *Pub. Health Rep.*, *26* (1911), 847–87 and *J. Am. Med. Assn.*, *57* (1912), 476–78.

J. F. Anderson and J. Goldberger, Collected studies on typhus, *U. S. Hyg. Lab. Bull.*, *86* (1912).

8 R. C. Williams, *U. S. Pub. Health Service*, pp. 190–92, 252–53.

9 *Ibid.*, p. 80.

10 Alice C. Evans, *Bacterium abortus* and related bacteria in cow's milk, *J. Infect. Dis.*,

22 (1918), 580–93.

Alice C. Evans, Studies on brucella, *U. S. Hyg. Lab. Bull.*, *143* (1925).

11 A. M. Stimson, *Hist. Bact. U. S. Pub. Health Service*, p. 21.

12 T. Swann Harding, *Some landmarks in the history of the Department of Agriculture*, History Series 2, 1942, pp. 1–4.

13 Alfred C. True, *A history of agricultural experimentation and research in the United States, 1607–1925*, Misc. Pub. No. 251 U. S. Dept. Agr., 1937, p. 177.

14 T. S. Harding, Hist. U. S. Dept. Agr., p. 47.

T. S. Harding, *Two blades of grass* (Norman, University of Oklahoma Press, 1947), p. 147.

15 J. Arthur Myers, *Man's greatest victory over tuberculosis* (Springfield, Illinois 1940), pp. 127, 272.

16 E. R. Krumbiegel, personal letter to author, 1958.

17 J. A. Myers, *Man's greatest victory . . .* , pp. 319, 343.

18 Jane's fighting ships, 1956–57. *Forrestal* cost $218,000,000 unequipped. It was designed to carry 90 to 100 aircraft of different types, besides other equipment so that its final cost would be much greater.

19 Charles W. Stiles and Albert Hassall, Index catalogue of medical and veterinary zoology, *U. S. Hyg. Lab. Bull.*, *37* (1908), 1–383.

Charles W. Stiles, A new species of hookworm parasitic in man (*Uncinaria americana* later *Necator americana*), *Am. Med.*, *3* (1902), 777–78.

Charles W. Stiles, Report upon prevalence and geographical distribution of hookworm disease (uncinariasis) in the United States, *U. S. Hyg. Lab. Bull.*, *10* (1903).

Charles W. Stiles, Hookworm disease, its nature, treatment and prevention, 3d ed., *U. S. Public Health Bull.*, *32* (1912).

Willard H. Wright, Obituary of Stiles, *J. Parasitol.*, *27* (1941), 195–201.

20 Bailey K. Ashford and W. W. King, Ankylostomiasis in Puerto Rico, *N. Y. Med. J.*, *71* (1900), 552–56.

Bailey K. Ashford, *A soldier in science—an autobiography* (New York, 1934).

21 L. A. Rogers and B. J. Davis, Methods of classifying the lactic-acid bacteria, *U. S. Bureau An. Ind.*, *Bull. 154* (1912).

L. A. Rogers and S. H. Ayers, Bacteria in milk, *U. S. Bureau An. Ind. Bull.*, *153* (1910).

22 James M. Sherman, personal letter to author, 1956.

L. A. Rogers, The preparation of dried cultures, *J. Infect. Dis.*, *14* (1914), 100–123.

L. A. Rogers, Studies upon the keeping quality of butter, canned butter, *U. S. Bur. An. Ind. Bull.*, *57* (1904), 24.

L. A. Rogers, Investigations in the manufacture and storage of butter, *U. S. Bur. An. Ind. Bull.*, *89* (1906), 13.

23 W. M. Clark and H. A. Lubs, The differentiation of bacteria of the colon-aerogenes family by the use of indicators, *J. Infect. Dis.*, *17* (1915), 160–73.

W. M. Clark *et al.*, Studies on oxidation-reduction, *U. S. Hyg. Lab. Bull.*, *151* (1928).

W. M. Clark, Barnett Cohen, an appreciation, *Bact. Reviews*, *16* (1952), 205–9.

24 Kenneth Raper, Obituary of Charles Thom, *J. Bact.*, *72* (1956), 725–27; *Mycologia*, *49* (1957), 134–50.

Charles Thom, Fungi in cheese ripening: Camembert and Roquefort, *U. S. Bur. An. Ind. Bull.*, *82* (1906), 1–39.

Charles Thom, An oxalic acid producing penicillium, *J. Biol. Chem.*, *22* (1915), 287–93.

25 G. T. Moore, Soil inoculation for legumes; with reports upon the successful use of artificial cultures by practical farmers, *U. S. Bur. Plant Ind.*, *71* (1905), 1–72.

26 L. R. Jones, Memoir of Erwin Frick Smith, *Nat. Acad. Sci. Biog. Memoirs*, *21* (1939), 1–71.

G. K. K. Link, Bacteria in relation to plant diseases, in E. O. Jordan and I. S. Falk, ed., *The newer knowledge of bacteriology and immunology* (Chicago, University of Chicago Press, 1928), pp. 590–606.

Erwin F. Smith, Studies on the crown gall of plants, its relation to human cancer, *J. Cancer Res.*, *1* (1916), 231–302.

Erwin F. Smith, Crown gall and its analogy to cancer, *J. Cancer Res.*, *8* (1924), 234–39.

Erwin F. Smith, *Bacteria in relation to plant diseases*, 3 vols. (Washington, D. C., 1905, 1914).

27 Charles F. Craig, Observations upon amoebas infecting the human intestine, *Am. Med.*, *9* (1905), 854, 897, 936.

E. L. Walker and A. W. Sellards, Experimental entamoeba dysentery, *Phil. J. Sci. B.*, *8* (1913), 253–331.

Samuel T. Darling, A protozoan general infection producing pseudo tubercles in the lungs and focal necroses in the liver, spleen, and lymph nodes, *J. Am. Med. Assn.*, *46* (1906), 1283–85.

Samuel T. Darling, Histoplasmosis, a fatal disease of tropical America, *J. Exp. Med.*, *11* (1909), 515–30.

CHAPTER XIII—*Bacteriology as it Developed in Three Types of Institutions*

1 Victor C. Vaughan, *A doctor's memories* (Indianapolis, 1926).

Victor C. Vaughan, Memorial volume, *J. Lab. Clin. Med.*, *15* (1930), 817 942. Complete bibliography.

2 Walter Reed, Victor C. Vaughan, and Edward O. Shakespeare, *Origin and spread of typhoid fever in U. S. military camps during Spanish War of 1898* (Washington, D. C., 1900–1904), abstract of report. (Complete report, 2 vols., 1904.)

3 W. J. MacNeal, and Frederick Novy, On the cultivation of Trypanosoma lewisi. *Contributions to medical research* (Michigan, 1903), pp. 549–77.

Frederick Novy, On trypanosomes, *Harvey Society Lectures*, *1* (1906), 33–72.

Frederick Novy, Ein neuer anaërober Bacillus des malignes Oedems, *Zeit. F. Hygiene*, *17* (1894), 209–33.

Ruth Good, Dr. Frederick G. Novy: biographic sketch, *Univ. Mich. Med. Bull.*, *16* (1950), 257–68.

Frederick Novy and Paul de Kruif, Anaphylatoxin and anaphylaxis. Trypanosome anaphylatoxin, one of a series, *J. Infect. Dis.*, *20* (1917), 499–535.

Wm. S. Preston *et al.*, *The history of bacteriology in Michigan*, Soc. Am. Bact., 1957.

4 Paul de Kruif, personal letter to author, 1955.
5 Alfred Charles True, *A history of agricultural experimentation and research in the United States, 1607–1925*, Misc. Pub. No. 251, U. S. Dept. Agr., 1937, p. 74.
6 C. E. Marshall, *Microbiology* (Philadelphia, 1911).
  C. E. Marshall, Microbial associations, *Science, 41* (1915), 306–12.
7 Ludvig Hektoen, Notes on the history of bacteriology in Chicago, *Bull. Soc. Med. Hist. Chi., 5* (1937), 3–21.
8 Thomas Burrill, Pear blight, *Trans. Ill. State Hort. Soc.* (1878), pp. 114–16.
  Thomas Burrill, Fire blight, *Trans. Ill. State Hort. Soc.* (1879) pp. 77–78.
  Thomas Burrill, *The bacteria* (Springfield, Illinois, 1882).
9 Ludvig Hektoen, Experimental measles, *J. Infect. Dis., 2* (1905), 238–55.
  Ludvig Hektoen, Experimental measles, *J. Am. Med. Assn., 72* (1919), 177–80.
  Ludvig Hektoen, The precipitin test for blood, *J. Am. Med. Assn., 70* (1918), 1273–78.
  Ludvig Hektoen, Formation and fate of antibodies, *Harvey Society Lectures 5* (1910), 150–91.
  Morris Fishbein, Ludvig Hektoen, a biography and an appreciation, *Arch. Path., 26* (1938), 3–18.
  Paul Cannon, Ludvig Hektoen, *Arch. Path., 52* (1951), 390–94.
10 Alice Hamilton, The fly as a carrier of typhoid, *J. Am. Med. Assn., 40* (1903), 576–83.
11 D. J. Davis, Hemophilic bacilli—their morphology and relation to respiratory pigments, *J. Infect. Dis., 4* (1907), 73–86.
  D. J. Davis, Chromogenesis in cultures of *Sporotricha, J. Infect. Dis., 17* (1915), 174–82.
12 Edwin O. Jordan, Some observations upon the bacterial self-purification of streams, *J. Exp. Med., 5* (1900–1901), 271–314.
  Edwin O. Jordan, H. L. Russell, and F. R. Zeit, Longevity of the typhoid bacillus in water, *J. Infect. Dis., 1* (1904), 641–89.
  Edwin O. Jordan, *Food poisoning* (Chicago, 1917).
  Ludvig Hektoen, Edwin O. Jordan obituary, *Science, 84* (1936), 411–13.
  Stewart A. Koser, Bacteriology at the University of Chicago, *Bios., 23* (1952), 175–91.
  H. G. Wells, *The Chemical aspects of immunity* (New York, 1924).
13 H. Kent Tenney, personal communication.
14 Edward A. Birge, talk to medical students, 1935.
15 William H. Welch, letter to Mall about Russell, 1892, copied by B. Cohen, 1950.
  H. L. Russell, Bacteria in their relation to vegetable tissue, *Johns Hopkins Hosp. Reports, 3* (1894), 223–63.
  H. L. Russell, *Tuberculosis and the tuberculin test*, Wis. Exp. Station Bull. 40, 1894.
  H. L. Russell, *Gaseous fermentation in the canning industry*, 12th Ann. Rep., Wis. Exp. Station, 1895, pp. 227–31.
  Merle Curti and Vernon Carstensen, *The University of Wisconsin* (a history), vol. 2 (Madison, University of Wisconsin Press, 1949), pp. 408–9.

W. H. Glover, *Farm and College*, the College of Agriculture of the University of Wisconsin (Madison, 1952), pp. 270–76.

16 J. C. Walker and A. J. Riker, Lewis Ralph Jones, *Nat. Acad. Sci. Biog. Memoirs*, *31* (1958), 156–79.

G. W. Keitt and F. V. Rand, Lewis Ralph Jones, *Phytopathology*, *36* (1946), 1–17.

17 W. D. Frost, Antagonism exhibited by certain saprophyte bacteria against the *Bacillus typhosus* Gaffky, *J. Infect. Dis.*, *1* (1904), 599–640.

18 E. G. Hastings, W. Wisnicky, B. A. Beach, and Janet McCarter, A detailed study of no-lesion tuberculin-reacting cattle, *J. Am. Vet. Med. Assn.*, *82* (1933), 565–83.

E. G. Hastings, The eradication of bovine tuberculosis, *J. Dairy Sci.*, *25* (1942), 1057–65.

19 E. B. Fred and E. J. Graul, The effect of soluble nitrogenous salts on nodule formation, *J. Am. Soc. Agron.*, *8* (1916), 316–28.

E. B. Fred, Ira Lawrence Baldwin, and Elizabeth McCoy, Root nodule bacteria and leguminous plants, *Univ. Wisc. Studies in Sci.*, *5* (Madison, 1932). E. B. Fred soon wandered from bacteriologic paths into administrative duties, first as chairman of important committees, and successively dean of the Graduate School, the College of Agriculture, and then to become the highly successful president of the University until his retirement in 1958. Baldwin was similarly lured from the microscope into administration; Elizabeth McCoy, always gracious, was the one of the triumvirate who continued productively in bacteriology. We do not intend to minimize the desirability of placing scientists in positions of administrative leadership; most of us are willing to sacrifice an occasional colleague rather than to turn administration over to someone from "education," business, politics, or the military.

20 W. H. Glover, *Farm and college* . . . , pp. 274–76.

Curti and Carstensen, *The University of Wisconsin*, pp. 409, 413.

21 Curti and Carstensen, *The University of Wisconsin*, pp. 485–86.

CHAPTER XIV—*Other Areas of the "Central Valley"*

1 Morris Fishbein, *A history of the American Medical Association 1847–1947* (Philadelphia, 1947), pp. 887–922. Especially the chapter on council of medical education and hospitals.

2 E. E. Ecker, Microbiology and immunology in the Western Reserve, unpublished, undated manuscript in Archives of Soc. Am. Bact.

3 Frederick Clayton Waite, *Western Reserve University centennial history of the school of medicine* (Cleveland, 1946), pp. 194, 346.

4 C. B. Morrey, letter of May 29, 1937.

Wm A. Starin, *Bacteriology at Ohio State*, Archives of Soc. Am. Bact.

5 L. S. McClung, History of bacteriology at Indiana University, *Proc. Ind. Acad. of Sci.*, *53* (1944), 59–61.

P. A. Tetrault, History of bacteriology at Purdue University, *Proc. Ind. Acad. of Sci.*, *53* (1944), 66–71.

L. S. McClung, personal letter to author.

E. W. Shrigley, personal letter to author.

B. D. Myers, *History of medical education in Indiana* (Indiana Press, 1956).

6 Frank F. Wesbrook, Laboratory methods and devices, *J. Infect. Dis.*, *Sup. 1* (1905), 304–24.

Louis B. Wilson and William M. Chowning, Studies on *Piroplasma hominis*, *J. Infect. Dis.*, *1* (1904), 31–37.

Wesbrook, McDaniel and L. B. Wilson, Varieties of *Bacillus diphtheriae*, *Trans. Assn. Am. Phys.*, *15* (1900), 198–223.

J. T. Syverton, personal letter to author.

7 Walter L. Bierring, The story of bacteriology at the University of Iowa, *J. Iowa State Med. Soc.*, *27* (1937), 555, 602, 656.

W. S. Jeter, History of bacteriology at the State University of Iowa, personal communication.

J. R. Porter, personal letters to author.

R. E. Buchanan, personal letters to author.

8 M. A. Barber, Reminiscences, bacteriological and otherwise, of earlier days in Kansas, unpublished paper, Archives of Soc. Am. Bact., 1938.

M. A. Barber, *A malariologist in many lands* (University of Kansas Press, 1946).

Noble P. Sherwood, Bacteriology at the University of Kansas, unpublished, undated paper, Archives of Soc. Am. Bact.

W. B. Blanton, *Medicine in Virginia in 17th century* (Richmond, 1930).

W. B. Blanton, *Medicine in Virginia in 18th century* (Richmond, 1931).

W. B. Blanton, *Medicine in Virginia in 19th Century* (Richmond, 1933).

9 O. B. Williams and W. B. Sharp, *The history of bacteriology in Texas*, Soc. Am. Bact. (Houston, 1956).

O. N. Allen and Gordon Worley personal letters and statements to author.

CHAPTER XV—*Rocky Mountain Area*

1 E. E. Maxey, So-called spotted fever of Idaho, cited by Ricketts, *Med. Sentinel* Portland, Ore., 1899.

2 Howard T. Ricketts, The study of "Rocky Mountain spotted fever" (tick fever) by means of animal inoculations, *J. Am. Med. Assn.*, *47* (1906), 33–36.

H. T. Ricketts, *Infection, immunity and serum therapy*, ed. 1 (Am. Med. Assn. Press, 1906). Excellent; our stand-by before Zinsser's *Infection and resistance*.

Russell Wilder, personal letters to author, 1958.

H. T. Ricketts, A micro-organism which apparently has a specific relationship to Rocky Mountain spotted fever, *J. Am. Med. Assn.*, *52* (1909), 379–80.

H. T. Ricketts, *Contributions to medical science* (Chicago, University of Chicago Press, 1911). This gives a fairly complete bibliography of the fields covered, including references to the men cited.

H. T. Ricketts and R. Wilder, The relation of typhus fever to Rocky Mountain spotted fever, *Arch. Int. Med.*, *5* (1910), 361–70.

L. Hektoen, Biography of Howard Taylor Ricketts, *Univ. Chi. Mag.*, *2* (1910), 259–62.

W. M. Reid and C. Donald Vogel, Three glimpses into the life of H. T. Ricketts, *Bios.*, *22* (1951), 75–79.

3   H. R. Cox, Use of yolk sac of developing chick embryo as medium for growing Rickettsiae of Rocky Mountain spotted fever and typhus, and Q fever groups in the embryonic tissues of developing chicks, *Science, 94* (1941), 399–403.

CHAPTER XVI—*California and the Coast*

1   Henry Harris, *California's medical story* (San Francisco, 1932). Excellent.
2   *Ibid.*, pp. 339–42.
3   Emmet Rixford and T. C. Gilchrist, Protozoan infection of the skin and other organs, *Johns Hopkins Hosp. Reports, 1* (1896), 209–51.
4   W. Ophüls and Herbert Moffitt, A new pathogenic mould, *Philadelphia Med. J., 5* (1900), 1471–72.
      W. Ophüls, Further observations of a pathogenic mould, *J. Exp. Med., 6* (1901–5), 443–85.
5   W. H. Kellogg, Plague, bubonic, pneumonic and sylvatic, *Am. J. Pub. Health, 10* (1920), 835–44.
      C. L. Williams, Diagnosis and detection of rodent plague, *Am. J. Pub. Health, 10* (1920), 851–64.
      V. B. Link, *History of plague in the United States*, U. S. Pub. Health Monog. 26, 1955.
6   R. Pollitzer, *Plague* (Geneva, 1954,) pp. 51, 52.
7   George W. McCoy, Tularemia, *U. S. Pub. Health Bull., 43* (1911), 1–71.
      George W. McCoy and C. W. Chapin, Tularemia, *J. Infect. Dis., 10* (1912), 61–72.
8   W. B. Wherry and B. H. Lamb, Infection of man with *B. tularense, J. Infect. Dis., 15* (1914), 331–40.
9   Edward Francis, Tularemia, *U. S. Hyg. Lab. Bull., 130* (1922).
10 H. Harris, *California's medical story*, pp. 131–44; 237–40.
11 L. S. McClung and K. F. Meyer, Beginnings of bacteriology in California, unpublished, undated paper in Archives of Soc. Am. Bact.
12 Wilbur A. Sawyer, A typhoid carrier on shipboard, *J. Am. Med. Assn., 58* (1912), 1336–38.
      W. A. Sawyer, Ninety-three persons infected by a typhoid carrier at a public dinner, *J. Am. Med. Assn., 63* (1914), 1537–42.
      W. A. Sawyer, Late history of a typhoid carrier, *J. Am. Med. Assn., 64* (1915), 205–53.
13 Jules Bordet, *Studies in immunity*, trans. by F. P. Gay (New York, 1909).
      Frederick P. Gay and Edith J. Claypole, The "typhoid carrier" state in rabbits as a method of determining the comparative immunizing value of the typhoid bacillus, *Arch. Int. Med., 12* (1913), 613–27.
      F. P. Gay and H. T. Chickering, Concentration of the protective bodies in anti-pneumococcus serum by means of specific precipitation, *J. Exp. Med., 21* (1915), 389–400.
14 Karl Meyer, Relation of animal to human sporotrichosis, *J. Am. Med. Assn., 65* (1915), 579–85. Since most of Meyer's active life comes after our period, I am giving one reference only to one of his early studies indicating his life interest in relation of diseases of lower animals to those in man.
15 A. W. Meyer, Zinsser at Stanford, *Stanford Med. Alumni Bull. no. 1, 6*, 1–16.

16 R. L. Wilbur and W. Ophüls, Botulism, a report of food poisoning apparently due to eating canned string beans, with pathological report of a fatal case, *Arch. Int. Med.*, *14* (1914), 589–604.

Ernest C. Dickson, Botulism, an experimental study, *J. Am. Med. Assn.*, *65* (1915), 492–96.

E. C. Dickson, *Botulism, a clinical and experimental study*, Rockefeller Institute monograph No. 8, 1918.

17 J. Russell Esty, unpublished paper, Archives of Soc. Am. Bact.

18 McClung and Meyer, Beginnings of bacteriology in California.

Wine Institute Bulletin 911, San Francisco, Dec. 31, 1957.

19 *Arnald of Villanova, 1478*, the earliest printed book on wine, trans. by Henry E. Sigerist (New York, 1943).

20 O. Larsell, *The doctor in Oregon* (Portland, Oregon, 1917).

CHAPTER XVII—*Our Means of Communication and Our Early Leaders*

1 Charles S. Slichter, *Science in a tavern* (Madison, University of Wisconsin Press, 1938).

2 National Academy of Sciences, *Scientific and technical societies of the United States and Canada*, ed. 6 (Washington, D. C., 1955).

Ralph S. Bates, *Scientific societies in the United States* (Massachusetts Institute of Technology, 1945).

3 H. T. Karsner, American Association of Pathologists and Bacteriologists, summary of transactions of Council, 1935.

4 Marion K. Sanders, Mutiny of the bountiful, *Harpers Magazine*, *217* (1958), 23–30 (Abstract, *Reader's Digest*, *31* (1959), 37–41.)

5 L. S. McClung, Early American publications relating to bacteriology, *Bact. Rev.*, *8* (1944), 119–60.

Thomas H. Grainger, *A guide to the history of bacteriology* (New York, 1958).

Arthur L. Bloomfield, *A bibliography of internal medicine; communicable diseases* (Chicago, University of Chicago Press, 1958).

CHAPTER XVIII—*Epilogue: From a Laboratory Window*

1 Irene B. Taeuber, *Population of Japan* (Princeton, 1958). Chapter on control of fertility.

Gregory Pincus *et al.*, Effectiveness of an oral contraceptive (in Puerto Rico), *Science*, *130* (1959), 81–83.

Annual Conference, *Interrelations of demographic, economic and social problems in selected areas*, Milbank Memorial Fund (New York, 1954), p. 200. Excellent, broad coverage.

Ibid., *Thirty years of research in human fertility: retrospect and prospect*, 1959, p. 404.

2 W. Lloyd Aycock and George E. Foley, An epidemiologic approach to the study of the biochemical mechanism of motor neuron disease—Landry's paralysis, *Am. J. Med. Sci.*, *210* (1945), 397–419.

Alphonse R. Vonderahe, Pathologic changes in paralysis caused by drinking Jamaica ginger, *Arch. Neurology*, *25* (1931), 29–43.

3 Theobald Smith, *Parasitism and disease* (Princeton, Princeton University Press, 1934).

4 Walter B. Cannon, *Wisdom of the body* (New York, 1932).

5 Norman Cousins, *Who speaks for man?* (New York, 1953).

6 Andrew D. White, *History of warfare of science with theology in Christendom* (New York, 1896).

Oscar Riddle, *The unleashing of evolutionary thought* (New York, 1954).

7 L. H. Allen, *Bryan and Darrow at Dayton* (New York, 1925).

Ray Ginger, *Six days or forever? Tennessee* v. *John Thomas Scopes* (Boston, 1958).

Faye-Cooper Cole, A witness at the Scopes Trial, *Sci. American, 200* (1959), 120–30. A personal and an excellent tale, one of the best.

8 Walter B. Cannon, *The way of an investigator* (New York, 1945).

W. I. B. Beveridge, *The art of scientific investigation* (New York, 1951).

E. Bright Wilson, *An introduction to scientific research* (New York, 1952). Includes excellent notes and references.

9 R. A. Fisher, *Statistical methods for research workers*, ed. 6 (Edinburgh, 1936).

R. A. Fisher, *The design of experiments*, ed. 2 (Edinburgh, 1937).

10 William Osler, *Aequanimitas*, ed. 3 (Philadelphia, 1947), pp. 349–71.

11 John Enders *et al.*, Cultivation of the Lansing strain of poliomyelitis virus in cultures of various human embryonic tissues, *Science, 109* (1949), 85–87.

A. B. Sabin and P. K. Olitsky, Cultivation of poliomyelitis virus in vitro in human embryonic nervous tissue, *Proc. Soc. Exp. Biol. Med., 34* (1936), 357–59.

12 I. P. Pavloff, *Testament to the youth of my country* (Chicago, University of Chicago Press, 1949), p. 110.

13 Homer, *The Iliad.*, 2 vols., classics in translation, trans. by A. H. Chase and W. G. Perry, Jr. (Madison, University of Wisconsin Press, 1952), p. 16.

14 A. B. Sabin and P. K. Olitsky, Influence of host factors on neuroinvasiveness of vesicular stomatitis virus, *J. Exp. Med., 66* (1937), 15–57; *67* (1938), 201–49. Parts of an excellent series on constitutional barriers.

15 E. M. Medlar, An evaluation of the leucocytic reaction in the blood as found in cases of tuberculosis, *Am. Rev. Tub., 20* (1929), 312–46.

16 C. E. Marshall, Microbial associations, *Science, 41* (1915), 306–12.

17 Oliver Wendell Holmes, *Medical essays* (Boston, 1911), p. 289.

18 Simon Flexner and James Thomas Flexner, *William Welch and the heroic age of American medicine* (New York, 1941), p. 247.

19 John Masefield, *Speech by John Masefield, O. M. Poet Laureate, in Reply to the Toast of the Honorary Graduands Proposed by the Chancellor at Luncheon Immediately before the Ceremony of Installation of the Chancellor, 25th June, 1946* (from a reprint supplied by the University of Sheffield, England).

Index